A B

After v
a decade, I
book, *In Mor*
in 2003. She   to promote
prevention and awareness of child sexual
abuse and researching for a Masters Degree
the phenomenon of emotional attachment
to the abuser and its long-term effects.
She divides her time between
Melbourne and Paris.

Relationships aren't here
to make us happy.
They're here
to wake us up.

ECKHART TOLLE
IN *THE POWER OF NOW*

What Price Redemption?

THE
ROAD
HOME

Barbara Biggs

MICKLIND

Published in Australia by
Micklind Enterprises
2007

Distributed wholesale by
Gary Allen Pty Ltd,
9 Cooper Street,
Smithfield, NSW, 2164
Telephone (02) 9725 2933

The Road Home
What Price Redemption?
ISBN 0 646 43122 6
APN 9780646431222

Editor: Bryony Cosgrove
Proofreading: Perfect Words
Final editing: Andrew Rule
Cover and internal design: R.T.J. Klinkhamer
Typeset in 10.5/12.5 Bembo
Author photo and back cover: Lissa Strauss
Printed in China at Everbest Printing Co

AUTHOR'S NOTE

Many readers will have already read *In Moral Danger*. For those who haven't, here's the story so far.

My life was devastated by one of Australia's most famous criminal barristers, Robert Roy Vernon. I began living in his home for nine months, ostensibly as a nanny to his two small daughters, when I was 14. He was 42, and a sexual predator.

Like many kids in similar circumstances, emotionally needy to begin with, then isolated from friends and family, I was vulnerable and became infatuated. When Vernon realized I was 'in love' with him and suicidal, he ordered me to leave his house and never come back. His legacy dogged me for decades, pushing me to the brink of insanity and increasingly desperate attempts to climb out from under the shadow of what he had done.

By the time I left his house I was imprinted with a self-image as a sex toy. I went back to my family home in Queensland (where I'd previously been raped as a virgin on my fourteenth birthday) and began a life of casual sex and drugs.

At sixteen, desperate for a rest from the world and my own tortured mental state, I admitted myself to a psychiatric hospital and enrolled at school.

During the following years, I see-sawed between depression and blind optimism; studying and suicide attempts; learning to play the piano and prostitution. I escaped from wartorn Cambodia only to get death threats when I triggered one of Australia's biggest transport strikes.

At the age of 22 (the point where *In Moral Danger* ends), I fell out with my closest girlfriend — and simultaneously found out I was pregnant to a man that I loved but who didn't love me. I decided to keep the baby. With that decision, my life was to change forever ... and become, if not more bizarre, maybe a little inspirational.

Barbara Biggs
Rome
November 2003

CONTENTS

LIST OF PHOTOGRAPHS

ACKNOWLEDGMENTS

I would like to thank close friends for their help in the past year dealing with the parallel universe that has manifested in my life as a result of the first book, *In Moral Danger*. And to thank Lucy Michot and Mina Gioia for opening their homes, hearts and cooking pots to me during the second draft phase of this book.

I would also like to acknowledge the input of my late sister Pommy for the moving and natural diary extracts used in this book.

As always, thanks to my son Dan for his support and for continuing to astonish me with his normality.

Thanks to editor Bryony Cosgrove for her advice and going beyond the call of duty and to publisher Andrew Rule and distributors Kristy and Gary Allen for their continued support.

To the hundreds of people who e-mailed after reading *In Moral Danger*, saying that it helped them realise they're not alone, I extend heartfelt thanks. It was one of the motivations for writing the story. I am grateful for your appreciation of the disturbing and confronting honesty I employed. There were times when I flinched and questioned if it were really necessary. Your comments validated the final decision to tell it as it happened.

Most of all, thanks to Peter Hollingworth for seeking me out and offering public support at a time when others turned me away. And for his courage and humility in admitting his blind spots and being prepared to open his mind. He has become an example to a generation of others.

MY FAMILY TREE

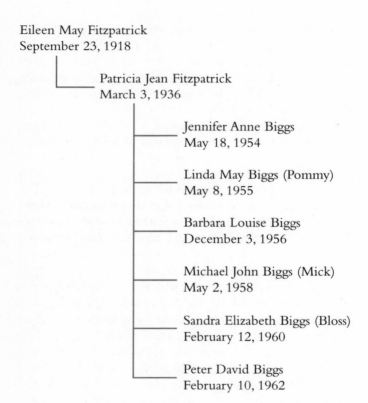

Eileen May Fitzpatrick
September 23, 1918

Patricia Jean Fitzpatrick
March 3, 1936

Jennifer Anne Biggs
May 18, 1954

Linda May Biggs (Pommy)
May 8, 1955

Barbara Louise Biggs
December 3, 1956

Michael John Biggs (Mick)
May 2, 1958

Sandra Elizabeth Biggs (Bloss)
February 12, 1960

Peter David Biggs
February 10, 1962

FOREWORD

As a society we have come a long way on the subject of child sexual abuse. When I began in ministry the matter was seldom discussed in public and, privately, people were often sceptical of allegations. Children and young people were sometimes accused in some quarters of fantasizing, 'making it up' or saying it 'to get attention'.

Today, with new understanding of children's rights to safety and protection, there are significant changes in public policy and practice at a professional level, though in some cases old attitudes die hard.

The transition has not been easy, because it involves confronting terrible situations and truths we would all prefer didn't exist. Yet they must be confronted, because abuse robs children of their innocence and makes a deep impact on their ability to form caring and loving relationships — sometimes for life. Tragically, it can also be passed from generation to generation as abusive or deviant behavior.

However difficult the past few years have been for me, one positive thing has emerged: media attention focused on child sexual abuse has brought this previously hidden issue to the full public attention. We have all been forced to look at this difficult and confronting issue.

I read Barbara Biggs' first book *In Moral Danger* soon after I resigned from office. She had left it at Government House with a challenging note suggesting that I needed to update my thinking about the long-term emotional and psychological impact on abused children. The fact that she had recently written a tough piece on me in the *Canberra Times* only added to the challenge.

Despite my work with the Brotherhood of St Laurence over 25 years, I had not been much exposed to the matter, and I was not as aware of its impact as I should have been. So I accepted Barbara's point that I did not understand the 'emotional mechanics' of child sexual abuse and the long-term destructive effect on a victim's later life. Other people had also written to me in similar vein and so I tentatively began a journey of discovery into a field of human suffering that was rather unfamiliar to me.

The most confronting element of *In Moral Danger* is the lingering emotional attachment and dependency Barbara felt for her abuser for so long. In her experience, and that of many others, this is the most destructive after-effect of such a relationship. It made me realise that it is one thing to understand an abstract issue – but another to learn of the personal impact from the victim herself.

If this is true for other abused children, they too may need to speak openly about it in their own way. For too long there has been a conspiracy of silence in the public domain. In *The Road Home*, the sequel to her first book, Barbara Biggs has certainly done much to break that silence. As she writes so movingly in her prologue, 'if we can't tell how our souls have been muddied, how can we ever clean them?'

But, for me, *The Road Home* is the most important part of her life story because it tells how she dealt with the psychological scars of her abuse and overcame them, along with other personal difficulties in her early life.

Her story will be an inspiration to others facing similar circumstances. Victims will see that they are not alone and will be encouraged to speak out about their own emotional responses to abuse. It will also help educate the wider community, as it has me, about these previously hidden and disturbing aspects of child sexual abuse.

Some will find the book morally confronting and difficult to embrace. They should remember that it describes a reality that too many young people have experienced. It is therefore better to try to understand rather than to judge.

I commend Barbara Biggs for her courage, honesty and forthrightness in banishing the demons in her past. She has shone a light into dark places so that we all might see more clearly.

The Right Reverend Dr Peter Hollingworth AC OBE

This book is dedicated to the millions of broken childhoods still under repair ...

And to my son, Dan, whose love helped me rebuild mine.

ONE

THE PROBLEM
WITH STARFISH

1979

Pommy's the first one I tell. Not just because she's my sister. But because I feel holy and she's been through it all before. Well, she doesn't exactly treat me like the Virgin Mary, but she does ask me to dinner.

I know everyone thinks I'm very intense and weird. I can see it in their eyes. My workmates and the two girls I'm sharing with as well. I know they're going to be nervous.

And they don't even know me that well. I can sense it in Pommy already, even though she hasn't said anything. I mean at least she has a reason to be nervous. I can see if you almost go and get yourself killed where there's a war going on and get yourself deported from foreign countries, and collect parking fines like football cards and try to knock yourself off every five minutes, of course people aren't going to think, oh, now there goes some really great mother material.

I wonder if that was the real reason Joanne said she didn't want to see me anymore. Maybe it was because she was scared I'd be even more needy and intense than normal. She hates me being needy alright. She made that pretty clear. I mean, she didn't know for sure. I only *thought* I could be pregnant when she told me she couldn't stand me any more and to stop calling and leaving notes under her door. Sometimes I can still hear her words ringing in my ears. 'Just piss off and leave me alone.' But mostly I try not to think about her at all. I've left so many people behind in my life I know how to block them out. She's harder than most because, well, she did say I was like the daughter she never had, even though she's only eight years older than me. Anyway, I've had a lot of practice at forgetting about people. I just pretend they're dead.

And Pommy, well, she's really been more like a mother to me than anyone else. If you think of a mother as the person you want to love you more than anyone else, then that's definitely true. Even though she doesn't really seem to like me, and she never likes any of my friends, she's still more like a mother than Mother, because she was always working and never there and wouldn't have a clue what you were doing from one year to the next. Well, almost.

Even though I can see Pommy doesn't think this is the best news around, I know everything's going to be okay. Nobody else believes me because they don't know how I feel. They don't know I've got this *feeling* of knowing that I've never had before, that everything's going to be okay.

When I arrive at Pommy's house for dinner, her little boy Christian is lying snuggled up on the couch with his head in her lap watching telly. She's stroking his hair and he's got his thumb in his mouth. He's six. Too old to be still sucking his thumb but I can't talk. My sucking went on until I was ten and I was terrified I'd still be doing it when I got married! Well, I guess there's no chance of that now. Ha.

Jacqui's in the kitchen cooking. Pommy gets down to tin tacks straightaway.

'Great. Are you going to tell him?' She's very practical, Pommy.

'I have to think about it.'

'What's he like? Do we get to meet him?' She's biting her nails. The way she goes at it you'd think there was actually some nail left to chew.

'He's pretty spiritual actually. He grew up in an ashram. He meditates and stuff. You'd like him.'

Jacqui comes in with a dish in each hand and puts them on the table in the dining room at the end of the lounge.

'Why don't you invite him over for dinner? Jacqui'll cook Chinese. Won't you Jac?'

'Sure. When?' Jacqui's always wanting to make Pommy happy. You can tell she adores her. Before they left Canberra she even bought a lounge and dining room suite on hire purchase in her own name for their gorgeous, huge new flat in Melbourne. It's in Walsh Street, South Yarra, right across the road from Fawkner Park. It's a pretty ritzy suburb so I guess they wanted everything new. After Jacqui signed up, they'd moved to Melbourne with no intention of paying for the furniture. Jacqui would never have done that before she met our family.

We start eating dinner at the table. It's pretty civilized. We

Biggs's only eat dinner at the table for Christmas lunch so it doesn't feel entirely normal. I know the table business is Jacqui's idea because she's the one with the Brady Bunch family.

Pommy tells me about her court-reporting course.

'None of the girls'll talk to me. They're real little bitches. I know I've always said only bitches call other girls bitches, but these ones really are. I'm thinking of leaving. Every day I have to steel myself to go.' The food's still there on the plate but she starts munching on the nails again.

'It's only for a year isn't it? Just ignore them and stick it out 'til the end of the year,' I say.

'I wish I could.' She doesn't look right. I think of Pommy as a person who always knows what she wants. She looks worried. Almost like she's in pain. 'Anyway, Jacqui's checking out this parlour on St Kilda Road.'

Jacqui doesn't look up from her food.

'What kind of parlour?'

'A brothel. She says we can both get jobs there. We need the money.'

It's like Jacqui's not part of the conversation. Like Pommy's not even talking about her.

'I've told you not to eat with your hands, sweetheart. Use your fork,' Jacqui says to Christian. She's really more like the mother in the family now.

'What about Christian?'

'On the nights I work Jac'll look after him and vice versa. Won't you Jac?'

'What?'

'Look after Christian.'

'Oh. Yeah.'

They'd started doing escort work in Canberra at nights before moving here. I couldn't work it out then and I still can't. Then they'd both had good jobs and didn't even need the extra money. Like private secretary to the Nigerian High Commissioner for Christ's sake. Pommy had been so proud when she got that job. It suited her, I thought. So why would they do escort work? Jacqui's told me she hates sleeping with guys because she's gay. She stopped after a few jobs but Pommy kept going. Not that *she* liked it either. But I know she lives with Jacqui not so much because she's gay but because she just loves Jac. Having sex with men doesn't make her skin crawl like it does with Jacqui. Still, I s'pose it isn't so different to me going back to Japan all those times after I'd tried to top myself. But Pommy's different. Even though Joanne isn't my best friend anymore, I still remember how shocked I was when she told me about my low self-esteem. She reckoned if I was wearing a price tag it would say about 20 cents. She said that's why I kept going back to prostitution. You could've knocked me over with a feather. You'd think you'd just know if you had low self-esteem but I didn't. I only believed her because Joanne's hardly ever wrong about anything. But Pommy, if she was wearing a price tag, I reckon it would say about a million dollars.

Maybe there's a crack in that glittery old price tag that I just don't see. Maybe people with price tags that say 20 cents have no idea about people with price tags that say a million dollars.

William's already told me he doesn't love me. That's why I moved over the other side of town to the share flat. Then he rang and invited me to a kite-flying day with his workmates a few weeks ago. If he doesn't love me, I wonder why he wanted to sleep with me that night. I know most guys will do anything for a root but William isn't like that. Well, at least I think he isn't. That's one of the reasons I'm in love with him, because he's so different to all the other guys.

I know I'd done the chance thing to help me get away.

The big pact with myself about going off the pill and not starting sex with him but letting him come to me to see if I got pregnant. I was sitting on the fence and didn't have the strength just to end it. So the idea was, if I got pregnant that would solve things in its own way, and if I didn't, that would give me the sign I needed to help me move away. Well, I didn't get pregnant and I moved. Then the kite-flying thing happened three months later and William pushed me into staying at his place that night even though I kept saying I should go home. Now here I am, pregnant after all.

The day after I've told Pommy, I ring him. It's a big thing because since I'd moved to make it easier not to see him anymore, I've done this big three-sixty. Not in my feelings for him but in my decision not to let him get to me anymore. Anyway, now his voice sounds surprised but happy to hear from me.

I ask if he wants to come for dinner to meet my sister and he says yes.

He turns up the next Saturday night with two bottles of sweet Riccadonna spumante. He and Pommy talk about meditation and Rosicrucianism and all kinds of religious and spiritual things. William reads more than anyone I've ever met. Books are strewn all over the floor in every room of his house. I can't believe how well Pommy and William get on. He's the first one of my friends she's ever liked.

I don't tell William the big news.

After that, every Saturday night for the next few weeks William and me go to Pommy's place for dinner. They keep getting on like a house on fire.

At Pommy's front door when he leaves one night, William gives me a really soft, gentle kiss on the cheek which I like much better than the usual stiff tongue lunge he used to do before we broke up. We haven't had sex since the kite night but I'm getting even more in love. If *that's* possible. I go back into the lounge room with this dizzy smile.

'You're going to have to tell him sooner or later,' Pommy says.

I know she's right.

I'm working at the Ministry of Transport so I'm busy, at least in the day. But at night, I think every second about telling William. While he doesn't know, I can build up this idea in my mind that he'll help me through it. Who knows, he might even fall in love with me. But if he can't, he can just be my friend. That will be enough. Well, it'll have to be, won't it. He's very honourable, William.

The next Saturday night at Pommy's, after dinner, we run out of Riccadonna.

'I'll just run down the road and get another bottle,' William says.

'I'll drive if you like,' I say. We're not a drinking family, but tonight I'm going for it because I'm working up to telling him.

We've just got back to the flat when I put my hand on his arm as he's getting out of the car.

'Just a second. Can we just talk for a minute?'

'What about?' I can feel him go stiffer, which is really something because he's like a steel pole even when some girl who's in love with him doesn't want to talk to him for a minute.

'I've been wanting to tell you for a few weeks now but I haven't known … well … you know … how. So …' I take a big breath and let it out. 'I'm pregnant.' Tact and subtlety aren't my strong points. Pussyfooting makes me annoyed so I'm hardly going to do it myself.

He sits there not saying anything but his face changes more into a thundercloud by the second. The air in the car is so heavy it could crush us. It's the longest five minutes of my life. I'm very surprised and realise pretty quick how much I've been kidding myself. I thought at least he was supposed to have equilibrium. That's what he said they taught in the ashram wasn't it?

'Who's the father?' He's like a bomb about to explode. But he's got self-control, alright. I can see that.

'You, of course.'

'How do you know?' When he says this he turns to look me right in the eye.

'Because I haven't slept with anybody else.' Then he looks away out the window again and even through his beard I can see his mouth become a line.

'I don't believe you.' Then he turns and gives me that look again. 'You're not exactly pure as driven snow, are you?'

His reaction is a shock. I remember again what he'd told me about how the ashram where he grew up is all about equilibrium, which is not feeling strongly about anything that happens to you, even if you're dying or winning the lottery. But I can see that equilibrium isn't where William's at. No sir. I can see he's struggling like a maniac to get that equilibrium back and, I try to hide it, but I feel sorry for him.

'How far gone are you?' He's staring at nothing again outside the front windscreen.

'About 10 weeks.'

'Are you going to keep it?'

'Yes.'

He still can't look at me. I wait. It seems like another whole eternity.

'I think that's a mistake.'

'Why?'

'Because I don't think you'd make a very good mother.'

He does the eyeballing thing again.

'William, I'm keeping it.' I can't believe he's saying this. He does more brooding and narrowing his eyes and squeezing his already stiff lips together. Even though I'm very crushed, there isn't a single thought in my mind about not having this baby.

'Well, we'd better go inside.'

We walk in with the wine and William doesn't talk to me for the rest of the night. He doesn't even look in my direction. After Jacqui goes to bed, I think Pommy wants to leave us alone because she can see that something's up.

'I'll just go to the loo,' she says.

'Can I come?' William says. Pommy looks at me and then at him. I'm embarrassed that William's said such a drooby thing, but worse than that, I know he's said it to make me feel jealous or something. He's not too adept at these kinds of games, William.

'I don't think so!' Pommy's embarrassed. You can see she thinks William's being weird. When she leaves the room it's obvious he's said the drooby thing because he doesn't want to be alone with me.

'I suppose I'd better be off then,' he says, standing up. 'I'll see myself to the door.' He takes some glasses to the kitchen and he's way too long in coming back. I know he's waiting until Pommy joins us again.

He comes back from the kitchen only after he hears the bathroom door open and close.

'I'd better be going. See you anon.' No-one else says anon. It's very old-fashioned. Very William. He says a pretty bloody cold 'Cheerio' to me from as far across the other side of the lounge room as he can possibly be without actually disappearing into the corner. I get up and start walking him out all the same. As he leaves he gives Pommy a kiss on the cheek goodbye and, to me, it looks like a very tender kiss. She goes to bed to leave us alone. I walk him to the door, but he doesn't even look at me when he says this formal goodnight, like he can't bring himself to be rude even though I can see what he really wants to do is push me over.

When I close the door I'm ashamed that my biggest feeling is jealousy. It doesn't have much energy because what's just happened is a lot worse than stupid jealousy. There's a baby involved here. But that's how I feel. I go into Pommy's bedroom.

She puts her arm around me, which is monumental for her.

'You told him, didn't you?'

'In the car before we came back in.' I'm almost crying.

'What did he say?'

I tell her.

'Bastard.' She looks at me while I cry. 'Maybe he just needs time to get used to the idea.'

When I go to sleep in the spare bed in Christian's room, I just lie there. I can't help it, I'm still jealous. I know he gets on better with Pommy than me. All my life everybody's got on better with Pommy than me. I can't sleep because I'm thinking that maybe the reason William's so angry about me being pregnant is because this last month he's really been falling in love with Pommy.

I go into her bedroom and wake her up.

'Just tell me the truth. I don't care if you are, I just want to know, are you in love with William?'

She looks at me with pitying eyes. I cry on her shoulder and she pats me and strokes my hair. I'm amazed. I've always wanted her to but she's never stroked my hair before.

'Don't worry, it's just because he's shocked about the news. I've seen the way he looks at you. It's you he likes, not me. He'll come 'round. You just wait and see.'

I have to wait alright. Every minute is like being nailed to the cross. But Pommy's wrong. He doesn't have any

intention of 'coming 'round'. He phones me two weeks after
I break the news.

'It's William here.' Like, really. He's very formal.

'Hi.'

'I just rang to tell you that I think the only decent thing
to do is to marry you. And I'm not going to do that, for
obvious reasons, so I think it's best if we don't see each other
again.'

'What are the obvious reasons?'

'Well, you've known all along I'm not in love with you.'

'Hmm. I know.'

'So, I think it's best to say cheerio.'

Whoever thought of cheerio doesn't have any idea how
un-bloody-cheery a cheerio can get.

I keep working at the Ministry. They still don't know I'm
pregnant. One day in the tearoom I stretch to yawn. I'm
wearing a snugly fitting little blue dress and one of the
professional guys stares at my stomach and then our eyes lock
for a second. That's when I know it's time to tell someone.

I ask my friend Elizabeth to spread the word. She's a
statistician and I help her sometimes when there aren't any
messages to deliver.

After she tells, I'm pretty surprised because nobody says
anything to me but they start being really friendly. Maybe
because they feel sorry for me being a single parent, who
knows. But anyway, I like it. I'm not used to it, but I like it.

I have to catch trams up and down Bourke Street to
Parliament House for my job. Even though my face was
plastered all over the papers and the telly for a few weeks, I've
forgotten all about the big tram strike I caused (I wouldn't
join the union) because that was a year ago. It might as well
be a lifetime for me. But the tram workers haven't forgotten.
Sometimes they find ways to remind me. One day I'm sitting
on a crowded city tram when people start looking at me. I'm

reading a book so I don't hear what's being said over the loud speaker.

When I see them staring I can't work out why because I've been sitting here quietly minding my own business. I think maybe I've got something showing. I look down to check myself. That's when I start listening.

'Yes, you. That's right, I'm talking about you. She's thick as well as a bloody scab. You're the bitch who cost us two weeks pay. I had a mortgage I couldn't pay because of you. That's right, you're listening now, aren't you? Yeah, I'd be embarrassed too if I was a bloody scab like you. Everyone take a good look. She's the one in the red skirt to match her face. She even looks like a scab, doesn't she Laurie? Happy to take union benefits but makes us all lose pay because *she* doesn't want to join.' It goes on all the way down Bourke Street. My heart's racing and my face *is* red, but I keep reading my book. Or pretending to, anyway.

Another time the driver stops the tram and says he's not going any further unless I get off. I refuse at first but after a few minutes the whole tram of people start getting pissed off because they don't want to be late for work. I get off and take the next one. Boy, have they got long memories. Who'd think they'd still be so pissed off after six months.

Early in my pregnancy I meet a girl at the family planning clinic who's just had a home birth. She tells me about doctors in hospitals forcing women to have caesarians, giving them drugs so they don't remember the birth, inducing labour to fit in with their golf games and not listening to what the woman wants. I still feel like an angel walking around. I'm already so in love with my baby I want everything to be perfect. Natural. I want to remember everything and for my baby to be born when it's ready. That's why I decide on a home birth. The only doctor who does it full-time has his rooms in South Yarra, just near where I live. Very convenient.

We've just moved to Black Rock and the house is right across the road from the beach so Pommy and me go every single day. Sometimes Jenny and Bloss come too but I like it better when just the two of us go by ourselves. We walk along with no shoes, skip stones in the water, climb the cliffs. We even swim way, way out to an old submarine called the Cerberus, stopping at little boats on the way to get our breath.

But the starfish are a problem. Pommy and me can't believe all the colours when we first see them in the rock pools. They're so beautiful we want to bring them home and keep them as pets, so we scrape them off the rocks with a sharp shell. They don't want to budge and they hang on for dear life. Then we bring them home.

Trouble is, they keep dying on us and when they do, all their bright colours disappear overnight. We wake up and instead of being all these brilliant blues and greens and pinks and yellows that made us bring them home in the first place, they're all washed out. We're told when they lose their colour they're dead. We try everything. The first time we put them in our bedroom on a shelf, but in the morning they're grey looking. Then we put them in water but they still die. Pommy says maybe they need salty water so we bring some with us from the beach. No luck. Then she says what they need is some rocks to hang on to so we bring some home with the bucket. Another batch dies. We decide we won't bring home lots until we know how they live so we only bring one home and try seaweed as well. It dies but now we're not sure if it died from loneliness, so we try the same thing with two. They both die. We feel bad because they're so beautiful and we know we're killing them.

Eventually we work out that, just like us, they don't like moving. After that, we leave them there and just go and look at them when we're rock-hopping our way along the beach.

I get a bee in my bonnet about buying a place so my baby will have a home and not have to move around like we did. I think of all the times we moved and decide there's no way my baby's going to have a childhood like mine.

I know I'll have to get a loan before my belly starts showing because nobody will lend money to a single parent. I've saved $3000 for a deposit, but I make lots of calls to banks and still no-one will lend me the $20,000 I'll need to buy a small, cheap house in the Dandenong Ranges in the foothills about an hour from Melbourne. I've saved the big deposit and have a steady job, so I go to the bank across the road from work. I dress like a nun and take my bankbook because I want that loan enough to jump through any hoops they want.

'How old did you say you were?'

'Twenty-two. I'll be 23 at the end of the year.'

'And why do you think we should give you the loan? You've had the job with the tramways for what, just over a year, isn't it?'

'Yes, but I've saved $3000 in that time. Isn't the ability to save something you take into account? And I've been paying rent as well and if I have a house I'll be saving money on rent.' I try not to let him know how much I want this loan. People hate it when you're desperate.

'Yes, but you'd have a mortgage and what if you lost your job or got married?' He looks over the top of his glasses at me and I can feel myself hating him. I'm powerless and he holds the future of me and my baby in his hands.

'I know I'll make the payments. I'll keep working no matter what.' When people hear you're desperate, there's something in them that makes them not want to help you. I try to cover it up, but it's too late.

'I'm sorry, it's just not stacking up I'm afraid.'

'What do you mean it's not stacking up? I rang and asked what you needed and I had every single one of the things on your list.'

'I'm sorry, but you only just scrape over the line with employment history.'

I have a lot of trouble telling people I know what I really think, but I don't have any trouble with strangers. In fact, I can be very rude, especially on the telephone. It's like they get all the frustration I've ever felt in my life. I'd hate to have me to deal with if I worked on telephone customer service.

That's who I really go to town on. It's not so easy in person but this man is making me very pissed off.

'I want this house more than I've ever wanted anything and if you give me the loan I promise to pay it back. If you knew what it meant to me you'd know I'd never miss a single payment.'

I'm losing him but I can't help myself. I want to punch him out. Mary from my student house was right. Feminism might be here, but we're a long way from women being treated the same as men.

'I'm sorry Miss Biggs. I'm afraid I'm going to have to decline your application.'

I can barely breathe while I'm staring at him with hatred. Then, I explode.

'Yes, you would, you patriarchal pig. If I was a man and had exactly the same employment history you'd be begging me to take the loan. You can keep your fucking money. I'll get it from somewhere else and I'll get a house with or without your help.' I'm leaning over his desk and I can feel my face going red. Then I storm out and run back across the road, crying.

Some crying is sad but this is angry and I can feel it setting me in concrete and making me more stubborn than anyone could ever be. I don't know how, but I *am* going to get a house for my baby no matter what I have to do. *Nobody's* going to stand in my way.

After that I pore over real estate ads in the paper every chance I get. A few weeks later I see an ad for a block of land in a place called Adaminaby, outside Canberra. It's 170 acres for $7000. That means I'll only need to take a tiny loan of $4000. I drive up one weekend and the neighbour, who's helping the owner sell it, puts me on a horse and takes me around the property. The horse is very big and the country is steep. I worry about falling off and hurting my baby, but the man tells me his horse is quiet as a mouse. The land's just below the snow line and although it's dry it has a rugged kind of beauty. Even though it doesn't have running water or electricity I talk myself into the romance of living like a pioneer because if I don't buy something soon, I'll be showing and if no-one will give a single woman a housing loan they won't lend a cent to one who's about to have a baby.

A few days after I get back, my work friend, Elizabeth, gives me some advice that changes everything. She's been a rock to me during my pregnancy. Outside work she's been taking me camping, something I've never done before. It makes me appreciate nature more. And the bush. She'd also told me about a yoga class she went to and suggested I join up because it would make the birth easier. I figured anything that helps. Now I do an hour of meditation and exercises every morning before work. Sometimes we go to classes together. When I feel depressed she listens and helps me through some really awful times.

I tell her about the land I've seen.

'When you go to the bank for the rest of the money, apply for a personal loan. Don't tell them you're buying land. If you tell them you're buying a car they'll be more likely to lend you money. Don't ask me why. It's something they can understand better than a single woman buying real estate. It's just the way men think'

It sounds crazy. Why would a bank think a car was a better thing to lend money on when it doesn't take Einstein to know cars depreciate as soon as you buy them and real estate doesn't? Anyway, I trust Elizabeth so that's what I do. I apply for a personal loan for a car.

It turns out she's right. The bank approves a loan for $5000. The repayments are $25 a week over four years. I can manage that even on a single parent pension. I buy the land, but can't live there as there's no money to build a house. So I sell my car to have money for a bond on a flat because I want to be alone with my baby as soon as it's born.

Chris, my flatmate, has been teaching me piano so I can learn *Für Elise* and I've been going at it like there's no tomorrow, and I mean like eight hours a day, until I drive the entire neighbourhood bonkers. With the leftover money I buy my own piano too. Chris has a grand which is so great to play on because you can really imagine that you're playing on a stage or something, but now I've got my very own piano in my very own place. It's an adorable one-bedroom flat in Darling Street, South Yarra. The courtyard garden is planted with roses and lavender underneath. I keep practising piano like a maniac and Chris keeps giving me a lesson every week. I've finished learning *Für Elise* and am getting ready for my fourth grade piano exam. All my spare time I spend practising. I drive everyone within cooee crazy.

TWO

BEING GOD

I'm happier than I've ever been in my life. I have my own flat, a piece of land where somehow I'm going to build a house of my own and I'm carrying a baby I love more than I've ever loved anybody. But somewhere about the fifth month of my pregnancy, the depression creeps up on me. It's like a person. Like that film, the *Invasion of the Body Snatchers*.

It gets inside and you just have to wait for it to leave. I know what's going to happen. It's mainly to do with William. I tell my doctor about everything. His name's Dr Stevenson.

'Sometimes men take a while to come to terms with having a child.' He's a bit of a nervous, humble kind of man. Not at all like any doctor I've ever met. He puts you at ease straightaway. You trust him without even having to talk yourself into it.

'Why don't you go and see him. Tell him he has a responsibility to the child, if not to you. Ask him at least to pay for the birth. I'm sure if he sees you again he'll feel differently.'

The birth is $300. I think William should pay, but more than that I want him to be at the birth. Dr Stevenson convinces me to ask him for the money but the thought of him rejecting me makes me want to start praying. I haven't prayed much since the convent days, but lately, with this holy feeling I'm walking around with, I've started thinking about God again. Sometimes I pray that my baby will be okay and that the birth won't hurt too much. I also pray that William can be with me when I give birth.

It takes weeks to get up the courage to visit.

One night I bite the bullet and borrow Pommy's car to drive to his place. I sit outside looking at the house for a long time before I get out and knock at the door.

It's a share house. I'm glad when he answers instead of his friends.

'What can I do for you?' He looks shocked and very pissed off at seeing me standing there with my stomach.

'Can I come in?'

'If you must.' He lets me in, like I'm some Jehovah's Witness trying to sell him the Lord, and takes me into the kitchen. My tummy's leading the way. When we sit down, it's looming in the air like another person, which it is I suppose. He doesn't look at it once.

'How are you?' I have to start somewhere.

'Fine, thanks.' I'm beginning to know this isn't a good idea.

'Are you okay?' He doesn't look fine at all.

'Can you just get on with it.'

'Well, I just wanted to ask if you'd consider being at the birth. Even if you don't want anything to do with me, if you miss the birth now there's no way you can make up for it later. It's your baby too.'

'It's completely out of the question.' He stares at me hard.

Then I stare at the floor and try not to cry. That would be the worst thing. The hate mantra starts. It's the first time it's come since I've been pregnant. I thought it had gone for good because of how special I feel now, but here it is and it's working – relieving the pressure building up in my head. Hate, hate, hate, hate goes round in my brain. Then I bring up the next thing, even though I know this isn't going to turn out at all the way I'd hoped.

'I've decided to have a home birth and it's going to cost $300. I think you should pay for it. After all, I'm giving birth. I don't think it's too much to ask.' I don't even care about the money. I just want him to give something. Anything. But that's when he stands up.

'I think you should just go.'

He doesn't give me a choice because straightaway he's walking towards the front door. You can see he's doing everything he can to stop himself from hitting me. Not that he'd ever do it but I can see he really wants to.

'Bye,' I say at the door, hoping stupidly that he'll change his mind at the last minute.

'Goodbye,' he says, and almost slams the door in my face.

Outside, I sit in the car and bury my head in my arms that are draped over the steering wheel. I feel this baby and me are completely alone in the world and I'm not sure I'm strong enough to do it, to be a mother on my own.

The next day at work, the drowning feeling comes at me like a tidal wave. When I got pregnant I thought those days were over. I go to the roof of our building. It's more than 30 storeys high. The loneliness is what gets me most. I've always been alone but when I feel lonely and it really suffocates me, I search around in my mind for someone I can talk to, who knows me and will listen. It's been William in the past, or Joanne, but neither of them want anything to do with me. Elizabeth is my friend but she's so different to me. She cares but she doesn't really know me. She's quite conservative.

Having this baby growing inside me, I have a feeling of responsibility that overwhelms me. It makes me smaller and more lonely than ever before. I look over the edge and imagine jumping. I stand there all through lunchtime. Thinking of the life ahead of me makes me squeeze my eyes shut and moan. I'm angry and sad. Desperate to escape the storm of feelings. I want to jump. My emotions almost split me into a dozen pieces. I climb up and sit on the edge and look at the ground so far below. It isn't the pain that worries me this time, but I keep thinking about my baby splattering on the ground with me. I'm nearly six months pregnant and when I heard its heartbeat for the first time a few days ago, I cried. Not because I was sad. It was the first time I'd cried because I was happy, pumped up with a love so strong it scared me. It's funny because it scared me and gave me strength at the same time. It was like fury and humility all rolled into one. Yes, they're the words. Furious and humble. It made me want to protect this baby. When I remember that feeling, I know there's no way I can kill myself with this life inside me.

I go down and take a paper and pen into the toilet because I'm not allowed to write letters at my desk. I sit in a cubicle for an hour writing and crossing out and rewriting a note to William. I believe in the power of words. I believe if

I can just say the right ones to him, I can change the way he thinks. It's just a matter of finding the *right* words. The reason he's feeling so bad is that he blames himself for getting me pregnant. I think if I tell him it was all my fault, that I got myself pregnant, he'd let himself off the hook and be able to be there for me. I know he doesn't love me, but maybe he can at least be my friend. I think if I accept all the responsibility for getting pregnant, he'll be able to see me without the guilt.

Every day I go to the letterbox hoping for a reply.

The pregnancy is one of the best and worst times of my life. I'm floating on air some days and the rest of the time puddling around in fire and brimstone. I keep riding my bike to work even when I'm hugely pregnant at eight months. I have my fourth grade piano exam a month before I'm due.

My 23rd birthday is only a few weeks away. No word from William.

Chris is getting married to a guy who's been in love with his first girlfriend the whole time they've been going out. Finally, when he nearly loses her to another guy, he proposes. Like they'd been going out for years and all along he said he didn't really love her because he was still in love with the other woman. Chris thought she'd never get him to marry her.

'If this can happen to us, I know there's still hope for you and William. Hang in there,' Chris tells me. I want to believe her but I don't.

I go to their wedding and cry so much people think I'm drunk even though I haven't touched a drop or smoked since I got pregnant. Chris and Clive are so in love now that he's decided he does love her after all. They're delaying their honeymoon and say when they take it in a month's time I can look after their house for six weeks. I'm beginning to worry about not being able to cope on the pension which is only $90 a week and I have to pay $25 off for the loan on my land. I decide to find somewhere cheaper to live and six weeks free rent will help me save money.

I spend a lot of time at Pommy and Jacqui's place because I like the company. But Pommy's changed. She's taking pills called Tuinols which she calls chewies and she's drugged out most of the time. She tells me why.

'The first night I worked at The Square I felt like killing myself the next day and I didn't want to go back. Then this girl Karen gave me some "chewies" and the most fantastic thing happened. I couldn't remember anything I'd done the night before. It made working a piece of cake. Only trouble is, I have to take more and more to forget.'

Jacqui stopped working after a couple of months because she couldn't stand it. She also hated Pommy working there. It's getting desperate around there. I feel sorry for Christian because he's gone from being a spoilt and loved little kid into one who's, well, neglected.

One day Jacqui was supposed to pick him up from school down the road but she didn't turn up. Christian had to cross Toorak Road which was very busy at that time of day. He waited for about an hour and then crossed on his own. When he got home he knocked on the door. Then he banged but no-one answered. He went around to the back window and looked into the lounge room and saw Jacqui lying unconscious on the floor. He went to a neighbour's house and they called an ambulance. She'd taken an overdose.

'Why don't you go and work in Japan,' I tell them when Jacqui's recovered. 'You can make a heap of money and come back and not have to work at all.' What I don't point out is that there aren't any chewies there. That's what's killing Pommy and making her manic and crazy. They say they'll think about it.

One night I'm looking after Christian and he starts

crying hysterically for Pommy. She's working at The Square.
Jacqui and Pommy are having a temporary separation.
Jacqui's gone home to stay at her mother's place for a while.
I can't get him to stop crying, so I drive to where Pommy's
working. What else am I supposed to do?

I go in to get her but she's half out of it already.

'What did you bring him here for?'

'He was so upset. I've tried everything, nothing'll calm
him down.'

Pommy comes out to the car and cuddles Christian and
tells him she'll be there when he wakes up in the morning.

'Now be a good boy and go home with Auntie Barb.'

'I don't want to. I want to stay with you. I won't talk. I'll
just go to sleep. I promise. I just want to be with you,
Mummy. Please let me stay with you. I don't want to go
home.' He's begging, clinging to her like he'll never see her
again.

'Darling, mummy has to go back to work. You can't stay.
I'm sorry, you'll have to go with Auntie Barb.'

He cries louder and she has to prise him off her to get
out of the car. She has a grim, determined look on her face.

'Why the hell did you bring him? You know he can't stay.
I don't know what you expected me to do? Just take him
home.' She's very pissed off.

I leave. It's the first time I've seen Pommy turn her back
on Christian. She's always given him whatever he wanted.
That's when I really know things will never be the same
again.

I haven't been close to Christian before but being
pregnant makes me tune into him and imagine how my baby
would feel if this was happening to him. I take him home
and we snuggle up in bed together while I read a bedtime
story. I stay the night and in the morning Pommy's sleeping
in. He goes and tries to wake her but she shouts at him and
tells him to go and play. When he comes out of her room his

bottom lip starts trembling. He isn't just sad, I can see he's worried about his mum. His whole world is falling apart.

We go to the park and I tell him about the wishing tree there.

'It's a special tree and if you stand under it and make a wish it'll come true. But you have to not tell anyone what it is.'

'Which one is it Auntie Barb? Show me.'

'Part of making the wish come true is that you have to be able to find the tree yourself. You have to just know which one it is.'

We go to Fawkner Park and spend all morning looking. We make a lot of wishes just to be sure. I think he's wishing things would go back to the way they were in Canberra.

Not long after, Pommy tells me she's phoned Vlad, the boy she'd loved when she was a teenager, ten years ago.

'I looked him up in the phone book. There's not a lot of Popovs around.'

'Why?'

'I think he's the only one who's ever really cared about me.'

'What about Jacqui? And me?'

'The only guy I mean.'

'What happened?'

'He's married.'

'Did he sound happy to hear from you? Is he in love with his wife?'

'I think so. Anyway it was like we were strangers. It sounded like he couldn't wait to get off the phone. I guess his wife was there. I can't believe how bad I feel … after all these years. Funny isn't it?'

She stops talking and stares. Perhaps she's remembering how she and Vlad laid naked on the bed, without having sex, holding hands as though it was the most natural thing in the world.

I want to work as long as possible for the money. I know it'll be the last time I can work for a while. Just before I leave I ask one of the professional guys in the office, who has a couple of kids, if I can talk to him. He seems like the sort of guy you can talk to about anything.

'Of course. What can I do for you?'

'I haven't got a name yet.'

He looks at me and shifts in his seat. I'm sitting on the other side of his office desk. It seems a funny place to be having a conversation like this but where else am I going to do it and who else am I going to ask?

'Yes.'

'Well, you've just had a baby haven't you? And I just thought you might have a few ideas.'

'Hmmm. Well, what have *you* thought of? You must have a couple of names up your sleeve.'

'If it's a girl I won't have any trouble there. But if it's a boy I don't have any idea. Sebastian's one, but Elizabeth thinks that's a bit pretentious. Do you think it's pretentious?'

'Sebastian. Sebastian. Hmm. I like the sound of it. Sebastian. Will it have your surname?'

'Mmm hmmm.'

'Sebastian Biggs. Hmmm … it doesn't really have a ring does it?'

'No, I guess not. How did you name your baby?'

'My wife bought a name book. Why don't I bring it in tomorrow?'

The week after that I leave work and they take up a collection for me. They're always taking up a collection for people. One of the guys tells me that they collected more for me than for anyone else who's ever worked there. It's the first big place I've been where people like me. I know I'm a little bit weird. Maybe even a lot. They give me a radio because I'll be at home a lot on my own.

One day when Elizabeth and I are out walking in the

bush, I talk to her about something that's been on my mind for a while.

'I know it's a big thing to ask, and don't feel you have to if you'd rather not, but, would you be there when my time comes? You know, for the birth?'

A big smile breaks out on her face.

'I wondered who you were going to have. I'd be honoured. But are you sure there's no-one else you'd rather have?'

'Well, apart from William, and that's not going to happen, you're the only person I really trust.'

A mutual friend tells me that William's gone to Papua New Guinea for his holidays. The news stabs me in the chest. Some part of me has been hoping he'll turn up at the birth at the last minute. Now, at least I won't have to worry myself sick fantasising about it.

My baby's due on December 2, the day before my birthday, but the day comes and goes. I start helping out in Dr Stevenson's surgery taking notes for him while he sees his pregnant patients and ones who've already had their babies. He takes me under his wing and we talk a lot about how I feel about William and my nervousness about giving birth. I keep asking about the size of my baby because I seem huge.

'Do you think it's normal?'

'Look, I can't really say but just average, maybe eight pounds. You're fine-boned so I wouldn't expect it'd be too big. And your tummy's not huge. That's my best guess.'

He could have fooled me. It feels like a beach ball sticking a mile out in front.

I go into labour about 1am on Saturday morning the 15th of December 1979. I phone Elizabeth and she comes straight over. We call Dr Stevenson and he says to phone again when the pains get to five minutes apart. They stop at dawn but start up again in the afternoon. He comes over to sit with me. He holds my hand and suggests reading me something from the Bible. I'm feeling terminal. 'Yea though I walk through the valley of the shadow of death ...'

'That's overdoing it a bit, isn't it?' he asks.

'It's beautiful. And if I die in childbirth I won't be the first and you can't deny that.'

Later that night he goes to deliver another baby, in the country. I worry he won't make it back in time for mine.

'I've delivered more than five hundred. Trust me, you won't have this before I get back. If anything happens you can contact me by phone. It'll only take an hour to get back if you need me.'

I can see Elizabeth is scared of the responsibility of being left alone with me. We talk and listen to music. She tries to take my mind off what's happening. I swing between being excited about seeing what my baby looks like to being terrified of pushing him out.

Dr Stevenson comes back early on Sunday morning. The labour pains are eight minutes apart but when they come they're excruciating. I'm not dilating. I'm chewing on ice so fast Elizabeth has to go down and buy a bag from the service station. At lunchtime Dr Stevenson stands me up and puts his fingers up inside me to try to manually dilate me. I scream in agony. Elizabeth furrows her brow and starts talking about hospital. I start thinking about it too. We're both worried but Dr Stevenson looks calm.

'If it just isn't working when do you decide to go to hospital?' I ask him.

'Not now. Just hang in there. You'll be all right. There's nothing they can do there except induce the birth and I really don't think that's necessary.' Dr Stevenson never railroads but tells you quietly what he thinks.

'But maybe I should go. It's been 35 hours and nothing's

happening. I don't know how much longer I can go on.'

'And she hasn't slept for virtually three days, since Thursday night. Maybe she'd be better off in a hospital.' I can see drops of perspiration on Elizabeth's forehead. I know it's not because she's hot.

'It's your decision, but I wouldn't want you to regret it later just for the sake of a couple of hours. You've been committed to a home birth all along. It's up to you.'

I breathe and crunch ice through another five hours of contractions. Dr Stevenson and Elizabeth take turns having the blood squeezed from their hands. By then I've been fully dilated for more than an hour but the baby still isn't coming out. I'm lying on my back after trying kneeling on all fours and on my side. All of a sudden I feel an overpowering need to push.

'Resist it. If you push you'll tear. If you can hold …'

But I can't. It's like having an overwhelming urge to rip yourself apart. I imagine someone being drawn and quartered and know exactly how they would feel.

The head's born. The thought of getting the rest out makes me panic.

'I can't do anymore. I just can't.' I'm almost crying.

'You can. The head's the biggest part. It's the hardest. The rest is nothing. You've already torn. Just breathe. On the next contraction, just push. Gently.'

But the next contraction comes and the urge to push hard is stronger than any emotion I've ever had. It *is* an emotion. I grunt and push hard without a thought for the pain, like I'm doing the world's biggest poo.

That's it. The birth is over. I have a big baby lying on my tummy covered in blood. I ask if it's a boy or a girl.

'Look and see for yourself,' says Dr Stevenson. And he turns my baby over.

It's a boy. The pain miraculously disappears and instead I

feel like God. God is love and I know it just isn't possible that anybody in the world can have ever felt this much love before. I can't take my eyes off the gooey, slimy little bundle on my stomach. He's so engrossing I barely notice when the placenta's born. I've tasted heroin before, but no drug can compare to this.

Elizabeth looks so relieved. It's 5.10pm on Sunday. I've been in labour for 40 hours. She runs a bath for me. Lucky she'd put a plastic sheet under the cotton one because there's blood everywhere. I'm paper pale. In the bath a blood clot the size of a cricket ball comes out. Dr Stevenson guesses by measuring what he can collect from the bed in a jug, that I've lost three pints of blood.

But I don't care about anything. I'm too busy being God. Only a woman knows how He felt on the seventh day when he sat back and looked at what he'd created and saw that it was good.

THREE

SOME KIND OF MIRACLE

Elizabeth had called Pommy to let her know I was in labour. She calls again after the birth and Pommy, Jacqui and Christian come to visit. Pommy calls to ask if I need anything.

'Some meat would be good. I've lost a lot of blood and iron's supposed to help make more.'

She turns up with some uncooked steak.

'Why did you say you needed meat. There's a plate of it on the table,' Pommy says.

'That's the placenta. I bought a book on placenta stew but it doesn't look very appetising does it?' It's a monstrous, gritty, three-lobed lump that's so unusual Dr Stevenson suggests that rather than eat it, we make a plaster caste for posterity.

Pommy looks at me like I'm crazy.

'Are you going to eat that stuff on the table Auntie Barb?' Christian's mesmerised.

'Maybe. What do you think of your new cousin?'

'He's little isn't he? Look at his teensy fingers. What's his name?'

'I haven't thought of one yet.'

'Here, come to Auntie,' says Pommy picking up my baby. She looks unsteady and out of it. I'm nervous but Jacqui helps her and at least *she's* straight.

'Isn't he the most gorgeous thing you've ever seen?' I'm still transfixed.

'He's fat. How much does he weigh?'

'He isn't fat. He's perfect. He's 9 pound 12 ounces.' I don't have the strength to argue. I'm so weak I can barely lift my head off the pillow.

'What are you playing the dying swan for? Anyone'd think you'd just been through a bloody war or something.' Doesn't she remember she was exactly the same when I'd visited her in hospital after Christian was born?

'Well, I have lost about half my blood and been in labour for nearly two whole days.'

'Linda, shut up! She's just had a baby for Christ sake.' Jacqui's great. She has hold of my gorgeous little baby boy and coos and smiles at him before giving Christian a hold.

They don't stay long. Pommy says she has to get to work.

Dr Stevenson goes off to deliver another baby and Elizabeth's so exhausted she heads home to sleep before work the next morning.

'If you need anything at all during the night and you want me to come over, just call.' I can't walk because I'm so badly torn. I won't let Dr Stevenson sew me up either. The thought of anymore pain down there's enough to make me want to punch out anyone who tries. He says it will heal itself. Eventually.

Finally I'm left alone with my little boy. He's snuggled in the crook of my arm and I can't stop looking at him. Every second I'm with him I think my heart can't stand it anymore. It feels like bursting. I'm overwhelmed by my responsibility to this tiny thing. How can you not be the best mother in the world when you have the world's most perfect baby to take care of?

It takes two weeks to name Dan. A Christian woman I meet in the street comes up with Daniel because it's a name from the Bible. It isn't very creative but it suits him and is better than anything I can think of. Even though it fits him I don't register the name with the Department of Births, Deaths and Marriages because I think something better will come up. No name seems good enough. How can you name perfection?

A couple of weeks after Dan's born we both catch bad colds. I can't recover because I'm waking up four or five times a night to feed him. It's during this time that my brother Peter rings.

'G'day Barbara. How's it goin'?'

'Not bad. Have you heard? I've had a baby. His name's Dan.'

'Yeah, I know. Mum told me.'

'He's beautiful. A bit sick at the minute but gorgeous anyway. How are you?'

'Pretty good. Pretty good. I just thought I'd let ya know I'm in the finals of a pool competition at me local pub. I was wonderin' if you wanted to come and see me play. I've got a pretty good chance of winnin', otherwise I wouldn't ask.'

I haven't heard from Peter in nearly two years. Since Mick died.

'When is it? At night I suppose.'

'Yeah, next Frid'y.' I haven't got a car. We're sick. I can't begin to imagine how we could get there and back at night on public transport. I say sorry, I'd love to but I just can't. I can hear he's trying, against all odds really, to be family.

'It's okay. Don't worry about it I just thought I might win that's all. I asked Pommy and she's workin'. I just thought, ya know, you might wanna see me win that's all.'

'Maybe we can come around in the day.'

'Nah, don't worry. I just thought you might not have anything else on, that's all.'

'Sorry, I'd really like to but with Dan being sick and being out at night and no car ...'

'Nah, don't worry about it. Like I said, I just thought I'd ask. It's nothin' really.'

After I hang up I think how strange that he'd asked me to come. He'd never invited me to anything before in his life. I didn't think he even liked me that much. Peter and I weren't what you'd call close. We don't dislike each other but we just don't have anything in common. That's when I realise the poor kid doesn't have anyone else he can ask. I feel bad but I don't see any way out of it.

I think about how close he and Mick must have been in boarding school for all those years. How it must have been for him, just 16, when Mick, really the one in the whole family he must have been close to, was found shot in the mouth in his room in the psych hospital where he worked. He'd just graduated. None of us understood. Maybe least of all Peter.

I regret selling my car. I can't go out at night or anywhere far away with Dan.

Then, just before Christmas, Pommy asks me over to her place.

'We've got a surprise for you.'

'What is it?'

'I know, Auntie Barb. I know what it is.'

'You shut your little trap, Christian. It's supposed to be a surprise!' Jacqui says.

They blindfold me. Outside they take the blindfold off and press a set of keys into my hand. It's a car!

'We thought with Dan you'd need something to get around. A girl at work was selling it. She says it's really reliable. What do you think?' Pommy can see me swallowing the lump in my throat and smiles as she takes Dan from me.

'Go on. Take it round the block.'

I give her a big hug and whisper to Jacqui to keep an eye on Dan. I take Christian for a spin.

'Now, when you move into Chris's house you've got no excuse not to keep visiting,' Pommy says when I get back.

A few weeks after I get the car, I go over to Peter's house and bake him a cake. I feel guilty about the pool competition. Now I'm trying to make it up, do what sisters do, but he's in the bedroom playing some kind of electronic game. He shows me his dope crop in a cupboard too and tells me all about how he's waiting for his long service leave from the railways. He's only 20. It's a beautiful day outside and his bedroom, where the computer is, is dark and depressing. I find everything about his flat lifeless and empty. I don't want to come again.

From the minute Dan's born I can't stop feeling like I've performed some kind of miracle. I felt a bit like an angel when I was pregnant, but now it's ten times stronger. I sit in parks with him in my arms and wonder if people know how special I am. I might as well be wearing a halo as far as I'm concerned. I know I'm not the first person to have a baby, but I keep thinking about the birth, about what I did, how I made life. I'm on a cloud, floating above my body wondering when this feeling will go and I'll be my old self again. Every now and then I dream that I'm covered in light, but then I become aware of this small, dark blob deep down that slowly starts eating me from the inside. As it grows, the light coming from my skin fades. I wake up in a panic before the light completely disappears.

A couple of weeks later, when Dan's maybe two months old, I move into Chris's house. I've saved some money from work but need more if I'm ever going to build a house. This will save me an extra $35 dollars a week in rent.

It's such a hot summer and Dan cries and cries with the heat. I ring Dr Stevenson so many times he gets cross and tells me to stop worrying. I lay Dan on a towel and put a wet singlet on him. I'm afraid he'll stop breathing. A few weeks ago he didn't exist and it seems like any minute he can stop being as easily as he started. From then on, on boiling hot days, I dress him in wet clothes to keep him cool. Like an air-conditioner. People think the way I mother is strange but I don't.

One day I have to hang some washing out. Going out the back there's a swing flywire door. I'm carrying Dan and the washing basket full of wet nappies. I carry him mostly in a sling but this time he's on my hip and I'm struggling to open the door. I stumble and for a second nearly drop him and save the washing. It happens in slow motion, like five years ago when I'd fallen asleep riding my motor bike and came off and rolled. It seemed like forever, until I stopped. At the last moment I drop the washing and hold onto Dan. I leave the washing on the ground and walk down the ramp into the backyard, shocked. I'm holding him, not tightly, but with as much body contact as I can get. I feel his little feet touching my sides, his cheek on my chest, his heart beating against my heart. It's the beginning of summer. Like the day itself is saying 'Don't ever forget me!' Maybe it's the crispness in the air you can almost touch. Jasmine's growing along the fence. Its scent swirls around us on the breeze as I walk up and down. If I'd dropped Dan, he'd be dead. A feeling comes over me that I've been blessed. Whatever the word means, I know it's the right one. Not because I haven't dropped him, but because he's here at all. I've created goodness, and if I've done that, I can't be all bad. Can I? No matter what else happens in my life, I know for the first time something that's absolute, that doesn't need anyone else to know or believe or tell me it's true, that in this moment, I've had it all. This is the best life has to offer. I suddenly know the only thing that seems important, that in this moment, *I* am love. And yes, I decide that there must be goodness somewhere in the black emptiness that sometimes threatens to swallow me.

I have to give up serious piano practice because Dan never sleeps for long. When he does, there are nappies to wash, floors to vacuum, food to cook. But sometimes when he's upset, nothing calms him like scales or exam pieces I used to practise. It's like he remembers the sounds from inside me.

My piano exam results come. An 'A'. Wow! I'm so proud I just stare at the certificate and smile like an idiot every time I pass it on the sideboard.

Sometimes I go to South Yarra and babysit Christian while Pommy's working at The Square. Jacqui and she are always splitting up over the work, then getting together again. Pommy's getting into it, trying to organise a Prostitutes Union.

She says the trouble is, girls who are desperate sometimes charge a measly $10. Then guys don't want to pay $15. It's not so bad for her, because her place has a set price, but the girls on the street are the ones who really suffer. They're so doped out on drugs they'd do it for a hit if they had to.

Pommy goes onto the street and hands out leaflets she's written and photocopied. She says it's not getting off the ground because the street girls are too far gone on drugs to get involved or even care about making their lives better. Never mind she's hooked on chewies and God knows what else.

I'm in the bath, laying Dan down with his ears under water with the tap running. His face becomes fixed with concentration and I realise he's listening to the water. I start turning the tap on and off, watching his face. I know he must be remembering the gurgling sounds he'd heard inside my tummy. It's then I realise I know everything about Dan's world. I know how he thinks and everything he's ever seen in his short life because I've spent almost every second with him since he was born. I wonder if my mother ever felt this way about me.

When Chris and Clive come back from their honeymoon, I decide to move to Adelaide. I don't want to be in Melbourne, too close to William where I know I'll exhaust myself with thinking about going to see him. Also, I've worked out that my savings are never going to grow into anything like enough to build a house on my land now that I'm on the pension.

Before I leave Melbourne, I decide to visit William. I figure that whatever reaction he has, I can handle it because I'm leaving in a week. I have to tell him that the social security people want to know who Dan's father is. They want to try to get maintenance money from him.

I phone and tell him I'm moving to Adelaide, hoping that will calm him down before saying there's something else I need to talk about. He agrees to meet me one night after work.

When I arrive at his house and take Dan out of the car, he wakes up and starts crying. He's been crying a lot lately and the only thing that stops him is driving around in the car. So when William comes to the door, I ask if he'll come out and talk in the car while I drive around the block. He looks fleetingly at Dan snuggled in his bunny blanket in my arms.

'Okay, I'll just get my coat,' he says. He's dignified. You can see he's holding himself in more than usual but that he's not exactly pissed off with me.

He comes back and gets in the front seat and doesn't even look in the back where Dan's in the bassinet, still crying.

We drive on the freeway near his place so I don't have to keep stopping. We try to talk but Dan's still crying. He won't stop. I tell William I have to pull over and feed him. He directs me off the freeway to a small quiet street. I get Dan out and bring him in the front seat and put him on the breast. William looks but pretends not to. He asks a few polite questions and I tell him what I'm going to do in Adelaide. We talk about everything except the small bundle on my lap.

Then I tell him about the maintenance.

'I don't believe he's my child,' he tells me.

'William, it couldn't be anyone else's.'

'How do *I* know that? I want a blood test.'

I don't blame him. After all, I was a prostitute when we met. It still stabs me in the chest a bit though. I say I'll organise one before we leave.

When Dan's finished I ask William if he'll hold him while I drive us back to his house. I show him how to burp Dan but he holds him like he's a block of wood and stares straight ahead out the window. He can't help himself, every now and then, he steals looks at this baby that he's trying to tell himself isn't his son. He thinks I don't notice because I've got my eyes on the road. But I notice alright. It's touching and sad at the same time. That William's so determined not to have anything to do with Dan that he can't even look at him. Even though I give him the privacy to look down in peace, by keeping up a patter of chat while I look at the road, I can feel him swell with pride. I turn around and catch a fleeting look on his face before he quickly resumes his stoic stare out the front window. I'm sure it's tenderness I see there. Seeing that look makes me want to cry. The only other person in the whole world who could love Dan the way I do, refuses it. He's shoring himself up against the storm that must be going on in him right now, as he's trying to tell himself this bundle that he's holding in his arms for the first time is not his son.

When we arrive back at his house, we say our goodbyes. When he passes Dan over to me, he does it stiffly, but there's a gentleness to his movement that brings on a lump in my throat. I can barely see the road all the way home.

Not long after I arrive in Adelaide, I see a cheap house. It's a Victorian sandstone place in Brompton, a few kilometres from the city centre. It's on a railway line, right near the bells. That's the reason it's so cheap: $19,000. I find a bank that agrees to give me a loan on the strength of my pension and the fact that I've been repaying my land loan and now have equity. What a difference in their attitude when you're already a property owner.

While I'm waiting for settlement, I enrol in an arts degree. If I become a teacher I can have the same hours and holidays as Dan when he starts school. I find a student house with two girls who love babies. Ellie's studying politics but being a country lass from Mildura, she becomes like another mother to Dan. I put him in the uni crèche while I go to lectures but I can come back and breastfeed between classes. Then my prac. teaching starts. I think I'm so lucky because the school's across the road from home. I only have to do two days a week, so Ellie says she'll look after Dan and bring him across to be fed. The first day she brings him, the headmistress nearly has kittens.

'What do you think you're doing there, young lady. Put that, that … put it away this minute.' She means my breast. I tell her I'll feed outside in the playground if she'd prefer it. She splutters. 'You certainly will not!'

Everything's too hard. I'm tired all the time and cry at the drop of a hat. I can't see how I can finish the prac. teaching and keep breastfeeding. I'm lonely. My sister Bloss has been living in Adelaide for years, since she nearly got caught with Ma in Whyalla for defrauding the government of all those pensions. She was only driving the car, at all of 14, but when she gave Pommy's name and date of birth they let her go and she hitched to Adelaide. She's been here ever since. Anyway, she and I hardly see each other because she's so busy. She'd got a job in a company and when they downsized she and her old boss lost their jobs and started their own company. Now she works all hours of the day and night and doesn't seem the slightest bit interested in Dan or me. I want to be back in Melbourne where at least I have Jacqui and Pommy, even though she is off the rails.

One day I ring Pommy in tears and tell her I want to drop out of the course. She tells me she and Jacqui are going on a world trip and then stopping off in Japan to work for a bit. She says I can look after the flat. I can't believe she's leaving Christian behind with Jenny in Sydney. I know she's the oldest of all of us kids but she's got four little kids of her own. And anyway, how can she just can leave him like that?

Bloss's lease has finished so I come up with a solution for both of us. She can rent the Brompton house from me after the settlement comes through and the rent will cover the mortgage. She agrees.

I move back to Melbourne to babysit Pommy's place. The rent is too much on my own, so I find another single mum to share.

Rachel and I have a lot in common. She has a son a few months older than Dan. Her mother died when she was eight and her father took her into his bed like a replacement wife. He'd call out to her at night, 'Come and turn the light off for Daddy would you?' She'd come in and he'd ask if she wanted a cuddle. She'd get into bed and turn her back on him and he'd 'seduce' her.

She said it was the only time she got affection after her mum died. He was a bastard to the other kids. He poured boiling water over her brother once. That went on until she ran away from home when she was 12 and ended up in Winlaton, a home for girls, where she was introduced to hard-core drugs and stealing. I understand everything she says.

'I'd scream at everybody, anyone who got in my way. Then when I got pregnant with Justin, I knew if I didn't do something I'd end up screaming at him too.'

So when she was four months pregnant she started primal therapy. Every time she had to bash pillows, her pillow would turn into her father. She tells me how late in her pregnancy she'd gone to Adelaide to see him.

'When he was seeing me off on the train he put his hand up my dress and tongue-kissed me. Part of me was so pissed off with him, but you know what? I kissed him back for a minute. I've never forgiven him for that. Or myself.'

The details of her story are different to mine. The man, the way he did it, our needing to be loved by the guy even though we know they've done something to us far worse than rape. The loving and hating them at the same time. In essence it's my story too. But the most important thing we have in common is knowing that having our babies saved us. *Is* saving us.

'It's like they've set your sexual computer from the very beginning and you can't change the programming,' she said about her father.

I remember my customer in Japan who had been condemned to a life of only gaining true sexual satisfaction when fat, white women sat on his face. He'd been a houseboy in a General's house after the Second World War and one day the lady of the house cornered him and sat on his face. She wouldn't let him up until she came. He'd been programmed at age 12.

A few months after I get back from Adelaide, the phone rings.

'BB. It's me. Joanne.'

It's been almost two years since she'd told me to bugger off.

'Hi.' I'm pretty cool towards her but my heart starts beating fast.

'How've you been?'

'Fine.' I'm not giving an inch.

'Look, if you don't want to talk to me that's fine. I know I've been horrible to you but I feel just so awful, you're the only person I've got left. Robert's left me. He's been rooting around with that floozy Jan. She was supposed to be my best friend. I'm desperately lonely.' By now she's crying.

'Well, I've had a baby since I saw you last.' What about when I could have used a friend? Where was she then?

'I know. I heard. I wanted to ring but I didn't know where you were.'

Right.

'So, you found me. What do you want?'

'BB, please don't do this to me. You're the only one I can turn to. Do you want me to crawl? I'm desperate. I'm lonely. All my supposed friends knew Robert was having an affair and not one of them told me. Talk to me. I need you. Don't make me beg.'

Joanne knows how to pull my strings. She may be begging but she's sounding angry and somehow it makes you respect her all the same.

She comes around and tells me the Robert saga from beginning to end.

'You know the worst, most humiliating part, is that after I found out, I took him back. And when he told me the reason he'd run off was because I didn't like sex, I bent over backwards to please him. So to speak. And still he rejected me. I keep thinking of all the things I did ... and you know how I find those body things a bit erky perky.'

'What sort of things?'

'I don't even want to think about it, BB. Just trust me, every fantasy he ever had, I fulfilled. I was so cross with myself later because it was like giving away a part of myself. Very fucking humiliating, let me tell you.'

Joanne still can't work because of her agoraphobia. She says when she has a panic attack she feels like she's hanging out of a plane by her fingernails. And they can happen anywhere and anytime without warning. At least she got the house from the separation. It was paid off too. She knows all someone has to do for me to open my heart is be needy and vulnerable. It only takes that one visit and we're living in each other's pockets again.

After I've been living in the Walsh Street flat for three months, Pommy phones to say she's coming back. Rachel and I find another place together in Pine Avenue, Elwood. It's covered in nicotine stains which make it dark and depressing. So we paint it, taking turns to babysit the kids. By the time we finish it looks a million bucks. It's huge and just across the road from the beach.

When Pommy gets back, she's lost a lot of weight. She's always been a bit chubby. Now she's like a stick. She says she's in love.

'His name's Jun. He's a Yakuza, it's the …'

'I know. The Japanese mafia. How do you know he isn't just saying that? Is the top of his little finger missing? All Yakuzas have that.'

'Yeah. He's a dealer. He sells shabu.'

I groan. Drugs aren't easy to get in Japan. Trust Pommy to find a dealer. Maybe that's why she's so skinny. I've never heard of shabu. Pommy says it's a man-made drug. At least it isn't heroin and it can't be worse than chewies. I hope.

'I'm going back to marry him.' Between biting her nails, she's picking sores on her skin, making them bleed.

'What about Christian?'

'He'll be all right with Jenny.'

Is this the same mother who spoilt him rotten, gave him everything he ever wanted? Now I've got Dan I just can't understand how she could abandon him so easily.

'I don't think he *will* be all right. I talked to him. He's missing you like crazy.'

'What else can I do? I have to work.' She's getting pissed off with me because I'm putting a spanner in the works.

'Look, you've just got to take him back with you. It's not fair.' I keep thinking how Dan would feel if I went away and left him for months on end.

'I can't. What if I can't cope? I'm working. What will I do with him?' Is she angling for something or about to turn on me?

'Can't Jacqui look after him?' I'm being careful. All I need to do is say the wrong thing and she'll just say no. I'm fighting for Christian as if he's myself. Or Dan. That's when I realise that the reason I love Dan so much isn't so noble after all. It's like he's myself. In bringing him up, I'm bringing up myself all over again at the same time. If I fail with him, somehow I fail myself too.

'She's not talking to me. She's stayed in Japan and got her own flat now.' Her foot's going up and down like a piston. We all get it from Mother. I wonder if Gran did the same thing.

'You should be earning enough to pay for a babysitter. Just think about it. Imagine how you'd feel if you were him.'

A week later, two days before she's going back, she rings me.

'I've decided I'll do it. I'll take him, but if I can't cope you have to come and help. Okay?'

I agree but figure she'll never really make a call on the promise.

Meanwhile Rachel and I help each other out with babysitting. She helps Dr Stevenson with home births and teaches me macrobiotic cooking. I buy a child seat for my bicycle for her son and carry Dan around in a backpack, dinking them both. We've read a book that's all the rage with New Age mums. It's called *The Continuum Concept* and written by an anthropologist who lived with a South American Indian tribe. It tells you how they let kids explore the world without worrying too much about the consequences. The theory is, if you let them play with knives, they learn through experience that knives are sharp. If you let them play near fire they learn fire is hot. We wonder what use it's going to be to them if we let them play near busy roads, and they learn you get squashed by cars. Some parents we know take the whole idea too far. Mums who've never heard of the concept think I'm irresponsible. Even though I know what they're thinking, I don't care. It's supposed to give kids lots of confidence in their abilities. I decide confidence is the main quality I want to give Dan. It leads to lots of funny looks from strangers.

He walks early and one day, at ten months, he climbs to the top of a slippery dip. I'm standing underneath, trying to hedge my bets about whether, once he's at the top where I can't reach, he'll fall off the left or right side of the slide. By now I'm used to the balancing act of being a Continuum Concept Mum while trying to head off spinal damage. How could I rob my baby boy of the pride of getting to the top? Some park mums look daggers at me, others shake their heads. They think I've got rocks in my head.

I get a reputation in the neighbourhood as a reckless mum. One old lady who lives nearby abuses me in the street for letting Dan play in the gutter with a paper boat after a heavy storm. 'He'll get typhoid,' she rants at me. I stick to my guns and weather abuse for breastfeeding in public, letting Dan pat strange dogs, picking him up by one arm, throwing him over my shoulder so he's hanging upside down on my back. I've got my reasons and having half of Melbourne hate me during the tram strike's given me lots of practice at being unpopular.

I'm loving being a mum, even if it's lonely sometimes. Then, when I least expect it, I get a phone call.

'Barb?' It's the middle of the night.

'Hmmm? Pommy? Is that you?' I get a sinking feeling.

'You said you'd come and help with Christian. Well, now I need you.' She sounds desperate. Her voice is breaking. 'If you don't come, I'm going to kill myself.'

'What's the matter?'

'Everything. Just come, okay? You promised.' Pommy isn't vulnerable very often. She doesn't do begging.

I don't have good memories of Japan. Pommy's somewhere I don't want to be. There's a cesspit out there and now my head's above water, I want to keep it there.

'I don't want to come and hang around while you get out of it on drugs. I can't stand it and I don't want Dan being around that stuff. If I thought I could actually help it'd be different, but I don't want to play babysitter while you get off your face.'

'I promise I'll go straight. I'll get off everything. Okay? I promise.'

What if she can't do it? What if it turns out a mess? I want to help Christian and her. I love Pommy more than anyone else, apart from Dan. I know she'd help me if the situation was reversed. Why is life so hard?

'Well? Are you there?'

'If you can't stay off the drugs, I'll come straight home.' I know she won't be able to. She's got no money for my ticket. The only thing I can sell is the piano.

A week later Pommy rings again and I tell her my flight number. She says Jacqui'll meet the plane. They're not living together anymore but they're still friends.

Rachel and I say goodbye at the airport. She says she'll look after everything while I'm away. Her boyfriend agrees to move in and pay my rent while I'm gone.

When I arrive nobody's there to pick me up. I have to stay in a hotel in Tokyo and phone Ma's friend in Canberra to find out their phone number. I only find out later that Jacqui had been playing with a Rubik's cube for hours and completely forgotten about me arriving, that she'd been on shabu that day.

From the moment I get to the apartment things are unreal. When I walk in the door, Pommy doesn't bother to stop putting on her makeup, like she'd seen me yesterday. Christian's excited as all get out. He gives Dan a big cuddle and says how much he's grown. At least someone's happy we're here.

Pommy's got a full, round, pretty face but she's slapping

on the makeup way too thick. She looks like a geisha. I'm not in the door two minutes and she asks if I have any money. I'm practically broke.

'We'll have to think about what to do tomorrow. I've gotta sleep.'

'I thought you were going out. Why've you just made yourself up?'

'I do that in case Jun comes. He's never seen me without makeup before. And he's never going to either if I can help it. Once he came and I hadn't made myself up so I locked myself in the toilet. He banged on the bloody door for ages but there was no way I was coming out.'

So, Pommy goes to bed.

And that's where she stays for the next week. She gets up to take her makeup off and put it back on again in case Jun comes. I don't lay eyes on him for weeks. I take Dan and Christian to parks and we go sightseeing.

When Pommy's feeling better, she decides to earn some money. She says she was offered a smuggling trip. She'll be paid $2000 to do a circuit of Korea, China and Hong Kong, taking electronic goods in and out so customs duty doesn't have to be paid. She's done it before.

'I don't want you to go Mummy. You won't come back. I know you won't!' Christian's eyes are full of panic.

'Darling, of course I'll come back. I love you. Mummy wouldn't go and leave her little boy. I'll just be gone a week. I promise. That's just seven sleeps. I promise. We need the money.'

Two weeks go by. We hear nothing from her. Christian and I are stretched like guitar strings. He's being horrible to me. Not doing what I ask. Throwing his food around. Swearing. He hasn't said anything about Pommy except to ask when I think she'll be back. Every day he nags me but I don't know what to say.

'Soon. I'm sure she'll call us soon.'

'It's been more than seven sleeps.'

I do my best to convince him that something must have happened to hold her up.

I don't know what's going on.

Then, one morning over breakfast, I snap. Christian's kicking Dan as he eats. I tell him to stop.

'Just fuck off! You're not my mum, you can't tell me what to do!' he screams, and hits Dan. I grab a broom. He runs out into the bedroom. I chase him and start hitting.

'I don't know why you're doing this to me. What have I done to deserve all this?' I scream at him.

By then he's squatting in a corner of the room, arms covering his head. I'm hitting and shouting.

He starts to cry, screaming like a dying animal.

'It's not you anyway! It's Mum. She's never coming back. She promised she'd only be seven sleeps. Now she's gone and she's never coming back.'

I feel terrible. I put my arms around him and we both cry. I rock him.

A few days later, while Christian's riding his bike, he's hit by a car reversing out of a driveway. He isn't hurt but an ambulance comes and the driver insists he goes to hospital to make sure there's nothing wrong. Christian's hysterical. I speak enough Japanese to tell them he's fine, that he doesn't want to go. He clings to me like he's about to be dragged off to the electric chair. His nails dig into my arms. The ambulance officers try to pull him away.

'Make them stop, Auntie Barb. Tell them I'm all right. Tell them I'm not hurt. I don't want to go.'

Everybody's in the flat; the ambulance people, the woman who'd run into Christian and all her family as well. I tell them Christian's mother's away and he's frightened. That he doesn't want to go and he isn't hurt. They keep insisting.

They're bullying me, saying he'll only be gone an hour, grabbing him by the arm. I explain that to Christian but he becomes more hysterical when he thinks I'm on their side and he's losing the battle

'They can't make me. Tell them they can't make me.' He's practically strangling me he's hanging on to my neck so tight. Suddenly I know what he's thinking. He thinks if Pommy doesn't know where he is she won't find him. He feels like he's disappearing down some crazy rabbit hole where nothing's like it's supposed to be. He's getting further and further away from the safe, secure world he used to know into a world that doesn't make sense anymore. No matter who explains it differently, he doesn't trust adults now. If his mum lied, how can he trust what anyone says? How can I let them take him? In the end, I stand in front of him.

'He's not going. He's frightened. He's not hurt and he's not going anywhere.'

They rabbit on too quickly for me to catch anything. I hear the word insurance and figure they don't want any claims later if we discover he really is hurt. I tell them we don't want any money now or later. They all leave.

A few days later Pommy comes back. She's been gone three weeks.

'They kept wanting me to do more and more trips. I earnt $5000 in the end.'

'Why didn't you call? Christian's been worried sick. He thought you weren't coming back.'

'It just wasn't that easy. Anyway, I'm back now. You know how much Mummy loves you don't you? You know Mummy would never, ever leave you, don't you sweetheart?'

Christian's face changes from hope to doubt and back again a hundred times as Pommy cuddles and reassures him. Later that night, when she's reading him a bedtime story, he clings to her as if she'll disappear before his eyes if he doesn't hang on tight.

I keep doing my yoga every day to help me not get too drawn into what's happening. Pommy's getting neurotic. She starts going back to work occasionally but hates it. She also starts stalking Jun and trying to track him down in the places where she knows he hangs around. After I've been here three months, I meet him. He's very tall for a Japanese, and skinny. He has so many missing teeth he could have a bit part in a horror movie. Pommy explains the attraction to me.

'I chose him because all the girls thought I should like this other guy Amano who's rich and handsome. But I hated the way they thought Jun didn't have a chance because he's ugly and a drug dealer. I think I went for him just to spite them.' She's always gone for the underdog.

I start writing a diary for Dan as a record of his early years that he can read when he grows up. But really, maybe I'm writing to stop myself going crazy.

FOUR

YOU HAVE TO GO
SOMETIME

February 28, 1981

WELL DAN, it's the last day of the month and we're moving from the apartment in Isogo to Honmoku, Yokohama.

You've been doing lots of things lately. When you see a pair of shoes lying around you put them on and strut around the apartment looking proud. One day Christian was mucking around and hugging me. You burst into tears. I couldn't believe it – you were jealous!

I'm still carrying you everywhere in the backpack. That's normal here in Japan. But you're so heavy.

Pommy goes out all the time and is sometimes gone for days. We're in this pokey little apartment which makes everybody on edge. Pommy, when she's home, Dan and Christian. And of course me. The last apartment was huge, especially for Japan. But here we're squashed into two small rooms. Pommy couldn't afford the rent on the other one and we got kicked out. I begin to resent being used as a babysitter so she can go running around after Jun. And who knows, taking drugs again for all I know. Also, I feel like me being here is just helping her to keep ruining her life.

After a couple of weeks in the new place, Pommy comes home after being gone for two days and we have a fight. I tell her whenever she doesn't come home Christian sobs and treats me like it's all my fault. I say I'm not going to be stuck in the tiny apartment with two kids for days on end so she can go out and play. That's when she tells me to pack my bags and go back to Australia.

I'm a bit devastated that she could kick me out. And reject me again. I've always felt like that with Pommy. I've always wanted her to love me like I love her. Fierce is a good word for how I feel about her. I always want more from her than she wants to give me, but when it comes down to it, whatever I do, however much I love her, it never seems like enough. Enough for what? Maybe I'm just a bottomless pit and nothing will ever fill me up. That's what scares me the most. I try not to think about it.

I can feel something brewing with Pommy and I don't want to be here for it. I know there's Christian and I don't feel good about leaving him with her, but I know there's no way on earth he'd come back to Australia with me. I know that's what Pommy really wants, but I'd have to drag him kicking and screaming. I think she knows that too. I leave the apartment in tears with Dan under one arm and my bag under the other.

I go to stay at a hotel until I can get a flight home. There isn't one for about a week.

When Pommy rings and finds out we still haven't left yet, she accuses me of plotting to stay in Japan an extra few days. I think she's going crazy. I'm very cut up about how much she seems to hate me. I know things are going to get worse.

Jacqui turns up to visit but doesn't seem to appreciate how crazy Pommy seems to be. Then one day I realise why. We're sitting around the hotel and she starts digging at the skin on her hands with a needle. She tells me she has little animals living under there and if we watch really close, I'll see one before it dives back under her skin. She really has me convinced she has parasites in the layers of her skin. Well, I've been to India and I figure it's possible. We don't see any and she keeps going at it for hours.

It takes me a while to realise they're both crazy because of the shabu they're taking. Even Jacqui. Sensible old Jac. I realise if this can happen to her, it can happen to anyone. Lives are going off the rails all over the place and I want to get myself and Dan back to a place where people are at least trying to be normal. I'm worn out by the dramas. I'm still cut up about Pommy and feel like my heart's been through the heavy wringer cycle. I can't wait to leave.

When we get back to Australia, things don't improve. There seems to be one thing after another. Rachel's boyfriend Des moved in while we were away and they've decided they want to live by themselves. So, I get a cold reception when I move back into my old room. For a few days I feel like I'm going crazy myself. I'm still desperate and grief-stricken about Pommy telling me to piss off and just know something terrible is going to happen to her.

While I was away, everything in her flat was taken to the tip by the agent. She'd left without telling them. I thought she'd organised something and never thought to ask. She had money. But just before I got back, when the rent hadn't been paid for three months and they got an order from the tenants tribunal, they came and took everything away. Everything. All the photos of Christian growing up, all his drawings from school that Pommy had kept. All his toys. A whole life taken to the dump.

When things are very desperate, my first thought is to get away. I've just been away, but now I need to do something on my own that stretches me to the limit. I need something to gather all my energies and focus them outside the mess in my head. It stops me from going crazy. That's why I decide to ride a bicycle to Sydney with Dan. It's something William would do. He doesn't have a car and cycles everywhere, on wild adventures all over the place. When I get lonely I think about him. I want to be more like him. Stable, happy, healthy, enthusiastic about life. Normal.

I decide I'm going to need money for a month's bond when I get a flat of my own, and I have to buy the bicycle too, so I decide to sell my car. That way I'll be more like William too. I only know how ridiculous and un-normal it sounds when Joanne's new boyfriend Bear laughs when I tell them over dinner one night. His real name is Russell but Joanne calls him that on account of how big and like Pooh he is. Joanne tells me later he'd asked, 'She won't really go, will she?'

'He doesn't know the old BB yet does he?' she tells me. Is she proud to know such a crazy person as me? Could she really be proud of me?

I get so busy organising gear and selling some bits of furniture that I don't have time to fall apart.

I'm worried about a few things – weight, because Dan's pretty heavy all on his own, carrying enough water, loneliness, boredom, hills, camping and bike problems. I've only been camping twice in my life, with Elizabeth, and the furthest I've ever ridden in one hit is 20km. I don't know what I'm letting us in for. With the money I get from selling more furniture I buy a lightweight specialty bike, a child seat to go on the back and panniers. Joanne takes a photo of us just before we leave.

We ride about four hours a day. Mainly in the morning.

In Seymour I send William a letter telling him about our trip. I also send some things home that I'd snuck into my pannier bags because there was room. But the bike's so heavy I decide to send them home. I'm thinking of sending my little stove home when the gas cylinder is finished. I cut my toenails today and wondered how much less weight that would be!

The Shepparton policeman pulls me over and threatens to have Dan taken away by welfare because we're riding to Sydney. He tells me to stop the trip and go home. I don't think he should be able to tell me what to do. He's just trying to scare me. I say go to hell, but not in so many words. You have to be careful with police because you never know how power crazy they might be. I call his bluff and tell him to go ahead and call welfare. Eventually he lets me go with a warning. 'You be careful, young lady.' As if because I'm a woman and a single parent I'm some kind of imbecile who doesn't know how to look after myself and my baby.

That night we pitch our tent in a caravan park. In the morning, a woman comes up and we start talking. I find out she's a single parent living in the park.

'I wish I could do what you're doing,' she says.

'There's no reason why you can't.'

'Oh, nah, I could never do something like that.' She looks shy. Her kid's younger than Dan.

'Why not?'

'I just couldn't, that's all. You must be really brave.' I feel kind of good about that but really, I don't understand why anyone would think riding a bicycle could be brave. Anyone would think there were murderers in the country or killer bees on the roads or something. Maybe she means being in an accident. Well, we could get run over by a truck but I've thought about that and decided that neither of us would know about it. We'd be dead and you have to go sometime, so what's to worry about there? And anyway, it's not like you'd miss seeing us riding along with all that gear and a bright orange seat with a baby on it.

The next morning when I'm packing up, a whole crowd starts to gather. I ask the girl what they're staring at.

'I think they can't believe how you can fit everything on,' she tells me. I look at the gear. She's right. It's hard to imagine how everything can fold down so small. There's Dan on the back, the tent and sleeping bag piled high behind him and the full saddle bags with pots and pans hanging out on the front wheels

I love the quiet in the bush. Often there's not much traffic at all. We take the smaller roads where we can. One day there are birds lined up on a fence, about six of them. They take turns to follow us. The last one flies to the front of the line, then the next last one flies to the front, like they're following and watching us, playing leapfrog.

I stop at a tiny town and go to the post office for a stamp for one of my postcards to William. A woman starts talking to me.

'Is that your bike out the front?'

I tell her it is and we chat. She invites me to stay the night at her house. She's married and has kids. Her husband is some important guy on the city council. She tells me all about the town. It's dry as a bone and not a blade of grass in sight. It's tiny. That's why I'm so surprised when she tells me it's actually a very rich town because of all the sheep. Once a year small plane loads of people come from Sydney and Melbourne, journalists and photographers and all these rich and important people and models and everything. They come to a fashion parade here at the beginning of the wool season in the middle of the bush.

It's hard to believe. She tells me how there's all this snobbery around and that the very rich farmers have a lawn bowls club.

'Lawn bowls in the middle of the driest town from here to Timbuctu!' she says. 'Do you know how scarce water is around here? And they use it to water a bloody lawn for bowls. It's so toffy you have to be invited to join too. We've been here for years, and even though Ted's the Chief Executive Officer, we can't get a membership.'

I wonder why she wants to if she thinks it's so silly.

Between there and another town I stop off to fill up my water bottle at an old farm house. It's very weird. The house has broken windows and paper covering them in places, the fly wire door is all torn and dropping off its hinges. There are dark, filthy, curtains in tatters at the window. I can't believe anyone really lives here but there are old men's clothes hanging on the line and a dog is barking. No-one comes out of the house so I fill my bottle and ride back down the long, long driveway. I'm nervous, as though someone's watching me. I get a creepy feeling, like someone's got a gun on my back. Maybe it's just my imagination but I breathe a sigh of relief when I'm back on the road.

A couple of hours later, when I get to the next town and ask where I can camp, I'm told to go to the showgrounds where there's a shower block. I'm barely there half an hour when a policeman comes and starts asking me questions. I tell him I'm on my way to Sydney.

'And how are you financing this little adventure of yours?' he says with a smirk.

'I get the single parents benefit,' I say. 'Why?'

'Well, I hear you stopped off at old man Kleitch's place.'

'How did you know that?' I'm flabbergasted. There was no-one around anywhere. And what business is it of his and why would he care anyway?

'I stopped at an old farmhouse to get some water. It looked like it was deserted. Except for the dog.'

He tells me the house is owned by one of the richest farmers in the area. Not only that he told me, within a couple of hours, word had spread around the whole town that I was a travelling prostitute. They thought I'd stopped off there to replenish my funds! Unbelievable. I wonder what kind of people live around here.

'I think it'd be better for you and everybody if you left first thing in the morning.'

I can't wait.

Between Wagga and Junee, on a lonely stretch of road, I take the safety straps off so Dan can stand up behind me for a bit of a stretch.

Not five minutes later the blanket Dan's sitting on falls into the back wheel. The bike stops with a crunch. When I try to disentangle the blanket, I see that the wheel spokes and gear system are mangled and the rim is buckled.

I know straightaway I can't go anywhere. I hitch a lift in a ute and put my bike with all the gear in the back. In the next town I'm told the bike parts I need to fix everything have to come from Melbourne. That's what you get for buying a specialty lightweight bike.

I'm tired. We're two-thirds of the way there but the Blue Mountains are between us and Sydney and the thought of scaling them seems too much. I decide to send the bike back to Melbourne on a train.

We hitch a ride to Canberra to stay with the family of the guy who'd given us a lift. He's got five kids and is a head-master.

As soon as we get there Dan's much happier with other kids around.

I still have to think about our future.

April 20

WE'RE AT JENNY'S HOUSE in Sydney for a couple of weeks. Because you're still sleeping with me you're waking up four or five times a night for a little suck of the breast. That means I don't get enough sleep and I'm always tired. I'm trying to let you cry, so you realise and accept that you can't have it whenever you want. It's so hard for me to let you cry though – especially since it's right in my ear.

Jenny lives in Heckenberg, which is a housing commission place a long way from the middle of Sydney. It's very depressing. There aren't too many trees and the houses all look the same. Years ago Jenny was the one who took me to the party when we all lived in Brisbane where I got raped on my 14th birthday. Those Mount Gravatt boys were pretty rough and, really, I guess that's one of the main reasons I ran away back to Melbourne. But even though the family moved to Sydney after I left, Jenny had kind of got stuck in the whole thinking of those people. She'd turned into one of the girls I was trying not to be. Girls who get pregnant at 16 and have babies to different guys and think of themselves, well, like they don't count for anything. Ma might have had six kids to five different fathers, but she always ran her own life. She was the one in charge and never had a man around telling her what to do. I'm here to visit because that's what sisters are supposed to do, but from the minute I get here I can't wait to get away.

On my second day here, Jenny corners me when I'm helping her make the bed. She tells me about her terrible life. She says her husband Michael didn't come to the hospital for three days when she gave birth to his own son and that he's always telling her how fat and useless she is. She cries and tells me she feels trapped, that I'm the only one who can understand. I don't know why she thinks that. She's the oldest, not me. I'm not even the second oldest, that's Pommy. I don't know what to do. I haven't seen her for years. She wants me to help but I don't even know where I'm going to live yet. And the things she's telling me about the way Michael treats Warren, who isn't his real son, are so awful. When she finishes I feel guilty. As if I should do something. But what? I wish she hadn't told me.

I decide while I'm in Sydney to go and visit a woman I'd studied with at Rydalmere Tech, Carol. She lives at Epping. While I'm visiting, I go to the shops to get something for Dan who has a cold. When I get to the chemist counter, I can't believe it. The guy in the white coat is Fabian, who I'd studied with at Sydney Tech the year after I met Carol. He was the first guy who'd ever asked me on a date. I'd been in love with him all year when we finally went out.

A couple of years after I finished studying at the Tech, after I'd come back from working in Japan and was trying to knock myself off again, I decided to try out how drowning would be. Before Dan was born I was always thinking about suicide. It was no accident that I chose a beach near Fabian's house in Rose Bay in Sydney. I'd nearly drowned by swimming out as far as I could go before deciding this wasn't my cup of tea. I'd struggled back to shore like a half-drowned rat. Afterwards I stopped off at Fabian's parents' place. Just to see if he was there. If he still felt anything for me. We hadn't had sex but we'd been on a couple of dates. Ever since then I'd fantasised more about him than anyone until I'd met William. The morning of the drowning experiment, it was 7am and I turned up on his doorstep wet, saying I was just passing by. He gave me a look, like this is very weird, and offered me a coffee. What else could he do? We sat in silence.

Neither of us knew what to say. I got out as fast as I could and decided never to see him again.

Now, I can't believe it. After all this time, like eight years, I'm so nervous. He'd wanted to be a doctor like his father. He did his final year of high school three times to get good enough marks for medicine but here he is a chemist. He mustn't have made the entry requirements after all.

He's serving customers and trying to ask me about the huge transport strike I'd caused before Dan was born. It was news all over Australia and he'd read about it in the Sydney papers.

The other customers who are waiting start looking at me and I go so red. He asks about Dan and if I'm married. I tell him I'm a single parent, but I just want to get away. When he serves another customer I call out that I have to go. You can see he wants to ask more questions but I'm not staying another second. When I'm walking out with Dan on my hip, I knock a ball off a shelf and when I pick it up the glasses stand nearby starts to wobble. I'm mortified. I leave before it crashes over and practically run the rest of the way out of the shop.

April 25

DEAR SON, I'm so sorry for lugging you around all over the place since you were born. I want so badly to find roots somewhere and feel that I belong – maybe I just don't wait anywhere long enough for that to happen. Also, I know my moving is in some way connected with William. Sometimes running away from him and other times coming back. Not that I see him, but being away from Melbourne makes it easier for me not to contact him.

In my heart, I know it's silly. He doesn't want us and I should be strong enough to accept that and go my own way. It should be over, finished completely by now. But I'm finding it so hard to let go – even after two and a half years. I've been thinking of ways I can be free of him: if one of us dies, if one of us gets married or I just get stronger. What I'd really like is to marry ... find a father for you, love someone and be loved.

But more than that, I want so desperately to be at peace with myself.

We're back in Melbourne staying with Elizabeth while I look for a flat. I thought at first maybe we should live out Belgrave way in the Dandenongs, so Dan can have a bit of nature around. I've been praying for guidance about where to live. I don't know why I'm praying at all because I haven't prayed or thought about God since I was giving birth. I want some kind of sign that wherever it is, is right. I have a thought about the flats where Dan was born. The next day Elizabeth suggests the same thing, seeing if there are any flats available in that block. And, I can't believe it, the next time I see Joanne, she suggests the exact same thing and *she's* never even seen the place.

The next day, when I go to the block just to have a look, I find out that of about ten flats, *ours* will be vacant in three weeks. It seems more than coincidence to me; it seems, in fact, like a sign.

When I ring the agent she remembers me. She said she didn't mind letting to someone with a child. This is a minor miracle because lots of agents have told me, in no uncertain terms, that their flats aren't suitable even when I think they're perfect. I know it's because I'm a single parent. When I get a few refusals in a row I feel really terrible.

Of course I haven't got the Darling Street flat yet but I feel confident about it. I just refuse to entertain the idea that they could give it to someone else.

Pommy rings to tell me she's back from Japan.

She arrives from Sydney with Ma and they stay in a motel and visit me at Elizabeth's house. She still seems to be winding up to something. Christian isn't with her. She's left him with Jenny in Sydney. Again.

She tells me she stopped in to see William at the zoo,

where he works. He'd told her he has another girlfriend. That's the second I've heard about since me. It seems, from what Pommy says, that he might be going into relationships to get away from me.

I visit him from time to time and he seems to have accepted Dan's existence in a grudging kind of way. Even though last time we saw him he came to Fawkner Park and held Dan up on a branch – like the little baboon he looked after a couple of years ago when its mother rejected it at the zoo. William looked really happy. We were all very happy that day.

But he's hardly put any money in Dan's trust account since he was born. I ring and ask why. He says he thought the money was for when Dan was 18 so there wasn't any rush. I'd told William the money would be for Dan when he grew up. Now I say I want to get something in writing about how much he'll pay. He says he only wants to pay from the time the positive results of the blood test came through, a few months ago when Dan turned one.

Because William is a very quiet person, it's easy to imagine that he's anything you want him to be. Like the deaf-mute in *The Heart is a Lonely Hunter* that I've just read. I've just begun to realise that maybe I imagine he has a lot of qualities I lack myself.

From the bits and pieces that I've been hearing about William, he's very disturbed by the whole business of being a father. I ask if he'll come and take Dan out for half a day.

'Absolutely out of the question,' he says in the English-major kind of way he's got. I don't understand it because when he's actually with Dan, he seems to like him. It's the idea of him having a son and some kind of responsibility that seems to spin him out. Funny really, because what I expect of him could be written on a two-cent piece.

I ring up for the final verdict on the Darling Street flat.

The answer is 'no'. I'm crushed after all the other turn downs, especially when all the signs seemed right. It's been nearly three weeks and there hasn't been even another 'maybe' in that time.

The pension's $90 a week and I pay $25 for our land. So originally I thought I could afford $35 a week, now that's up to $45. I even considered looking at more expensive flats. Since I found out about Darling Street I want to run away or cry on someone's shoulder but there isn't anyone. I don't trust Joanne so much anymore.

Since I sold the car, Pommy drives me around in her old yellow Renault to get some references to give to an agent in the hope of getting a nice flat in Westbury Street, East St Kilda. The rent's half the pension and not far from Joanne's place. While I'm in seeing the agent, Pommy takes Dan to an expensive children's shop in South Yarra, where she spends $60 on Ma's bankcard. It's totally irresponsible (a tiny jumper cost $34!), but she couldn't resist a beautiful little toy horse with a wooden soldier riding it that Dan pulls along with a string. She leaves with Ma to drive back to Sydney the next day.

FIVE

STARS, HOLES AND KEYS

We've got the flat in Westbury Street!

It's huge with two bedrooms. I'm excited when we move in. It's a home of our own at last. Joanne brings around some flowers and things I need for the kitchen.

On the second day, I discover on my way to the shops

that there's a crèche down the road. It's run by the parents, who all have to do a half-day roster a week. It's only $6 a week which I can afford. Just. The rent on the flat's half the pension and then there's the land payments which only leaves $20 a week for bills and food. My bike's fixed so no transport costs and I buy all our clothes from the op shop. But I'm happy.

We go to the crèche together for a few days, then I try Dan out on his own for just an hour while I go shopping. All day long I keep coming back to take him home but he doesn't want to leave. I finally persuade him to come with me at four o'clock, when his eyes are so tired he can barely keep them open.

When Dan gets settled in I get friendly with all the parents. They seem very nice.

I also visit Joanne almost every day and we sit around her kitchen table drinking endless cups of tea. Often she invites us for dinner. She's such a great cook and I start to learn lots of recipes from her. She keeps telling me I'm her surrogate daughter again. Joanne doesn't want kids and neither does Bear. She pampers him like he's a God. She even irons his undies! He's started his own nursery business and Joanne's finally let him borrow against her house to finance it.

Not long after I move into the new flat, I get a call from Pommy. She's back from Sydney and wants to stay with us for a while.

When she gets here, I discover she's been taking heroin. She's very sick. She thinks everybody is an alien trying to get at her so they can take over the world. She's tormented by fears and voices.

When she first tells me about the space people it sounds so real.

'Imagine if there really was life on another planet. You can just imagine it. Everyone would think the first person who found out was crazy.'

Well, that's probably right.

'I know how crazy I must sound but put yourself in my position. I'm the only one who knows and if I tell anyone they'll think I'm crazy.' She really has me half believing her. But then Gullible's my middle name.

But when she starts accusing me of persecuting her and being one of 'them' I know there's something seriously wrong. She yells at me and says I steal her cigarettes or hide them on her and all kinds of other stuff that I don't really understand. I hardly even smoke. That's when I know for sure that she really is going crazy.

I get a psychiatrist from the yoga centre where I go in Chapel Street to come around and take a look at her. But when he asks about aliens she says she doesn't know what he's talking about. She's so smart Pommy. Even in the middle of being crazy, she still knows that she sounds crazy. The shrink thinks I'm the neurotic one for trying to have my perfectly sane sister committed.

It's a big strain. I don't feel safe living with her anymore. She's suffering so much and sits in her room all day building up to such mental anguish that it's hard to tell what she'll do. I hear her sobbing but she screams at me if I go in. Because she doesn't trust me anymore, it's completely useless to talk to her or try help in any way. I worry and wonder if Dan's safe. I never leave him alone with her.

Then one day Ma arrives to pick her up and take her back to Sydney. I'm glad I don't have to worry about her myself anymore.

June 6

I THINK YOU'VE STARTED TALKING! If 'lookada' means 'look at that' and 'pena ba' means 'peanut butter' then you're on your way! You've started going to the toilet in the mornings, too. I put you on your pot with some raisins on the floor in front of you and as you bend over to get them, out it all comes! Now you won't eat anything but raisins!

As I watch Dan grow and do things, I think about my own childhood. I've been thinking a lot about Ma and how she brought us up. I've always thought she was a terrible mother but now that I've had Dan I realise she did so many things that most mothers never would, especially in her situation. Six kids and she somehow managed all those classes for us. The cooking and deportment classes; speech therapy for Pommy and me because we lisped; ballroom dancing; the marching girls that cost a fortune every weekend when we went off to the country for competitions; basketball, even though she never came to a match; piano lessons, even if only for six months. The classes were never followed through because we were kicked out of everywhere for not paying the rent, but she tried. When she was a single mum there was no pension like I've got. And when she'd worked as a prostitute for a month every year to give us the biggest best Christmas ever, she told me later she'd hated the work. She did her best, just like I'm trying to do with Dan. But it isn't until now I see that. And that's why I decide to stop calling her Mother. It sounds so cold. Now I'll call her Ma instead. It's friendlier and I respect her more because now I know what being a mother means. I still can't call her Mum though. It doesn't feel right.

Before, I've always had a little bit of money in the bank. Now I have almost none. I'm very touchy about it. I'm liable to burst into tears when I get an unexpected bill.

When I had the car I used to get parking tickets. Being on the pension, there's no way I could pay them, so I just ignored them. I must have dozens by now.

August 24

YOU'RE SUCH A PRECIOUS JOY in the mornings – still. After I've accepted that I can't have another minute's sleep, we go and get you a drink and then come back to bed to read stories and cuddle, play hidey under the covers and talk to the birds outside our window. After half an hour, or an hour on lazy days, we get up and have a bath, have porridge and peanut butter toast for breakfast and go off to the crèche.

I felt I was leaving you at the crèche too much so I stopped taking you every day. I didn't feel we were as close as we used to be. It's better already after a week.

You're discovering lots of things; the moon, sun and stars, holes, keys, the word 'fuck' (from crèche), how to be jealous, how to hit me, how to water our plants.

We've been here three months. You know where everything is, you know the ladies next door and downstairs. We have a steady routine and you know all the kids at the crèche and I'm friends with the mothers. It might look like a boring life but we're both content and happy. The weather is blustering and summery. I'm in love with life.

A man asked me out. I met him at Joanne's. He's a friend of Bear's and his name's Marcus. He brings me flowers and everything. I don't know if I want a relationship. I like the attention more than the man. Life without a man or sex is so uncomplicated. But it's spring and it's been two and a half years. I feel like a woman again.

We see each other for a while but he turns out to be pretty weird. When we have sex, he makes me come but he doesn't seem to want to, or maybe be able to, get it up. Still, he's intelligent and kind and I get used to him until one day after we've been seeing each other for a month or so, he announces he's going to live in Adelaide. He's gotten under my skin so that I can't concentrate on my yoga, even housework. And just before he tells me, he's especially affectionate.

On the day he leaves I feel abandoned. It feels like he's running away from me, the relationship, his feelings? Who knows. Bear tells me he's done this before and that he's quite neurotic. Why don't people tell you these things *before* their friends start messing with your heart?

When Marcus leaves, I feel like writing. Not about him but about my life. I write a story called *In Search of the Nitty Gritty* about my year at Sydney Tech and my first date. I laugh out loud when I'm writing. Joanne thinks it's a hoot. I read my story over and over. I wonder if maybe one day I could be a writer.

Even though I ride my fixed bicycle everywhere these days, one day the police come and tell me I have to pay my traffic tickets or be arrested. I checked it out a while back and found that you can serve all the tickets concurrently. That means if I don't pay the worst one, which is for speeding and has a default penalty of three days in jail, that's all I have to do. The rest are for one or two days in jail so when they're all served concurrently with the three day ones they'll automatically be wiped out. Well, when you know, after the first parking ticket, that you're never going to be able to pay on a pension anyway, what's the point of ever parking legally again? I mean, I don't go out of my way to park illegally, it's just that being a Sagittarian, in my mind when I set out to go somewhere, I'm already there, so looking for a legal spot just slows me down from getting there in person. That's the same reason I've got speeding fines in the past. The whole idea is to get there as fast as possible so my head isn't separated from my body. This is a tricky idea that I don't try to explain to police.

Then there are the seatbelt infringements and going through red lights when I'm sitting there waiting when there's no-one even coming the other way. All in all, I don't like to be a sheep and obey the law just because it's the law. As long as I'm not hurting anyone, the law and me have to work around each other.

The good part is I haven't had any tickets since I sold the car. Having a bike has a lot of financial benefits.

I've found out I can take Dan with me to jail because I'm still breastfeeding. Some people in the street think I'm weird to still be feeding when Dan's almost two, but a lot of the mums at crèche have done it even longer than me. Anyway, that's pretty handy because if it wasn't for that I'd have to move to avoid going to jail because there's no way I could be away from Dan for three whole days.

So the police tell me if I don't turn myself in at Russell Street Police Station in the city, they'll come and get me themselves. They're quite polite and matter-of-fact about it and I appreciate that. I've dealt with them a few times and if I'm nice to them they're usually nice back. Well, they're just doing their job and I'm obeying the law in my own way, so there doesn't seem any point in making it unpleasant.

So, I turn up one afternoon at Russell Street but it's too late for them to take me to Fairlea Women's Prison which is where I'm doing my time. They put me in a cell where there's no-one else. We just hang about until dinner time reading the graffiti on the walls. The place is quite dark and depressing. It doesn't smell very nice either. I think it's old wee and damp from rain coming in the roof. And there's nothing in there except wooden benches and chipped everything and vinyl cushions scattered about. I wonder where we're going to sleep. Well, I soon find out about that.

At about nine o'clock, they bring in some smelly grey blankets and tell me we have to sleep on the vinyl cushions. It doesn't sound so bad until you try to actually do it. You line three up and lie on them. Dan and I fit okay because I cradle him in my arm. (He doesn't care where he is as long as he's with me.) But then, every time you move, like turn over or breathe too much, the cushions separate and you start to fall between them onto the concrete floor. At any one time your bum and knees or your shoulder and hip are touching the concrete. Well, me anyway, because Dan fits quite nicely on one cushion.

If that isn't bad enough, they don't turn off these glaring lights all night and a guard comes in every hour and clangs open this gigantic noisy door, shines a torch in your face and makes you talk to him to make sure you're not dead. After hours of this, getting up to squash the cushions back together, again, dozing off and being woken up by the clanging, I'm so miserable I'm ready to scream. Finally, when the guard comes in for the fifty-sixth time, I burst into tears.

'I came in here to try to do the right thing and serve my time,' I shout through my snot and blubber. 'But how could you treat people like this? How do you expect people to get any sleep with you coming in here every hour and banging the doors waking us up just when we've just managed to fall asleep. It's inhuman. And I've got a baby here and he hasn't done anything wrong. Why do this to him? I just need some sleep. I want to go home.' And I sob, hugging Dan, who's still sound asleep.

I thought they'd laugh in my face and tell me that's what I deserve for breaking the law, but boy am I wrong. The guy goes away and comes back ten minutes later and tells me to follow him. He puts us in this room with a bed. And clean white hospital sheets. And blankets. It's the most beautiful bed I've ever seen in my life. It's the sick bay and he says I can stay here until morning. Bliissss. I fall straight into a deep sleep.

I'm so grateful that I'm all chirpy the next morning, even though I'm going off to Fairlea Women's Prison that everyone thinks is such a tough place. I know it can't be worse than last night.

I arrive and they do a body-search. No-one likes being naked when the other person isn't but it doesn't bother me. When you've been a working girl, taking your clothes off in front of strangers is no more intimate than brushing your teeth. I'm polite to them and they're polite back. Like we're all just doing our jobs. They put Dan and me in a special wing of the prison for mothers who are breastfeeding. There's only one other mum here. She's in for drugs.

We mums don't have to do anything because we have to look after our babies. We get special food and everyone's nice to us. Out in the prison yard where the others hang about when they're not working, we chat after lunch. I meet this woman who killed her two kids and then shot herself but, of course, she survived. She did it because her husband thought she was crazy because she breastfed for two years. He had a psychiatrist friend who committed her to a psych hospital. That meant she could never get custody of her kids again. She still saw them sometimes on the weekends but they could never live with her which must have been terrible because she doted on them. Then one day, a couple of years later, when her husband had said she couldn't see them for months, she ran into her kids on the beach with their grandma. She said they cried all over her and begged to go home with her. That's when she snapped.

One weekend before she had an access visit with her kids, she said she went to see her old boyfriend from before her marriage. He was a psychiatrist and she thought he could help her. She told him she'd bought a gun and couldn't stop thinking about killing her kids. She even told him she had them the next weekend. You wouldn't believe what he did. He seduced her. The next weekend she shot her kids.

Anyway, she's very nice and not crazy at all. In fact very intelligent I think. She's grateful that I let her play with Dan and cuddle him.

I do my time in there and then go home. If you ask me, apart from the vinyl cushions it was a pretty easy way to deal with thousands of dollars worth of parking fines.

September 3

FOR THE FIRST TIME last week you spent the entire night without me. When I rang you at the crèche the next morning, we had a whole conversation together. You said "Lo … 'lo … 'lo' (Hello, very loudly) then I said 'Mummy' and you said 'Hmm' Then you started to cry, so I jumped on my bike and raced over to the crèche where I had to stay with you all day. You wouldn't let me out of your sight.

I get a call from Ma. She tells me that Pommy has gone back to Japan and got herself arrested there. Deliberately. Jun had been arrested for dealing and she wanted to be with him so she shoplifted something and made sure she was caught. Now she's in jail. But the biggest news is that bloody Neville has turned up after all these years to claim Christian. How very convenient. Ma says he's changed and that he's inherited some money and wants to come and buy a house in Melbourne. He wants to come and stay with me while he looks for a place. I'm suspicious but say okay.

They arrive on a Sunday. Neville's driving a brand new Commodore. He says he's had therapy in jail and changed. He certainly looks pretty good. He and Christian move into the second bedroom and Dan moves in with me.

Christian's so happy he's living with his dad after not having seen him for six years. Seeing his face when he looks at his dad makes me want to cry. Christian's the reason I'd said they could stay, even though I'm a bit worried.

But it seems like Neville really has changed. He bought Dan a bike. He says most of his money's in a trust account so he can't touch it for another month. He bought the bike with a cheque. He's paying half the rent which is great. We go to Mornington to look at a really swish house he wants to buy when his money comes through. He even buys me a new dinner set. It takes me about three hours to decide because I can't imagine when anyone would ever buy me a new dinner set again.

Christian enrols in a local school. Looks like they're here to stay for a while.

I start getting letters from Pommy. She tells me she's writing a diary on toilet paper. The letters are bad enough. I don't show them to Christian. They'll just upset him.

SIX

THE FARE HOME

Yokohama Immigration Detention Centre, September 18, 1981[1]

I'M AT PRESENT being 'detained pending trial'. I've been here about three days. When they came in a little while ago I actually thought I might be getting out but instead they reprimanded me for sleeping with my head up the wrong way.

I only wish somebody was able to get in touch with my new lover, Amano. As yet nobody at all knows I'm here – not even Jun – they won't tell him, the bastards. They didn't believe I was married to him. They think I'm crazy because I sleep with my head facing south.

I've just finished talking to the guy from the embassy. He tells me the cheerful news that the last Australian caught on a shoplifting charge was given a 12 month sentence – suspended because she had a ticket home. I, of course, do *not* have a ticket home.

---

1 Pommy's prison diaries which I read six months after they were written.

I've got a letter from Pommy asking if I have money to pay for her ticket home. There's no way I could find $1500. I shouldn't be struggling so much financially now that Neville's sharing the rent, but for some reason that I can't work out, I seem to have less money than before. I think I have a certain amount in my purse and then I find out I've got less. I've never been good at keeping track of money.

Christian starts talking about his new school. He doesn't like the teacher. She shouts at him. It makes me start thinking about what kind of school I want Dan to go to. At the crèche nobody bullies the kids around or raises their voice. I want the same thing for him when he starts school. This new mum I meet at crèche called Beacon, because she has a red nose, is into Krishnamurti, who is an Indian guru type of guy. She tells me he has a school in India where they teach kids in a spiritual kind of way. I've stopped doing yoga since Neville and Christian moved in but I still like all those Indian ideas.

I decide to write to the Krishnamurti school in India. I also start thinking that maybe I could check out the school where William went, in the ashram in Pondicherry. William's the only good guy I've ever met. He's got morals – even if he hasn't been so great on the responsibility front. That's what I want for Dan. Morals. So, I decide to write to his old school too, and ask how I could get Dan in there. A few months ago I wrote to William's mum in Pondicherry, care of the ashram. Amazingly, she answered. She's been sending me little books written by Sri Aurobindo, the head guy who's dead. I just told her I was a friend of William's.

Neville's going out with this woman from the crèche. He takes her out to dinner and buys expensive wine and brings her flowers and everything. Boy, has he changed. Everyone at the crèche thinks he's great. I like him too now. Specially after he bought the bike and the dinner set.

I asked if he could buy Pommy's ticket home and he said he can't even think about it until his trust fund matures. Fair enough.

September 21

NOTHING MUCH HAPPENS HERE.

The day starts at about 6.30. After being woken up with an almighty clanging of doors, our futons have to be folded and the rooms cleaned. In a room seven feet by fourteen feet (my feet that is - size 7b) there's really not much to do. I finish in about three minutes, but the other women (who I can't see but hear crashing about), are kept busy for half an hour or so. I can't for the life of me imagine what they're doing. In their favour, I must say that except for futons and a small table, the only other items are cleaning apparatus. Perhaps that explains something. After cleaning, there's roll call then breakfast. They make special meals for gaijins[2], so breaky is cold egg and camp pie. Everything I get to eat I make into a sandwich with mayonnaise for butter. I've taken a great fancy to Japanese tea - it's really very refreshing.

Lunch starts at 11.30 and finishes at 11.35. Tea starts at 4.30 and finishes at 4.35. Apart from this the day passes completely without interest—oh, except for a bath on Tuesdays and Fridays. I am yet to experience the Tuesday bath. That's on tomorrow's agenda.

I don't know why, but whenever it's time to sleep, they start playing this ridiculous music, which for all the world sounds like Andy Pandy (they're playing it now). It's at bedtime they really excel themselves. For some reason we get three hours of non-stop football results. At 9pm the radio finally goes off but the light stays on—all bloody night.

I put in a complaint at the Equal Opportunity Board. I can't get a concession card because I'm a single parent. If I have the card I can get public transport, phone, gas and electricity concessions. If I'd been married and divorced or widowed I

---

2 Foreigners

could get it but because I'm a single parent I can't. That seems like discrimination to me. They tell me about ten other single parents who've put in complaints too.

I go to the tribunal hearing on my bike with Dan. We don't have to do much. Because it's a class action, they appoint lawyers who do most of the arguing amongst themselves. They talk to each of us women and ask why we think we're being discriminated against. We all say the same thing. You don't have to be Einstein to work it out.

I leave early because they're going on with legal arguments I can't be bothered listening to and Dan's getting tired. A guy follows me down in the lift.

'You *are* the same Barbara Biggs who was involved in the tram dispute a couple of years ago aren't you?' he asks.

'Yeah, that's me. Why?'

'Well, transport seems to be big on your agenda doesn't it? First this, then trying to get a transport concession for single parents.'

'The two things don't have anything to do with each other actually.'

We're downstairs and he keeps talking while I'm undoing the chain on my bike.

'So, you're a single parent now? And this is your form of transport? If you use a bike why did you want the transport concession card?'

'Because with that card I can get concessions on lots of other things as well.'

The next day my photo and the story about how we won the case are on page three of *The Herald*. I think that guy was stretching a pretty long bow tying those two things together but at least now other single parents will get to hear about the new concession card.

September 30

I'M WAITING FOR LUNCH. I'm really starving for some reason and my arm's throbbing from the cigarette burn.

When I was kicked out of the apartment I went into some weird kind of mental state for a few days. I'd walk across Honmoku Dori at any time of the day or night without even attempting to look for traffic – and I was hardly scared at all. I didn't want to get run over but I did want to make some kind of protest. It was in this frame of mind that I took a cigarette to my arm and tried to burn a hole in my wrist. I made a bloody mess in the laundromat where my crime occurred and now all that's left is a leathery looking scab that promises a lot of pain when I pull it off before it's ripe. That's on tomorrow's agenda. I'm okay now. I don't feel the least bit sorry for myself – at least not for that – I just wish somebody else would feel sorry for me, that's all. The needle marks on my arms are clearing up quite well. By the time I get out of here they might even look ordinary.

My chocolate has arrived. Oh joy. Oh bliss. I'm not kidding. Dinner has arrived and I'm hardly interested.

I've come to the conclusion that I should only write in the day. It's too easy to fall over the edge at night. And just a little thought-action is all it takes.

When I'm cleaning the room I decided to give my face a drink as well. I first washed my face in soap and left the soap on for five minutes or so but that just made my pimples break and bleed – ugh. This sounds disgusting. Anyway, I then washed my face in shampoo to see what that would do – I'm still hoping for miracles. Tomorrow I'll try toothpaste; again I'm ashamed to admit. I hope the guard wasn't watching. They already think I'm a little touched, what with still sleeping up the wrong end of the futon and everything.

Sometimes my friend at crèche, Beacon, visits and stays the night with her son Dennis who calls Dan, Dan Pigs because he can't say Dan Biggs. When they stay at our place they sleep on the foldout bed. Other times we stay at their place.

Beacon's married a Scottish guy so he could stay in the country. It was an arrangement but then she fell in love with him and had Dennis. She went with him to live in Scotland but he didn't do any fatherly things and practically ignored her. He was studying to be a vet. She said it was like having two kids instead of one. That's why she left him and came back to Oz. So many of the married people I know say that and it makes me feel glad I'm a single parent with just one real kid to take care of.

One morning Beacon and I sleep and when we get up the kids have been awake for a while. In the lounge we find that Dennis has shat on the fish and chip paper on the floor of the lounge room. He and Dan think it's the funniest thing. How gross.

October 2

TODAY I'VE BEEN THINKING BACK to when I was last in Australia. I know it really was the worst time in my life, up until now that is, but a lot of really funny things happened during that time. But I also think that I reached some kind of peak. Sadness certainly, but some other kind of evolution (or revolution, that's better) of self or soul; that I completed myself – perfected myself. In the midst of sorrow there is perfection? Well, that's a new one at least.

I'm afraid to go back and read this last bit. I'm afraid it won't make sense and I want it to so badly.

The world is about to close down around me for the night once again. It's the moment in time during the whole day that I hate the most. The guards, at exactly some pre-destined time – I don't know when – come and 'shut-down' the cellblock, and boy, then you know what it's really like to be alone. The sound of the closing window is so final – and everlasting and forever lasting. I'm starting to brood.

I get another letter from Pommy. She says she's hungry and wants me to send food, chocolate, biscuits and magazines. I don't even buy those things for myself because they're luxuries. I can't help thinking she got herself into this situation herself. Why didn't she buy a return ticket last time she went? I write back and say I'll see what I can do, but really, I'm not going to rush off to send a relief parcel.

I do feel sorry for her though. She sounds so unhappy. She said Ma hasn't got any money for her ticket home either. That means we're really just relying on Neville. I told her about how he'd turned up out of the blue. I really hope his trust fund does mature at the end of January. He says there's a small chance he'll have to wait another three months after that!

I get a letter back from the Krishnamurti school in India. They say there aren't any vacancies in their school and won't be for another seven years!

I haven't heard from the school in William's old ashram. Maybe I'll have to go there to find out. I decide I'll find a way to do that in a year or two before Dan gets to school age. I've heard you can get the pension overseas and we could live like kings there. We could even borrow the money for the airfare and pay it back from the pension. I start day dreaming about living like a queen and never having to worry about money again.

October 10

FINALLY GOT A LETTER from Jacqui today. She went crazy in Hokkaido and ended up in a mental hospital. Her family paid a fortune to get her home with a psychiatrist in tow. She has to pay them back though and is at the moment completely broke with no prospects in sight. But there is good news! Mother rang and told me Neville's turned up after all this time to fulfill his fatherly duties. Big deal, but he says he can pay my fare home! Please, please let it be true and fast!

Jacqui wrote: 'I wanted to have a fulfilling life like other people seemed to have. Now I don't believe it's possible, probable, or profitable. Nobody I know is interesting or happy or inspiring: least of all me. I cannot visualise myself ever fitting into anything here and see no reason to try.' Touché Jac, but you've depressed me terribly.

I hope tonight isn't going to be as bad as it promises. If I can just keep my mind off Amano I know I can make it. That's the very worst thing – thinking of being with him and knowing that I can't be. Oh well, it doesn't matter. When I get out of here I hope to be able to see him straightaway. By now he should have got my message. I had the guy from the Embassy leave one at one of the coffee shops he hangs around at. Who knows, I might even get a visit from him tomorrow, or at least soon.

At night I always seem to be on the verge of tears – sometimes hysteria. I think if I had someone to talk to things wouldn't be so bad.

I've just been cleaning out my cell to calm myself down. And I've just re-read some of the notes that other prisoners have written in the books they lent me – and added a few of my own.

One guy, Stephen Wong, was arrested for 'theft', he writes: 'First arrest on 31/7/79, moved here on 19/8/79, first trial 30/9/79, second trial 23/10/79, third trial?' Doesn't sound very promising. He also writes: 'Amigo, good luck'. From a stranger written two years ago, it's kind of beautiful.

Reading these has calmed me down a lot.

Ma comes to stay with us for a few days. She has to sleep on the couch. She's here to see a specialist about her leg. She'd fallen asleep at the wheel and rolled over a cliff a couple of years ago. She had broken legs and ribs and they didn't find her for three days. Now she limps pretty badly and the pin in her leg keeps breaking because of her weight. The doctors are also talking about giving her a stomach stapling operation so she'll lose weight.

When she's here she tells me about when Pommy was last in Sydney after she'd stayed here.

'You know she got me to drive her to bloody Brisbane to meet the aliens?'

'Why did you do it?' Ma is sometimes very weird.

'The main reason was I wanted to stay with her to make sure she didn't take anymore drugs. Do you know she thought Christian was the devil?'

I'm flabbergasted. Even though she's been leaving him all over the place, I know she adores him.

'Why?'

Ma looks worried. She shakes her head and stares into space. 'She thinks everyone's out to get her. As soon as she got to Sydney, Christian was that happy to see her. You should've seen him. She only stayed three days and then she nagged me in the middle of the night to drive her to Brisbane because the aliens were sending messages to meet her in some paddock up near the bloody Gold Coast. When we got there she said they kept shifting the rendezvous point and we had to go back to Melbourne.'

'And you did?'

'You know how bloody stubborn she can be. I also thought at least while she was with me she wasn't taking drugs.'

She said they drove up and down the coast half a dozen times, doing thousands of kilometres before Pommy finally said she was going back to Japan.

I told her about how I'd got a psychiatrist to come and see her last time she stayed with me.

'She's very good at pretending she's normal,' I say.

'You're not wrong. I don't know what else to do. And Christian. I feel that sorry for the poor little bugger.' Ma stares at the wall some more.

She also brought a letter to Christian from Pommy which she must have written before she'd found out he was living here. It nearly breaks my heart.

My Darling Christian,

Hello sweetheart, how are you? Nana has probably told you that I'm in jail but she probably didn't tell you that I'm in the same jail as Jun. It's bedtime here in prison and I'm writing this just before I go to sleep. It's winter here in Japan and it's very cold. I bet it's hot in Australia now. Do you go to the baths very often?

Well, it's nearly Christmas isn't it? I hope I'll be able to be with you at that time but the way things are at the moment I don't know where I'll be. I hope not here.

How is everybody at Jenny's place? Are you doing well at school and getting along with the teachers? I hope you've made lots of new friends. Have you? I've been to see Jun twice since I've been back. He asked how you were and sends lots of love. Jacqui's back in Australia. Has she been in touch with you yet?

Well, that's all for now darling. Try to write back as soon as possible. I know mummy doesn't deserve it because I never write to you. I'm very sorry I'm such a bad letter-writer sweetheart – please, please don't think it's because I don't love you. I do – very, very much.

Bye for now.

Lots and lots of love Mummy xxx

October 25

STILL DON'T KNOW whether I love Jun or not but I do know that my obsession for him has gone. I'm beginning to think that unless you feel sick thinking about somebody you love, then you don't love them. What a pity. It would have been nice loving Jun now that the pain has gone. I still think about him a lot, but mostly it's in connection with Amano (I hope against hope he got my message) and how to hurt him the least if the time must come when I have to tell him I want a divorce. I'm dreading this moment greatly. I want to marry Amano – I really do. I'm never able to picture myself living with Jun in any normal kind of way. But with Amano it's different. I can even eat in front of him: mind you, I still like egg sandwiches but Amano makes me feel guilty if I want one. The last time I ordered one when we were together I got a cucumber and potato sandwich. But was it a genuine mistake?

It's become bitterly cold lately. Autumn must be here. Does October begin autumn, or is it September? I have nothing but the summer clothes I came in with and they stink.

... Geoff Williams from the embassy just came. He gave me ¥7000 from the Emergency Relief Fund. He also told me that Amano rang and said he didn't want anything to do with me anymore.

I get another letter from Pommy. She tells me the reason she's in solitary confinement is because she keeps attacking the guards. Why is she making this harder for herself? She says she's really lonely and it's freezing cold over there. I know how bitter it can be. She also says she wants to kill herself when she gets out. She says she doesn't know how she can ever make it up to Christian, everything she's done to him. She says he'd be better off without her.

I write back and say that we could go up the coast to Byron Bay. Rent a place together for a few weeks and just lie in the sun and get her healthy again. I also tell her Christian would be devastated if she died.

Money's missing from my purse and I ask Neville.

'Look, it must be one of Christian's little mates, ay? You're too bloody trusting, Barbara, that's your trouble. You just can't trust people these days.'

Then I get a phone call from the agent saying the rent hasn't been paid. I ask Neville because I give my share to him and he pays it because he has the car. The agent's in South Yarra.

'I've paid the bloody rent. They've made a mistake with their books, ay? Bloody agents, they're always doing that. They've prob'ly got fuckin' hundreds, maybe even thousands of places so they'd have to make a bloody mistake sometimes. Don't worry about it Barbara. You bloody worry too much you do.'

Bloody agents.

Konan Prison, November 26

WHEN I FIRST CAME HERE (this is the same prison Jun's in) I broke a window to try to kill myself so they put me in a green tin with no furniture and a peephole. I'm freezing. So freezing cold in here. You'd think in Japan, of all places, they'd understand a wish to die. But it's my totally undignified cowardice about life that they hate me for.

After I got out I stopped eating and broke a fluorescent tube to cut my wrist so they put me back in the tin; this time in chains so to speak. They put handcuffs on me and then some kind of belted thing around my waist with my arms inside arm holes which were attached to the belt. Every time I went to the toilet and tried to pull my jeans down I nearly fainted from the pain. I've got bruises everywhere.

Now I'm back in the 'normal' cell. Possibly this place is even worse – it doesn't have the fan but it's bitterly, bitterly cold. There aren't any physical beatings but the verbal and mental abuse is worse and they continue non-stop all day, every single day, on and on forever.

I want the peace of death so badly. I cry for the wanting of it. I yearn for it. I need it. I deserve it.

Neville isn't coming through with the ticket money. Mother wrote: 'Do you need anything? I hope not because nobody here has any money.' I just don't believe they can't get it. It's such a little bit of money.

Pommy writes back to me and says how dare I tell her not to kill herself, when and if she ever gets out of there. It's her life and none of my business. She also tells me how she's moved prisons and attacked the guards again. She says they're horrible to her. If she'd just be a bit civil to them they wouldn't treat her so badly. She sounds totally and utterly miserable. I feel so sorry for her but she's bringing it on herself. I write back and I'm very pissed off. I say: 'Why tell me you want to kill yourself and then expect me not to mention it? If you don't want my help, don't write and tell me.'

I haven't heard from her since. That was weeks ago.

I hear about a housing loan for single parents in Adelaide. Three per cent interest and it's not only okay if you're on the pension, you have to be to qualify. I send away for the application forms. I'm so excited; it means we can build a house on the Adaminaby land. The South Australian government's been wanting to acquire the Brompton house to build a prison on it. They've offered good money so I tell Bloss she'll have to move out soon because I'm going to sell it.

A couple of days before Christmas I get another call from the agent. They say my rent hasn't been paid for three months!

Neville. Maybe he'd run out of money while he was waiting for his trust fund to mature. I ask him about it.

'I'll go in and talk to them as soon as they open up again if it'll make you feel better. I've got all the receipts and the cheque butts and everything, ay. I'll get 'em from the car later. I gotta go down when I pick Christian up.'

An hour later he leaves.

When he comes back I get distracted.

'Look, it's bloody Christmas and you've got fuck all for Dan. Why don't we pick Christian up and go shopping and get a few bloody decent presents and some food and shit. You can't have Christmas without a tree and food and shit, ay?'

We go to Coles and Woollies and he buys a pile of stuff. Neville pays with a cheque as usual. I forget about seeing the receipts and when I remember the next day I can hardly ask after he's been so generous about the Christmas shopping. Same when he asks to borrow some money when we get home. Well, how can you say no when someone's just spent all that money to give you a nice Christmas?

On New Year's Day Neville finds out the phone number of the prison Pommy's in and rings her so Christian can wish her Happy Christmas and New Year. Wow. How nice of him. I wish I'd thought of it.

'Mum, it's me. How are you?' He's shy because he hasn't seen her for so long.

'Yeah, I'm living with Dad now. It's great ... Yeah Christmas was great. When are you coming home? ... Dad says he's getting you home at the end of January, that's only a few weeks away. He's paying for your ticket Mum. You'll be home soon.'

Christian gets off the phone and gives it to Neville. Christian tells us Pommy's crying.

'... Yeah, the bloody trust fund should be through in a few weeks ... I said I'd do it and I bloody well will okay ... look, if you don't bloody believe me you might as well forget the whole thing ay? ... well, you are the mother of me son, ay? ... don't worry about it okay? ... well, we'll see ya in a few weeks then, ay? And hey, Linda, Happy New Year.'

Kagacho Watch House, January 12, 1982

GOOD NEWS AT LAST! Jun's sister Misako came to see me today and gave me enough money to get home: or I think it's enough ¥150,000. I'll probably be home in a few days. I can't believe I'm really getting out of here. I thought at the end of perfect suffering was perfection, now I'm not so optimistic.

I've put on a lot of weight since I was arrested. I'm now about the same as when I first came to Japan – FAT. I'm so depressed about it. Oh well, a few weeks back in The Square and onto chewies should fix it – I hope so.

I'm not looking forward to coming home.

After New Year everything starts to hit the fan.

As soon as the real estate agent's office opens again they phone and tell me we're being evicted. They say if I'm not out in two weeks someone will come and put my furniture on the street. I get the call at lunchtime.

Neville and I argue and he tells me he'll show me the receipts after four o'clock when he picks up Christian.

In the meantime I visit Joanne.

'What will you do if he hasn't paid it?'

'I'll have to leave. There's no way I could pay back three months rent.'

I get home at 7.15. It shouldn't be a shock, but it is. I'm gullible, just like Ma. Neville's room's completely empty. All his and Christian's things are gone. He's done a runner.

Now everything's clear. How could I have been so stupid?

I ring the police and give them a description of Neville and his no doubt stolen car. He'd asked for Bloss's address a few weeks earlier. I ring and tell her what's happened and say if he turns up to call the police. And me.

He lands on her doorstep the next day. Bloss rings the police and he's arrested a few days later. But he gets out on bail the same day. He calls me the second he's out.

'You fuckin' bitch, Barbara. I'll get you, ay? You better not sleep too bloody sound at night 'cause I swear I'll get ya. After all I did for you, ya fuckin' cunt.'

What! After everything he's done for me? I'm speechless and he hangs up.

Everything falls apart.

Not only do I have to get out of the flat, I have to get away from Neville. I don't scare easily but now, with Dan to look after, I feel so vulnerable.

I start thinking about where I can go. India comes to mind. I want to get as far away from St Kilda as possible. Somewhere where Neville won't find me.

I talk to Elizabeth and she says she'll lend me the money from her bankcard for the airfare if I pay the interest. I go to the library and look up a Lonely Planet book. I work out with the cost of living there, I'll be able to pay off my land loan, pay her back maybe $25 a week and live on the rest of my pension there.

I have a garage sale and sell a lot of my stuff. I store some of the best pieces of furniture at Chris and Clive's place. It happens so fast, all the things I have to do are stopping me from being completely devastated. I'm leaving in a few days.

Just before I'm about to leave, I find out Pommy's arriving home from Japan the day after I'm due to fly to India.

I can't cancel the ticket. There's no refund. If I do that I won't be able to pay Elizabeth back and I won't have anywhere to live either.

Dan and I fly out in mid-January. Joanne comes to the airport.

'Don't forget, open my mail and let me know straight-away if you hear from the housing loan people,' I tell her. 'Post Restante, Pondicherry.'

'You know how I hate responsibility BB. Don't blame me if you miss out or I send you the wrong thing. Anyway, you'd better go or you'll miss the plane. I don't know why you leave everything to the last minute. Go, go, go! It's the last call. Remember, keep yourself nice over there. If you need anything write and for heaven's sake don't catch any of those nasty tummy bugs. I've heard they get into you and you can never get rid of them.'

'You worry too much. We'll be fine. I just hope Pommy's okay when she gets back.'

'I don't know why you worry about her. She doesn't have a lot going for her that girl. It's you I'm worried about. Every time you go off somewhere I think I'll never see you again. Write! Now go.'

When we arrive in Madras we catch a bus to Pondicherry.

Wow. This is it, the town where William grew up. We

book in at one of the ashram hotels. The Lonely Planet book says we can live in India on $5 a day. We buy a daily ticket for the ashram diningroom for $2 a day. At this rate I can pay Elizabeth back in a year.

I know William's mother still lives in the ashram. I'd written to her earlier in the year and asked her to send some of Sri Aurobindo's writings. She doesn't know who I am except that I'm a friend of William's.

I make an appointment at the school and ask about Dan enrolling but they say they aren't taking any new students. But I do find out that because William grew up here Dan's eligible.

Someone from the ashram stops me in the dining room.

'You are Barbara Biggs?'

'Yes. Why?'

'We have a message for you to ring home urgently. It is your mother.'

My body goes still and everything stops. Ma barely phones when I'm in Australia. There's only one reason she'd call here.

I go to the post office. Everything takes an eternity in India. I wait three hours for a phone line.

Ma tells me Pommy's dead. But really, by now I've figured out that's the only thing it could be. The only thing I don't know is how. That's the big shock. Ma tells me she jumped from an 11 storey building. I collapse down on the phone.

'It's probably all for the best,' she says.

'I know what you're saying,' I tell her. 'She was such a mess.'

'I can't see how she was ever going to get out of it.' I know what she means.

'When did she do it?' It could only have been just after I left.

'The funeral was a couple of days ago. She went to your

grandmother's old block of flats the day after she got back. Apparently she knocked on one of the old lady's doors and asked for a glass of water before she did it. The police think it was a cry for help.' I feel like all my organs are melting and trickling down to my feet.

Neither of us say anything after that. I keep seeing Pommy falling.

'She called me before she did it.' Poor Pommy. Normally Ma would be the last person she'd turn to.

'What did she say?'

'She told me what she was gonna do and I told her to wait a week and I'd go with her.'

Ma. I wonder how she could be so weird. Like that's what Pommy wanted to hear when she was about to throw herself off a building. She falls again and again in my mind. It must have taken so long to hit the ground. What if she'd changed her mind on the way down?

'Did she say anything about me?'

'She told me thanks very much for nothing and said to say the same to you.'

That's when I hold the phone away from my ear. Then I slam it down. I don't even cry.

Two weeks after I hear about Pommy, I meet Abbas, an Egyptian professor who's living in Sri Lanka. He's offered to take us to his place for a holiday. We're on our way there, in a hotel in Madras, when a strange thing happens.

I'm in the bar with him and suddenly I feel nauseous. Dan's upstairs sleeping in the hotel room. I leave Abbas with his friend and go upstairs and lie on the bed. Suddenly, I don't feel sick at all. Instead, I feel Pommy at the end of my bed.

I sit up. How am I going to explain I had enough money to pay for my airline ticket but not hers? I didn't even send the chocolates and magazines. Not even some measly warm clothes.

I talk to her quietly. Say I'm sorry for not doing enough. I tell her she'd been the only one in the family who'd cared for me when we were little. I tell her I love her. When I've said enough, I lie down again. I try to think of her in a moment when she was happy and I think she could have been saved. When she was with Vlad lying naked on the bed holding hands as though it was the most natural thing in the world. But the only image that keeps coming back is her falling. Over and over. I don't cry.

SEVEN

BURSTING WITH LIFE

I stay with Abbas for two weeks. He's a sophisticated man with a wife and three grown-up sons back in Egypt. He says he doesn't love his wife. He's too old but we have a short affair anyway. He's built exactly like Robert Vernon (the barrister who 'bought' me when I was fourteen). He's tall and big. He thinks like him too. He's so determined to seduce me it's easier to give in than put up with his bad moods and sulking. Once I give in, a few days after we arrive, he takes us up to the hill country and to white sandy beaches. He buys Dan a dog and me a sari. He takes me out for dinner and tells me I'm an attractive, intelligent woman.

Back in Pondicherry. I start thinking about how to get Dan into the school. I know they'll let him in if they know William is Dan's father.

Last year, Pommy had told me William was planning a trip to India some time this year, so it isn't a complete surprise that he turns up while I'm here. He comes to my hotel to visit. I'm sitting on the grass on a banana lounge watching women, still wearing their saris, laughing as they splash around in the churning waves on the beach. I imagine how their saris must feel, clinging salty wet to their bodies when they come out. What women do to save men the trouble of keeping themselves nice as Joanne would say. Dan's asleep in our room. There's an Indian gardener working near me when William arrives.

'Hello. How are you?' He says, coming around a corner, straight and dignified.

'William! What are you doing here?' I'm happy to see him. My heart is in my throat.

'Just visiting. More to the point, what are *you* doing here?' He glances at the gardener to see if he's within earshot. He's hovering.

'I wanted to check out the school here for Dan.' My heart's beating so fast.

'What's wrong with schools in Australia?'

'I want a school with some kind of spiritual base. I went to see them and they said they're not taking new kids.'

'I could have told you that and saved you the trouble.' He keeps looking at the gardener. His back's very straight sitting on the banana lounge.

'I've actually met some friends here and they say there's one way I can get him in.'

'And what would that be?' The gardener's sweeping towards us and I can see William getting edgy.

'They say if the school knew you were his father they couldn't turn him away.' The smell of the sea, talk of William being Dan's father. It's a heady mix. I'm not sure I'm prepared for the answer.

'That's totally out of the question. If anyone here found out I had a son and I'm not married I'd never be able to come back. And it would make life here unbearable for my mother.'

When William's angry he gets even more stiff. How can someone be so stiff on a banana lounge? Calm anger is so much scarier than the loud kind. He's a living, breathing pressure cooker about to blow, but no matter how angry he is, he still keeps looking at the bloody gardener. I've already discovered that 'Pondy' is a gossipy community like any other small town, but here William's supposed to be as spiritual as all get out. Now here he is more worried about what the gardener might hear than what I think or feel. Or about his son's education.

I feel anger rising out of my gut and rumbling up like a volcano. I've got a dragon in my belly that's been asleep for as long as I've known William.

Then he lays the next one on me. That's what finally does it.

'Do you know what you being here's doing to my life?'

This dragon that hasn't even squeaked before, comes out roaring, spitfire and all.

'*Your* life! Your bloody life! What about what you've done to mine? Did you ever stop to think for a second how all this has affected *my* life? How it's affecting *Dan's* life? Ever since I got pregnant I've done nothing but apologise for having fucked-up your life. If you'd stop thinking about yourself for a second you'd realise there's something more important than your life or mine. There's another human being involved here whether you like it or not, someone that, for better or worse, we brought into this world together. We're both responsible.'

I feel very upset but fantastic at the same time. Like I've been carrying a truck around on my shoulders and I've just slammed it on the ground with a bang. I also see, not without some satisfaction, that the gardener's pretending to concentrate on his sweeping, but his ears have grown big as cabbages.

'You don't have to raise your voice. I'm not deaf you know,' William says, looking nervously over his shoulder.

'I'll talk as loud as I want.' I'm on a roll.

'Have you ever thought about apologising for all the pain and suffering you've caused *me*? Has *that* ever crossed your mind? It takes two to make a baby and that night I got pregnant, *I'm* the one who wanted to go home. You're the one who talked me into staying. You're the one who came onto me. You never once asked about contraception. What about a little "I'm sorry, Barbara". Did you ever think about that?'

He's staring at me. Finally he's stopped worrying about the gardener. I look at him and then watch some bees buzzing around a bush near us. I can feel tears coming and I try to stop them but the relief from having got all that off my chest is too much. I run to my room and throw myself on the bed. Three years of tears soak the pillow.

William appears at the door. He comes over and puts his arms around me and says the only thing I really want to hear.

'I'm sorry. Shhh. I'm sorry. I'm sorry.'

He holds me while I cry, more quietly now so I won't wake Dan. It seems to go on forever.

When the heaving ends we sit on the bed and talk.

'Do you know, that night you told me you were pregnant? If I'd had a gun, I would've killed myself.'

I'm shocked. I knew he felt bad but I didn't know he was even capable of feeling like that. He'd told me once ages ago, that when he was young, a pregnant girl and the responsible guy were both kicked out of the ashram and sent away in shame. But it never occurred to me that he'd taken on those old-fashioned morals. He doesn't even live here anymore.

'But why? Wouldn't it have been easier to accept the situation instead of pretending it hadn't happen?' I still see William as more grown-up, mature, disciplined than me.

'You'd have to have grown up here, in this place, to understand.'

It's the first time we're honest and stand, so to speak, naked in front of each other.

William leaves Pondy a few days later and I keep thinking about telling his mother about Dan. I know he'll be mortified, but this is Dan's grandmother. There's blood between them. I don't know my father and I don't want to let an opportunity pass for Dan to know his family.

Dan's two now, but when he was a baby I tried to find my father. I'd never thought about him before. But when I had Dan, I wanted to know what kind of genes I'd passed on. I'm curious. Ma had told me my father's name was Max Miller. I'd phoned about seventy Max Millers or Millars in the Melbourne phone book. I told the people I was tracking down my family tree and that I thought he was a distant relative. My father had been a mechanic in Springvale with a withered hand or arm. How many one-armed mechanics could there be? I didn't find him.

The day after William leaves, I go to the main centre in the ashram and do my meditation there. I ask for guidance. When I finish I do another deal with myself. I'll tell William's mother the situation and ask her advice. If she thinks I should stay and try to send Dan to the school, I will. If she says I should go home, I'll do that.

I find out where she lives and go one morning. Anxiety leaches into my too loud knock on her door. It's way too soft and I have to bang again.

'Mrs Bryson, I'm Barbara Biggs. William's friend. I wrote from Australia and you sent some books.' I try to slide a smile over dry teeth.

'Oh, dear me. Yes. I think I do remember. Yes. Aurobindo's little books. Yes. Come in dear. Fancy seeing you here! What can I do for you?'

She's a tiny, frail old thing, with white hair and a hunched back. She wears loose white pants and smock, the ashram uniform. Her home has the shutters down against the heat and there's cool shade with filtered light in the neat little room.

'This is my son, Dan.'

'Well, how do you do young man. And how old are you?'

'He's two and a half.'

'You're a big boy aren't you? Yes. Now, what can I do for you dear?'

'Well, I've actually come to talk to you about something personal. Something that's quite difficult for me to say.'

'Yes, dear. What is it? How curious. Tell me. I do love a mystery.'

'It's about William.' Now she doesn't look quite like it's such a fun, curious little mystery.

'Yeees. Go on.'

'I first met William about three and a half years ago when he hadn't been in Australia long. I met him through a mutual friend ...'

The story tumbles out. I leave nothing out, the prostitution in Japan, how William helped me find my way to some kind of normal way of seeing the world, how he'd opened my eyes to some kind of morality. And then, of course, about Dan and the school and why I'm here. While I'm telling my story, she barely looks at Dan. He's wandering around her flat picking up the knick-knacks and she occasionally looks over at him to tell him not to touch or gives him something he can play with. But just like anyone would do with any child. No scrutinising looks. No checking him out for similarities to her only son.

'Are you sure William's the father dear?' It's the first thing she says when I finish my long story. Like mother, like son, I think.

'There *was* no-one else at that time.'

'Well dear, I don't know what to say. Why are you telling me all this?'

I tell her about my pact with myself. That I want her advice.

'I really don't know about these things. I don't know how William feels. You say he doesn't love you. But one thing is certain, that if you stay in India and he's living in Australia, there's no possibility that the two of you can have a relationship is there? At least if you're in the same place, there's a chance that things might work out between you, don't you think?'

'Maybe.'

'Well, there's certainly no chance if you're halfway across the world from him, is there dear? Does William know you've come, that you've told me?'

'No.'

'Well, I won't mention it and it's probably better if you don't either, dear. I think it would only make him feel uncomfortable, don't you?'

We exchange a few pleasantries and I say goodbye. She doesn't ask me to keep in touch. She doesn't ask for a photo of her grandson. It's clear she has no interest in a relationship with Dan or me.

A few days later, I almost keel over every time I stand up. I think it's the heat. It takes at least a week of being plastered to the bed for most of the day to realise my period's late. I go to a doctor for a test. It's confirmed that I'm pregnant. It's Abbas.

I had morning sickness with Dan, but nothing like this. Every day I manage only to get to the dining room and back before collapsing again on the bed.

I ring Abbas and he wants me to have an abortion. After having Dan, I tell him there's no way I can do that because life is a miracle and who am I to play God?

That's my first reaction. But within three weeks I'm a changed woman. Three weeks of continuous, gut-wrenching vomiting and nausea's all it takes to change my mind on that score. I ring Abbas and tell him I want an abortion after all.

He flies me back to Sri Lanka and I stay at his house again. Then he changes *his* mind. He decides I should have the baby. My God. Why is a female rejection such a turn-on for men?

A week later, while I'm in hospital recovering from the abortion, a package arrives from Australia. It's from Joanne. Full of all kinds of lotions, potions, creams and vitamins. One of her typical injections of nurture and love from the other side of the world. I wish Joanne was my mum.

Actually, I don't need pimple cream at the moment because, although I have enough paranoia to warrant it, I don't have any pimples to bother about since Dan was born. But the soap reminds me of sweet things almost forgotten: shampoo (Mill Creek), conditioner, cotton buds, tweezers, face masks, cotton wool and most, most of all, dear, underestimated toilet paper ($6 a roll in India!). Not to mention tissues which cannot be begged, borrowed, stolen, or comprehended. When I tried to find some during the height of my hayfever I'd sniff, make like I was blowing my nose, go red in the face with exertion and they would look sideways at each other and wonder what to do with the hysterical foreigner.

The first couple of days here in hospital haven't been too bad. I'm a bit of a penicillin/flagyl/aspro-induced mess, recovering from a bad uterine infection after the operation, but without Dan shadowing my every move, I've managed to read a book.

The night after Joanne's relief package, I see a cockroach. It's about 10pm. I ring for the nurse and sit in a foetal position under the sheet. I hate cockroaches more than anything. And here they fly. The nurse comes and laughs at me! She kills it and leaves. She's so casual it makes me nervous. Then I see another one. I mean, it's supposed to be a hospital, isn't it? I duck under the sheet again, this time whimpering, crying and laughing at the same time. I can see how ridiculous I must look but I'm also really terrified. I have to admit to screaming a little bit as well.

The same nurse comes back but this time she brings half a dozen other nurses with her who think I'm the funniest thing they've ever seen. One of them kills the cockroach and carries it towards me by the leg to show me it really is dead while the others fall over themselves laughing again.

When they leave, I whimper shamelessly, get dressed and run for the stairs. They're all crazy and I decide I'm not staying here another second. But before I get far, they grab my arms and try to convince me to stay. What they don't know is that I'm one stubborn girl and I'm not going back in there for anything. They ring the doctor and he says he's busy but that he'll send a *psychiatrist* over right away.

I tell them I don't want any bloody psychiatrist, I just want to go home. If it'll make them any happier I'll come back and finish being sick in the morning.

The shenanigans go on but I finally escape in a taxi at 11.30pm. Back at Abbas's house I have a terrible night with crazy thoughts: that Dan's a corpse on the bed next to me, that Abbas is going to stab me in my sleep. I see eyes and shapes in the dark.

Abbas takes me back to hospital in the morning.

Now, here I am in bed with a hoard of ants, obviously with an unbalanced diet, carrying one of Joanne's multi-vitamins up the wall to their nest. At least somebody's benefiting from her relief package.

I'm glad I'll be back home with her soon.

After I recover from the abortion, Abbas wants to keep having sex with me like nothing's happened. Why don't men realise what an emotional odyssey it is to have an abortion? Being pregnant again reminds me how holy my body is and I don't want a horrible dick inside me after a baby's been in there. But Abbas won't leave me alone.

'You're just like all the other guys. You think with your dick,' I say.

'Nobody has ever said this thing to me.' He's absolutely incensed. 'Why do you say this awful thing? You think I am some kind of, of ...' and he storms off.

But it's true. He doesn't care about my feelings. He only wants to have more sex. Three weeks go by and the strain of him being horrible to me when I'm still so emotionally fragile is more than I can stand. In the last week I give in. I go numb and let him do what he wants at night so he's kind to me in the day. I can't wait to get home.

Back in Australia, I've only been staying with Joanne for a few days when my housing loan's approved. The only trouble is, they'll lend me money to buy a house but not to build one. It also has to be in Adelaide. I'm tired. Tired of moving and feeling like I have no roots. I want to give Dan a home. I decide to pack up everything and move to Adelaide. I think about what William's mum said. But the idea of pinning my hopes on William again, after all this time, makes me feel hopeless.

I see William when I get back, but it's too hard. I want to

be far enough away that I don't think about visiting him, don't think about wanting him to love me and most of all, don't keep wishing he'd be a father to Dan.

I put everything I can fit in the car and we drive the 800km to Adelaide in one long day. After falling asleep when I was riding my motorbike at 17, the anxiety about nodding off while driving makes me incredibly sleepy. The more I worry about it, the sleepier I seem to get, but we arrive in one piece.

I stay with Bloss for a couple of weeks and then move in with Ellie, the girl I shared the house with when I had my prac. teaching disaster. She never finished her politics degree because she got pregnant. She's now married and has a daughter six months younger than Dan.

I can't start looking for a house to buy until my land's sold and settlement comes through on the Brompton house. I've decided to sell the land and buy a house in the Adelaide Hills. It's a compromise but the itch to put my roots down is consuming me. I want it now.

I put my name down for second year arts at Adelaide University. They say they'll give me credit for the Japanese year I did in Canberra before I had Dan. Now I'm a mother and Pommy's dead, I want to forget about everything to do with Japan. Instead I enrol in anthropology, English, linguistics and maths.

Ellie's unhappy in her marriage. Chris is a nice guy and a good dad, but Ellie doesn't love him. She copes by smoking dope from morning until night. I soon get into the routine. We get up late, smoke a joint, have a lazy breakfast with the kids, gossip, watch telly still in our pyjamas; *General Hospital*, *Days of Our Lives*, *Beauty and the Beast*, telly off before Chris gets home at 4.30pm.

Occasionally the time gets away with that last cup of tea and one of us yells out.

'Shit. 4.15! Quick!'

We tear around like mad things getting dressed, dressing the kids, gathering our dishes from the lounge room, washing them and the dishes from dinner the night before, peeling potatoes for dinner – trying to create the impression for Chris that we've had a productive day.

'Put the oven on. I'll put some bread in. He'll think we've been cooking.' Ellie has a slow, stoned way of hurrying. Not me. I'm in a panic.

'But Ellie, what happens if he looks in the oven and sees a loaf of sliced bread in there?'

'He never looks in the oven. Anyway, we'll be peeling veggies when he gets home. As long as there's a meal on the table at six he's happy.'

Ellie has lots of tricks. Sometimes we go to the shop and buy a family pie and Ellie says she cooked it. Made the pastry and all.

'Tastes just like the real thing. You're a damn good cook, Ellie,' Chris says.

And she has the perfect solution for the odd late joint.

'I'll put some fresh coffee on. It'll get rid of the smell.'

She has other tricks too, to avoid having sex with him.

'Well, for a start I've told him you can't have sex when you've got your period. And of course my period goes for about ten days doesn't it. Then I get stomach cramps and migraines for about a week before my period. That only leaves about two weeks where I have to either go to bed earlier than him and pretend to be asleep when he comes in or stay up late and sneak in when I know he's asleep. The going to bed late works better because then I'm in a coma in the morning so there's no danger there, is there?'

'Does he ever get any?'

'Oh, yeah. Course he does. I'm not that cruel. About once a month if he's lucky.' And we laugh.

I don't see Bloss often because she works 16 hours a day in her new company. She's the boss now and has a staff of a

dozen people. She thinks I'm an overindulgent mother and
that Dan would be a lovely boy if I only I gave him a good
whack now and then.

One day she rings me at Ellie's and says Christian's
coming to live with her. She's split up from her boyfriend
and now spends all her time at work. I wonder how she'll fit
in having a kid. She's become a tough old nut over the last
couple of years, a metamorphosis from the vulnerable thing
she'd been when we climbed Ayers Rock together a couple
of years ago. Now she's hard as nails. Or pretends to be.

'They found him in an orphanage in Canberra.'

'What do you mean *found* him? How did he end up lost?
I thought he was with Neville. I can't believe even *he'd* dump
him in an orphanage.'

'He didn't. He took up with a girl who lived in a caravan
park who already had four kids. When he pissed off, he left
Christian there. She took him to welfare and they put him
in a home.'

Bloss talks like a bullet train. Everything fast and efficient.
It's like she's at work. No emotion. No intonation. Robotic,
you might say.

'How did you find out?'

I can't help mimicking her. You get the distinct
impression she's too busy to talk about anything except
essential facts, relayed quickly. When Ma moved to
Queensland from Melbourne, her best friend, another fat
woman called Betty, moved with us. So did Betty's daughter
Nicole. They kept living and moving with us for ten years
until Betty got sick of moving and stayed in Canberra when
Ma moved on.

'Nicole. Remember Nicole? Betty's daughter. She told
Betty her school friend said there was a new kid in her class
whose mum had jumped off a building and he'd lived in
Japan. Nicole told Betty it sounded like Christian. Betty
checked it out and found him there.'

'When was all this?'

'A few months ago. He's been living with Neville's sister in Canberra since then. She wanted to take him but Christian fights with her kids. It's not working out. I said I'd take him.'

'But you're at work all the time.'

'I can get babysitters and cut down when he comes. I'll manage.'

Her machine gun assessment of the situation brooks no opposition. Monotone works for her. I wonder how it will go down with Christian.

She goes out and buys everything new for his room: a bunk bed, desk, clothes, football, toys, map of the world on the wall.

When Christian arrives and sees his room he's so happy. The only time I see a soft side to Bloss is when she cuddles up to Christian on the couch. Whenever Christian stayed with me without Pommy he fought with Dan because he was jealous. Dan has a mum and he doesn't. Now, Bloss hasn't got anyone but Christian and he at last has someone of his own like he had before Pommy spiralled off into another world.

Three months after I move in with Ellie, my land's sold. I paid $7000 and it sold for $18,000. Wow. I sold the Brompton house for $7000 more than I paid for it too, which means I'll have enough money for a decent deposit on the house *and* $8000 left over to pay Elizabeth back and buy a piano and some furniture for the new house.

I start looking straightaway. Every weekend when the Saturday and Wednesday papers come out. I want a house in Stirling or Aldgate in the Adelaide Hills. I'll have all the benefits of country living but it'll only take 15 minutes to get to uni. It's quaint up there with sandstone houses and big, old gardens everywhere. A garden. A little spring of happiness bubbles up at the thought.

The trouble is, the Ministry of Housing's set a limit of $45,000 on the house I buy. I can afford more than that but the government says if you can afford more you don't need a concession loan. There are hardly any houses around in Stirling for that price, so I start driving miles to look at dives. I want a house I can fall in love with but everything I see is ugly, depressing, on a main street or falling down.

I fall in love with a house built in 1890 that's falling down. It's in Aldgate on a half-acre block of rambling garden. It's built of sandstone with a verandah and two birdbaths and winding paths leading to secret stone seats dotted around the garden. The place is crawling with nostalgia and the romance of it seduces me. I don't care that the floorboards are like waves and everyone says it'll cost a fortune to fix.

The day of the auction I have my finance organised. The Ministry has inspected the house and tentatively approved the loan. The agent says it'll go for around $35,000.

It's a spring day and the birds are singing their heads off. I've already planned where to put a hammock between two liquid ambers, where in the lounge room to put the sideboard I stripped all those years ago, where I'll have breakfast outside in the spring and how I'll put chairs in the old greenhouse in winter.

The bidding starts at $20,000 and climbs in $2000 lots to $30,000. I put in my first bid at $32,000. I think the bidding will start to slow down when it gets near the price the agent says, but it doesn't, it keeps going up in $2000 lots as fast before. At $42,000 the auctioneer accepts $1000 bids, I put my hand up at $43,000 and finally the bidding slows down. It takes a few minutes for the next bid at $44,000. Straight-away I jump in with my final bid and hold my breath. I hold everything in. I can't go any higher or I won't get the loan.

'We have $45,000 with the lady on my right. Do I have $46,000 for this fine property. $45,000 going once, $45,000 going twice. Thank you madam, $46,000 I have.'

I'm in shock. I'd willed this house to be mine. Hadn't allowed myself to contemplate not getting it. Now, I howl like a hyena and run down the side path and through the front garden moaning like I've been shot. It doesn't help that I'm premenstrual. I sit on the step of the gutter outside, put my head in my arms and sob. I stay until the auction's over and the other bidders shuffle past like I'm an escapee from a nuthouse.

I've been looking for two months and that auction's exhausted me so much I decide I'm never going to find a house I love that's under the price threshold. The next weekend I see a property with two houses on the one block. One's fibro and the other sandstone. But there's no garden and it has no charm. It's half an hour further out from the city than I want but I decide it's a good investment. It's exactly $45,000. I'm sick of looking.

'I'll take it.' I tell the agent.

'We've got someone else who wants it. They're coming back this afternoon to sign.'

'What time?'

'Four.'

'I've got one more house to see in Stirling. I'll be back before then.'

This last house is only $43,000 with two bedrooms. It sounds too good to be true, so it must be a dump. But when I get there I can't believe it. It's exactly what I've been looking for. The house is in a street called Tingaling Grove and, my God, it even has a name. Linga Longa, in Tingaling Grove. Is this for real? There's a hawthorn hedge enclosing the garden with a double, green corrugated iron gate set into it. When I enter, it's like walking into a Monet painting. I almost cry with relief. It's paradise. I thank my lucky stars I've been rescued from my good investment down the road. Charm drips from the rafters. The little Victorian weatherboard house with a verandah at the front is set in a 100-year-old garden with apple and pear trees, old roses and a vegetable garden out the back. In front of the verandah is a Japanese maple, one of Joanne's favourite trees, radiant with new lime green leaves. Inside there's a fire going in a slow combustion stove with a glass door. It's the cosiest house I've ever seen and I want to curl up in front of it and go to sleep like the cat lying there. Two gay girls own it and they're splitting up. They've fixed it themselves. There's nothing left to do. The fact that the main bedroom window's ten metres from the railway line to Melbourne where the freight trains pass is a factor I'm determined to gloss over.

'After about a month you won't even hear them,' says one of the girls.

'You've convinced me. Where do I sign?'

Two months later when Dan and I move in I feel like I've won Tattslotto. Blessed. A shade short of giving birth, but without the pain. The work of house hunting, the dream I've had since way back when I was a teenager, of having my own garden, wanting to give Dan what I didn't have, a permanent home, having a place in the world that's all mine and nobody can take it away. I think of all these things as I walk towards the front door in a blissful daze. I turn the key and walk in. It doesn't look as cosy without the girls' furniture but what I have left is arriving this afternoon in a removal van from Melbourne. I've only kept the good pieces and I have enough money to buy more. I've already bought a tiny baby grand piano, not kidney-shaped but a semi-circular one that will just fit in the corner of the lounge room beside the French doors that lead out to the courtyard overlooking the veggie garden. I think I've seen everything until I walk into the kitchen. There, outside the wall of windows looking onto the boundary fence, which isn't a fence at all but a ramble of garden, covering almost the whole view, is a tangled canvas of purple wisteria climbing an oak tree. I'm a greedy girl and can't believe it's all mine.

We go outside again to breathe in the garden. Along the path at the side of the house is a raised garden wall at hip height lined with grey, weathered railway sleepers. Dripping over the side is a row of strawberry plants heavy with fruit. I pick one and give it to Dan. As his teeth sink into it, his eyes grow wide and his face breaks into a smile. It's the first time he's eaten something picked straight from a garden. He thinks fruit comes from shops.

'Yummy food Mummy! More!'

Half an hour later he's marinating in strawberry juice. It's summer and the twisted old apple and pear trees are drooping with fruit. The garden's bursting with life, and so are we.

Before I start uni in March, I look for a local school for Dan. I've heard about the Montessori system and, as luck would have it, there's one just a short bike ride through bushland at the back of our house. I try him there for a week but he doesn't like it. They have such a prescribed way they think kids should be. I think kids are fine exactly the way they are. If we talk to them nicely and leave them alone I think they'll grow up to be everything they're supposed to be. Then I find a small Anglican school in Goodwood, down the hill on the way to uni. It's perfect. There are only 20 kids and one teacher. Just the right size for a little person.

Adelaide Uni's old and gracious. It only takes 20 minutes from leaving home to drop Dan at school, find a park and get to lectures. Life is a fairytale. I've been reborn.

At Dan's school I hear from one of the mothers about Suzuki piano lessons. It's a method of teaching kids Dan's age how to play. I find a teacher in Stirling and enrol Dan for a term. He likes the lessons but hates practice. I bribe and coerce him in every way but in the end it seems like I'm pushing my fantasy of playing onto him. He wants to stop but I've already paid for the term, so I take up the lessons instead.

I meet a girl in my English Literature class. Mari has a boyfriend Roy who's doing a PhD in philosophy. They have an open relationship. Roy tells me how it took Mari five years to realise an open relationship was no threat to what they had. He believes in it philosophically. What can you expect from a philosopher? He says the whole thing works really well when they both have another lover but that if one has one and the other doesn't, the one who hasn't feels left out. Roy and I talk a lot. He tells me how he and Mari have sex for at least an hour every day. I feel sorry for Mari. I tell him I think that would be boring. Secretly I think Mari must only do it because she wants to please him. I can't believe anyone would really want to have that much sex. One day I'm telling him about how I felt about Abbas after the abortion.

'I didn't want his disgusting dick inside me afterwards. Ugh.'

'Do you realise whenever you talk about sex it's like that?'

'Like what?'

'Like you just did.'

'Like, how was that?'

'Well, this is the first time you've said they're disgusting, but whenever you talk about men and sex, it's as though it's some dirty, horrible, disgusting thing.'

'Really?'

'Yes. Maybe you don't realise how offensive it is. Penises

aren't disgusting. They're beautiful. Just like vaginas. I don't see how you can enjoy sex if deep down you think about men's sexual organs in that way.'

I go home and think about what he said. It's the first time I realise sex is a gooey mush in my head that maybe isn't that healthy.

At home we don't have a telly. I want Dan to learn to entertain himself. He's always had kids stay over and gone to their houses – imported and exported surrogate siblings. When he goes to bed at night, I practise the piano. I do at least three hours most nights. I go through the Suzuki books like wildfire. Book One a few days, Book Two three weeks, Book Three a month, Book Four five weeks, Book Five two months. I'm not interested in my Arts degree, all I want is to play piano. It feels like I can express all the tenderness and drama inside me that has never found a home. I'm absorbed. Sometimes when I finish, I feel if I looked up and saw The Holy Ghost sitting on my shoulder, I wouldn't be the least bit surprised.

I start teaching Suzuki piano to little kids. I don't have any qualifications but my teacher says I'm good enough because after just six months I've finished the whole Suzuki course and am playing eighth grade pieces. My teacher says I should think about doing an audition for the Adelaide conservatorium.

'But people doing the audition will have been playing since they were little kids. And I can't even sight-read.'

'As far as I know they presume you can read but I don't think it's part of the audition process. And as far as I'm concerned, you're good enough. You've probably practised as much as anyone else, but just over a shorter period. Just give it a go. You've got nothing to lose.'

That's where she's not quite right. The thing is, I can ride to Sydney if I want or learn piano in a few months because it just depends on me. I'm not competing against anyone or, more importantly, giving someone else the power to tell me I'm not good enough. It's a private thing. This is different. I'd be giving total strangers the power to say no. Sometimes I think it would be safer staying anonymous, on the edges of society instead of trying to venture near the mainstream. I'm bloody wary.

I decide to go for it but steel myself not to care about the outcome. I really don't expect to get in anyway. Hell, how could I when I'll be competing against kids who've learnt since they were little kids for Christ's sake.

I go like a maniac, memorising three eighth-grade pieces for the audition. I practise every spare minute, often five hours a day.

On the morning of the audition I have a beer to calm my nerves. When I walk into the room I don't even look at the assessors. I tell myself I'm just going through the motions. I won't get in. My hands and legs shake as I play. I fight my nerves every inch of the way and get through the pieces. Just.

At home, I wait weeks for the results, trying not to torture myself with the possibility of being accepted.

We have Dan's fourth birthday party with some kids from crèche. One of the mums, Jane, stays late with her French husband, Dan, their son Oliver and their new baby. We've started calling Dan, Dan Biggs, and Jane's husband Dan Ranson. I like Dan Biggs, it's got a ring. We have dinner together and then Jane tells us to come outside. She's brought sparklers. We light them and Dan Biggs's face looks like he's just seen paradise. His eyes are wide, his mouth's open and it's smiling at the same time. I've never seen him look so beautiful. It's the first time he's had sparklers. I wish I'd thought of showing him earlier, but I wouldn't have missed this moment for anything. Sometimes I still can't believe how lucky I am.

Just before Christmas a letter with Adelaide University on it arrives. I'm still kidding myself that I won't care if I'm rejected, I don't expect it anyway, right? I open the envelope.

'We would like to inform you that you have been accepted to the performance degree, Bachelor of Music at the Elder Conservatorium, Adelaide University ...'

I cry and read the letter again. And again. I ring my piano teacher, Bloss and Ellie. That night I ring Joanne on off-peak rates so we can talk for a long time.

'That's fantastic BB? You must be very good. I can't wait to hear you play. When are you coming over next?'

'If I can stay with you, I'm thinking of coming these holidays.'

'You know there's always room at the inn for you, BB. Just let me know when, so I can work on Bear a bit.'

It's on that trip back to Melbourne, before I start my first year at the Conservatorium, that I see Vernon again for the first time in more than ten years.

EIGHT

THE ONE IN CONTROL

Joanne and Bear want to have a picnic at Rippon Lea estate
near their house. It's a National Trust mansion and there's a
music recital on there as well. We bring champagne and make
a day of it. Dan's visiting one of his little friends from crèche.

Late in the afternoon when we're packing up and about to leave, a couple of girls run up to me. I think I recognise them from somewhere.

'Is your name Barb?'

'Yes. How do you know?'

'Do you remember us?' It's the younger girl.

'You look familiar but I can't quite remember where I've met you before.'

'I'm Kate and this is Nita. We think you looked after us when we were little. Is that you?'

My heart is in my shoes. Where is he? The question breathes fear into my pores. Joanne and I look at each other.

'Oh, that's right. Look at you two. You're so grown-up now. You're both so gorgeous looking. How did you know it was me? That must've been about, what, 11 years ago. You were only two.'

'Wait 'til we tell Dad. Nita, let's take her home. Dad'll just be so surprised!'

'Hang on. Where do you live?'

'Here! We live here, in the gatehouse. We're the caretakers. Well, not really, we're just here for like, security. Wait 'til we tell Dad. Come on, can we call you Auntie Barb? Remember we used to call you Mummy Barb?'

'Yes, I know. Look, maybe your dad's busy.'

'No, he isn't. He's just home with Jean. He got married again. They're just home not doing anything. Oh, come on. Please? Dad'll just be so amazed.'

'Well, look, go and tell him I'm here and if he wants to see me, he can. Okay?'

'But will you promise to wait here?'

'Yep. I'll be right here.' My voice is breezy even while my world somersaults.

'Don't go away. Okay?'

The girls run off and Joanne raises her eyebrows.

'Well, they were a couple of happy little bunny rabbits, weren't they? What about you? How do you feel?'

'A bit sick.'

'We don't have to stay, you know.'

'It's funny, I can't believe how totally nervous I am. I feel like I'm about to face a firing squad. But he shouldn't make me feel like this after all this time. Maybe I do want to see him to put it all in perspective. It's like he's grown larger than life over all these years.'

'It's up to you. I wouldn't do it, but I wouldn't mind seeing what a real live pervert looks like, all the same.'

The girls come tearing back and each grabs one of my hands and starts dragging me off.

'Come on. Dad says to bring you home. He just can't believe it!'

I look at Joanne.

'If you're going to his house, I'll wait for you at home. Bear has to get to work anyway. Are you sure you want to go?'

'Might as well now.'

They drag me in the front door and I first see Vernon in the hallway coming out of the kitchen. He hasn't changed much. He still has the moustache and watery, piggy eyes. He does his uncle number on me. I feel like a trapped bird with no way out. Stupid birds, curious enough to go through windows into stray houses, but getting out is another thing.

'Barb. How lovely to see you. What a surprise. When the girls told me they'd seen you, I said to Jean "That's young Barb who was such a big help when poor Jane was sick", didn't I Jean?'

He's bringing me into the kitchen to meet Jean. I'm amazed to see that she isn't young like me and Jane had been, but an older woman, about his own age. She seems nice. The girls are hovering around like jumping jack-in-the-boxes.

'So, how have you been dear? What have you been up to all this time? But wait a minute, we can talk later. The girls are just too excited. Girls, why don't you take Barb into the lounge room and put some of your records on. You can show her how you dance. Auntie Barb's a pretty good dancer too, aren't you Pet?'

'Not really. But do you want to show me your records?' At least this way I can get away from Vernon to collect myself. But I'm wrong there.

The girls take my hands again and pull me towards the lounge room.

They put their records on and they're jumping around dancing and telling me to join in. So, I do. A few minutes later, Vernon puts his head around the door and looks me up and down.

'I told you Barb was a good dancer didn't I?'

He stands in the doorway, undressing me with his eyes. I have a flash of him catching Pommy and me dancing one night after our baths when we were little, dancing like princesses with our towels on our heads making veils down our back. How he'd offered us money to dance naked for him. Of how he made me dance for him when I lived with him all those years ago.

I feel trapped now, not by the house, but an emotional time warp. Even though I'm more than a decade older and, in so many ways, another person, I feel exactly the same as when I lived with him. I want him to like me. I don't want him to leer at me. I want him to admire the way I dance. I want him to stop watching me dance with that look on his face. I can't find my tongue.

I listen to a couple of songs with the girls and then say my friends are waiting and I have to go.

'I hope you come back and see the girls again. They'd

love to see you, wouldn't you, girls?' We're back in the kitchen with Jean.

'Yes, Auntie Barb, come back and visit. Why don't you come tomorrow? Can she, Daddy?'

'Well, you'd better ask Barb about that.'

'Can you, Auntie Barb?'

'Well, I'm actually living in Adelaide now and I'm just here for a few days, so probably not. Maybe another time.'

'Oh, that's a shame. What are you doing in Adelaide, dear?'

'Studying. I'm playing piano. I've just passed an audition for the conservatorium there. I start this year. I've been doing an Arts degree.' Like me. Respect me. I'm just like you. I'm not something to undress with your eyes.

'That's wonderful, dear. Marvellous. Well, we'd love to see you next time you're in Melbourne, wouldn't we girls? Now, you'd better let Auntie Barb go if she's got friends waiting.'

'Aaaww, do we have to?' They put on their sad faces and say goodbye.

I leave feeling ridiculous. I was trying to impress him. Why? And why was he still leering at me after all this time? On the way home the Melbourne weather turns and rain buckets down. I run to Joanne's house, confused and overwhelmed. Joanne lives around the corner from Rippon Lea and knowing he's so close is unnerving. I don't feel myself again until I'm back in Adelaide.

That summer, before I start at the conservatorium, Dan and I eat our way through the strawberries and apples from the garden. I make strudel, apple pie and strawberry milkshakes. I buy a trailer of mushroom compost for the garden and grow my first veggies ever; lettuces and tomatoes, broccoli and carrots, spinach and basil for pesto that Joanne had taught me how to make in Melbourne. I weed and prune and poison blackberries. I buy a yellow rose bush. Pommy's favourite flower. I tell Ma about my plan and she sends over her ashes and I bury them under it. Now she has a home where she can finally be at peace. I hope she'll stop falling in my dreams.

When I start at the conservatorium I'm so excited I can't sleep the night before. The first day I meet my new piano teacher. Mary Warneke's a short, frumpy woman with an ocker accent who chain-smokes when she can get away with it. Not at all what I expect. When she asks me to play, I choose Mozart's *Fantasy in C*.

'Okay, that's fine. Now go from here.' She points to a place on the page. I stare at the page. I don't know where 'there' is without doing Every Good Boy Deserves Fruit with every note of the first few chords. It'll take up the whole lesson. But I know the notes from the sound they make and the shape of my hands on the piano.

'Where's there?'

'What do you mean, where's there? Where I'm pointing.'

'Can you play a couple of bars so I know where you mean.'

Her mouth falls open and she widens her eyes like a mime artist. I pucker my mouth and cross my eyes. We both laugh.

'How on earth did you get in here if you can't read music?'

'I can, but I can't read and play at the same time.'

'How did you learn the pieces then?'

'I read them slowly and then memorised the bars.'

'Everything you know, you've memorised?'

'Mmm hmm.'

'And I thought I'd seen everything. Well, I s'pose we've gotta work with what we've got, haven't we. So how are we gonna do this?'

'If you just show me what "there" looks like, the place on the piano, I'll play whatever you want. Just play a couple of bars.'

She does and we're away until she asks about a perfect fifth.

'What's that?'

She does her mimed shock horror.

'Do you know anything about music or can you just play a couple of pieces? Have you done any theory?'

'What's theory?'

'My God! I can pick 'em. You haven't done *any* theory? How long've you been playing?'

'Six months this last spell and nine months while I was pregnant with my son five years ago. But I practise for hours and hours a day.'

She gets up from her chair and paces the floor while she's rubbing her chin, looking over at me every now and then, narrowing her eyes. I can see she's thinking of kicking me out and I'm not about to go without a fight. I haven't come this far for nothing. I stand up and put my hands on my hips. I'm about to cry.

'Look, I came here to learn piano. Do you want to teach me or not?'

We glare at each other. Her eyes are hard as nails and mine are watery with unshed tears.

'You're a feisty one for someone who doesn't know a perfect fifth from their eye teeth my girl. Now get back to that piano. We've got a lot of work to get through before I'm done with you.'

She works her teaching around my handicaps. She teaches me how to relax my wrists, how to break a wide chord with my tiny hands and most of all, how to use rests and rubato to pull the timing around in a way that makes every piece my own unique interpretation.

Almost every lesson I have dirt under my fingernails because of gardening. Miss Warneke, as she insists I call her, mentions it every time.

'Bring the garden with you again today did you? You really should do something about those nails. You've got the hands of a charwoman.'

In the hallways and grounds of the conservatorium, the sound of pianos, flutes, cellos, violins, oboes, even recorders, floats on the air, a symphony of middle-class gentility. I can't believe I'm here. I feel like an impostor and wait to get found out. I go into the piano rooms to practise, hoping I'll feel more a part of the scene. It works, at least temporarily.

Piano lessons are the only part of the week I enjoy. I go to lectures but can't understand a thing they say. I have a hard time picking classes because anything that involves sight-reading's out. For electives I take Bach Choir where I can follow everybody else and pretend to be reading the music. I take Tribal Singing where we learn songs from corroborees that they call Inmas, taught by an Aboriginal tribal elder from the centre up near Alice Springs. There's no music to read. The elder comes once a month and the rest of the time a white, lanky guy called Ian Knowles takes the class. He's kind and patient and thinks I learn fast.

There's no way I can get out of Aural Training, Orchestration and Composition. I can't do them. Most lectures I go to I can't follow at all. I sit there feeling like an idiot wondering why I'm here. I go to a class and tell myself that it's logical and if I concentrate hard enough I'll be able to understand. I go in and will my mind not to wander for a second. But I'm lost in five minutes and have to leave the class before anyone sees me in tears. It gets so I'm crying every day.

I also have to do a half-hour recital at the end of the year for my instrumental exam. My performance nerves have got worse, not better. I can't play in front of anyone, not even in my own lounge room in front of friends. My confidence ebbs away with every passing week. There's no way I can give a half-hour recital in front of examiners. I feel like a fraud.

It's near the end of first term and I'm making my debut at the conservatorium this Saturday. It's not for assessment or important in any other way, but it's the first time the other students will hear me play. I think I'll take a little pill to help me along. The others seem to have to take something to perform. The campus GP has referred me to a hypnotherapist. He's supposed to be the best in Adelaide. He must be good because he's booked up until November but the doctor will probably be able to get me in before then because they're friends. He can see I'm desperate. I went to him in tears after running out of yet another lecture.

I'm getting better all the time on the piano, though. I've been spending an hour a day on scales and finger exercises and then my pieces on top of that.

I feel like every moment's put to good use. Precious in fact.

I've started kung fu on Thursday nights. I have to get out and meet people. I still hardly know anyone here.

I'm lonely.

I start seeing the hypnotherapist in second term. I tell him everything that's happening. About the lectures, the crying every day and about my past, about Vernon. He puts me on anti-depressants and makes a hypno tape for me to take home. I listen to it every morning when I wake up and every night before I go to sleep. Sometimes two or three times.

'Relax your toes, now your feet …' All the way up the body.

'Now Barbara, I want you to imagine that whenever you play the piano, it's something that you enjoy. No matter who's listening you feel as though you're playing alone, in your own lounge room, in your own home …'

On the anti-depressants I sleep every time I sit down for a spell. I keep going to classes but at home I fall sleep in front of the fire on the floor in the afternoons. Dan often comes in from playing to wake me up. I manage my three hours practice at night after Dan goes to sleep. Not much gardening or housework gets done that winter.

Earlier in the year I'd sold my old bomby car to get a better one. A young, handsome guy called Lindsay bought it. He lives locally and drops in to visit from time to time. I don't know why. He's only nineteen and as country as they come. I'm 27. We have nothing in common.

When winter comes, he starts visiting at night and staying for hours. He tells me he doesn't get along with his dad and his mum isn't around anymore. He lives in a shed in a paddock he rents from a farmer for practically nothing. He's unemployed and will take any job he can get, but without much experience, paid work is thin on the ground. His 18-year-old best friend from primary school suicided last year because he was so depressed after applying for hundreds of jobs and being turned down. I feel sorry for Lindsay but he's interrupting my practice.

'I don't mean to be rude, but the only time I can really get my three hours in, is when Dan's in bed,' I say one night.

'That's alright. I don't mind. You practise away and I'll just sit here and listen to ya. Don't worry me. I can listen to ya play for hours.'

So, two or three times a week through winter, Lindsay sits in my warm lounge room while I practise. It helps my performance nerves. It doesn't take long before I'm playing like no-one's there. When I finish, we have a cup of tea, then, after kissing me chastely on the cheek, he leaves.

I visit him once and am shocked at his living conditions – dirt floor, rats running around, gaps under the shed doors big enough for dogs to get in and a pile of dirty blankets on a mattress in the corner of the room where he sleeps. It's only then I realise why he prefers my lounge room on cold nights.

After six months, he brings a joint around and we smoke together. Dope makes me horny and I haven't had sex for a long time. We end up in the sack and I'm so surprised. His touch is like poetry, even though he's only slept with a girl a couple of times in his life. Through touch, he expresses all the longing, quiet desperation, sadness and hope of a boy in love. I'm charmed by his innocence and passion. In him, I see myself before I met Rick and Vernon and all the others. I want to nurture it and look after him. We begin spending more time together. He's uncomplicated, sweet and honest. He fixes my kitchen cupboards and tunes my car. He adores me. We have nothing in common.

By the end of the year, I'm off the anti-depressants. I've passed everything except Aural Training. They play tunes and I have to write them in musical notation. I can't hear whether an interval's a fifth or an octave or a second apart.

I get through my half-hour piano recital and get a B plus. I've fallen seriously in love with Ravel and Debussy. I learn Debussy's *Submerged Cathedral*, Ravel's *Sonatine* and a Chopin *Nocturne*.

I become friends with Steven half way through the year because he's so encouraging. He's Chinese, born in Singapore, adopted there and the best pianist in the whole con. I have a crush on him before I find out he's gay, but after that brutal discovery, we become best friends. His adoptive parents in Singapore think he's studying engineering but he's changed to music without them knowing. They've been supporting him financially over here for two years.

Half way through the year his parents find out that he's changed uni courses and they're livid. They threaten to cut off his allowance if he doesn't enrol in a more sensible degree. Steven refuses. If he can find someone to marry so he can stay here he can be independent.

'I've always wanted to have a white wedding,' I tell him.

The paper work's complicated because it means I'll have to go off the pension while we're married. He says he'll compensate me for any money I lose through the deal. I send out invitations and make wedding plans. A friend from the crèche still has her mother's 1950s wedding dress that fits me like a glove.

The day's set for mid-January. Even though everyone knows it isn't a real wedding, Ma and Jenny are coming from Sydney and Peter from Melbourne. Some mums from Dan's old crèche in Melbourne also agree to come.

'Is there anything you want me to bring?' asks Ma.

'No, not really. I can't think of anything.'

'How about a bucket of Kentucky Fried?'

'Ma, most of my friends are vegetarians.'

'I'll bring it anyway.'

The morning of the wedding I'm running late as usual. Someone gives me a bouquet of parsley because it's a fertility symbol and they figure with Steven being gay I'll need all the help I can get. Ha. I have something old, my oldest possession, a ring an old boyfriend gave me for my 18th birthday. Knickers are new and blue.

I drive myself to the ceremony that's being held in a grand, historic registry office in King William Street in the city. Everyone's waiting on the pavement and I'm running so late I speed up, almost doing a wheelie when I park out the front and emerge, a small whirlwind of white veil and taffeta. Steven whisks me into the registry office with trails of brightly-coloured friends scurrying after. We say our solemn vows. We all feel embarrassed because we've been treating it like a joke and now we're here. Really getting married. One of the singing students at the con, a religious girl, sings a Vivaldi aria. She says later she's mortified even though she knew what she was letting herself in for. She'd forgotten how Catholics run on guilt.

Back at my place we eat, laugh too loudly about the wedding and play music.

Ma arrives late. She's missed the service. I'm shocked when I see her. I know she's had the stomach stapling operation but she's aged 20 years. She'd always looked so young for her age but now she's gone from 30 stone to 12 stone in a year and her skin hangs off her bones in billowing folds.

She's been in and out of hospital on drips and had countless operations, but she's lost the weight only because she's been living off her own body fat for the past year. Her jet black hair's gone completely white in the last year.

'Barb! How are you? Sorry we missed the wedding but bloody Jenny was fart-arsing around in Orange looking for something. How was it? Good?'

'It was great, but look at you! Ma, you look so skinny. You must feel so ... so light.'

'Well, I don't feel any different actually.'

'You must. You've lost two-thirds of your body weight. You must feel fantastic.'

'Well, it's good to be able to buy clothes off the rack. That's real good. And walkin's easier 'cause I don't have the weight, but inside meself I don't really feel that different.'

'How did you lose it? You always say you can't lose weight.'

'It was only because I threw up everything I ate for a bloody year. The only thing I could keep down was flat coke.

But I don't want to talk about that on your special day. Are you having a good time?'

'Mmmm. Great.'

'Are you happy?'

'I am, but not because of Steven. You know it's not a real wedding don't you, Ma? He's gay.'

'Yes, I know. But you never know what can happen.'

Ever hopeful.

'Did you notice the Kentucky lasted about two seconds? I thought you said they were all vegetarians. I should've bought two buckets.'

'I guess there's nothing like the smell of meat to get a drunken vegetarian thinking about meat.'

I haven't seen my brother Peter in ages. He still has the long straggly, grey-streaked ponytail, even though he's only 23.

'Are you still with that girl Peter?'

'Barbara, I told you about three years ago we'd split up about a year before that. Don't you ever listen to anything?'

'I hardly ever see you. No wonder I forget.'

Jenny's still as roly-poly as ever. She's short, Jenny, and drinks about two litres of Coke a day. Bloss is with her new man Bernard who seems to be an emotional baby like her last boyfriend. I don't know why such a grown-up person like Bloss goes out with such immature guys. Bernard's being horrible to Christian, ordering him around and being a prick. Christian, he's 11 now, is being naughty and causing disturbances all over the place, making Bernard pay.

We cut the wedding cake and sing. Steven performs a couple of his exam pieces and I play my Debussy. Audiences don't worry me now. None of the family have heard me play before and Ma's so proud. The hypno tapes have worked like a dream.

After the wedding, I've planned to go to Melbourne to

visit Joanne again. And maybe William too. He's being nicer to me these days. I also want to try to find my father. Since having Dan I've realised how much like William he is and think I must be like my father too. I'm curious.

But the main reason I want to go is to get something out of my system that's been there for too long. I decide to visit Vernon.

'I want to demystify him, that's all.'

We're in Joanne's kitchen, smoking like chimneys. In the middle of the table is a carousel she's making with Australian animals instead of horses. I'm making us a cup of tea.

'But why now, BB? After all this time? What can you possibly have to say to him?'

'I want to tell him what effect he's had on my life. Why shouldn't he know?'

'But why? What do you want out of it? And what's all this demystifying business anyway? It's hard to keep track of your obsessions.'

'I don't know. One of those self-help books. All I remember is that you're supposed to confront the guy if he's still alive because when I was younger he would've seemed much bigger than he really was. If you see them as an adult you're supposed to be able to cut them down to size.'

We always make pots of tea in Joanne's house. She never uses teabags. It has to be just so, the pot heated, water boiled for three minutes, one spoon of tea for each person and one for the pot. I pour us both a cuppa. Like her and everything in her house, they're exquisite – fine Victorian china.

'You don't take sugar do you?'

'Yeeessss. I doooo. Twooo.' She sighs and looks exasperated.

'I didn't think you had sugar in tea.'

'BB, ever since you've known me, what is it? Ten years

now? You've been asking that and every time I say "Yes, thank you, two" and every time you say, "Do you take sugar?" like it's the biggest surprise. Then you say, "I thought you didn't," with this puzzled little look on your face. Then! Then, you give me tea without sugar!'

'Do I? How rude! You should've said something.' I'm mortified. It's a short-hand way of taking in lots of information quickly. If I get it wrong the first time I never review it.

'This little brown duck knows when she's banging her head against a brick wall. I gave up years ago. Anyway, what would you say to him?'

'Vernon? I just want to see what he's got to say for himself. You know, I'm not the same person I was then, but in relation to him, I don't feel grown-up at all. That's the problem. When I saw him at Rippon Lea last year it was like nothing'd changed. But I've just got this idea that if I see him I'll get unstuck somehow.'

'What did he say when you rang?'

'He sounded suspicious. He wanted to know why I wanted to see him after all these years. It's so weird. I can't believe the power he's still got over me. My voice was shaking. Anyway, he said he'd meet me in a coffee shop in Fitzroy Street. Topolino's.'

'When?'

'Saturday, 10 o'clock.'

'At least it's in the day.'

'He tried for night but I said no. That's when he started sounding nervous.'

'What about you? How do you feel? Are *you* nervous?'

'Yeah. A little bit. Not really.'

The next day, Vernon rings Joanne's – I'd left her number. He says he wants to change the meeting to the sea baths at St Kilda.

'It's a bit of a sleazy place, BB. I think you should make it somewhere else.'

'I don't want to piss him off. He wasn't sounding that enthusiastic anyway. I'll just leave it, I think.'

That night I lie in bed thinking about seeing Vernon again and get the shakes so bad I can almost hear my bones rattle. I've had the shakes before when I've been cold, but it isn't anything like that. My teeth chatter and my whole body shakes violently in waves from head to toe. It goes on all night. I'm so exhausted I will myself to think of something else but it only lasts for a few minutes before the thought of seeing him sets me off again. It's one of the longest nights of my life. I hope my body will become so exhausted it'll shut down and get some rest. No way. I try yoga breathing, taking a deep breath in and letting it out slowly, trying to relax. Again the trembling stops for a minute and then starts more violently than before. It's hard to believe a body can have so much nervous energy. I get up to make a cup of tea but that only calms me while I'm actually vertical. When I lie down again it feels like I'm working out on a fat reducing machine. But the shakes aren't coming from the surface. I know it's fear that comes from the depths of my being.

At dawn, I fall into an exhausted sleep.

When I get up I dress in a skirt, shirt and flat sandals. It's summer. I look plain but attractive. By the time I walk into the sea baths, I have myself under control.

Joanne was right about this place. There are old guys in hot pools everywhere. They look me up and down when I come in. Vernon's in a pool way down the back. The last thing I expect is that he'll be in his bathers.

'Barb, there you are. How are you, Pet?'

'Fine. How are you?' How are we supposed to talk with him in the pool and me here?

'Couldn't be better. It's gorgeous in. Did you bring your swimmers?'

'No.' The thought of it makes my heart sink.

He starts getting out of the pool.

'I might be an old bloke but I run an hour a day and swim 20 laps. Not bad for an old fella. We can go upstairs to talk. There's a place on the roof.'

I follow him doing a quick mental sum about how old he is: 42 when I was 14. I've just turned 27. He has to be 55.

On the roof we sit on the ground with our backs to a low wall. Although the sun's shining it's muggy and polluted. I can hear the waves rolling in. The place we sit is private. Too private?

'Alright then. What's all this about? Tell me.'

I take a deep breath. As I start to talk, terror rises in my throat and my voice warbles.

'I've been thinking for a long time that I wanted to tell you about how you've affected my life.' I'd planned it while I was lying awake last night.

'I thought it might be something like that. So you've come all this way from Adelaide, after, what is it, 13 years, to tell me off for ruining your life.'

'I come to Melbourne anyway, but yes, I *do* want you to know. I don't think you realise, well, realise how much effect you had. On my whole life. Not just then but for years afterwards. After I left your place I had sex with anyone who wanted me. Remember you kept telling me how life's about sex and you should get as much as you can? Then, when I was 16 I ended up in a mental hospital ...'

'And that's my fault?'

'Not entirely, but partly, yes.'

I know I'm not going to get through this. I feel my resolve leaking out of me every time he opens his mouth.

'Look, there's a saying that unless you've walked a mile in someone else's shoes, don't go around judging people. You've got no idea what was going on for me at that time. I can't see any point in going over it. I would've thought at your age you'd have realised you can't go around blaming other people for what's happening in your life.'

He's talking to me like I'm a real person. For the first time. Even though he doesn't seem to be understanding anything that I'm saying, at least he isn't being sleazy.

'My life's actually going really well at the moment. That's why I decided to tell you because now I *can*.'

I tell him about my study and Dan. I happen to have the wedding photos in my bag and I show them to him.

'So, you're into chinks now.'

I'm shocked. I always thought he was into equality. He's supposed to be a communist, isn't he? I thought he loved Chairman Mao.

'He's gay. I married him so he could stay in the country. He's a friend.'

'I think we've got too bloody many here already.'

'Too many what?'

'Chinks. Asians. Before you know it there'll be more of them than us.'

We talk more and, part of my plan at least, starts working. Yes, he's narrow-minded and bigoted. When I had no education he seemed like an intellectual giant. Now I know about political correctness. He's like any other old guy his age with racist opinions and rigid views.

Then he floors me.

'You know I followed the tram strike when it happened. What was that you said about me not paying you enough?'

'What?' What's that got to do with anything?

'In the paper. You said you were disillusioned by communism because I didn't pay you enough. You thought I should've paid you half of what I was paid, didn't you? That's a bit rough isn't it? I don't think I deserved that.'

I'd forgotten about it. Over all these years *that's* the thing that stuck in his mind about me? A slight? A dig at him in a newspaper that hurt his pride? His narrow-mindedness and inability to see the chasm of difference between what I'd done to him, for which he expected an explanation, and what he'd done to me, that he had no intention of even explaining let alone rationalising or apologising for, just blew me away.

'I said what I believed, that's all.'

He changed the subject and asked if I had a boyfriend.

'There's a young boy I see. He's only 19.'

'Can't find a real man to satisfy you like I did, eh?'

There's a glint in his eye. Suddenly I'm only Pet again. In that moment I realise what I've wanted from him more than anything is to be taken seriously. Seen as a grown-up. For all those years, that's what I wanted. And this hunger, eats you away. The power he had over me then, is still here, now. It comes crashing down on me and I can't get out from under it.

'Apart from all the weird stuff you did. Sometimes you did actually satisfy me.'

'Did I now? And how did I do that?'

'There's one thing that no-one's ever done to me since.'

I can't believe I'm getting into this. Like I'm still trying to prove I'm sophisticated when it comes to talking about sex. I *am* grown-up. Nothing fazes me.

I tell him what it was. There's a war of shame and guilt and longing going on inside me. I'm supposed to hate the guy. I know there's no way I can tell Joanne or anybody else what I'm doing here.

He puts his hand up my dress while I'm telling him. I take it away.

'I'm the one in control now,' I say.

And I kiss him on the mouth. Memories of sex with him fling me back into the past. We aren't here, in St Kilda, in 1983. It's 1972 again. Don McLean and Leonard Cohen are playing in my head. We grope for a few minutes before someone comes up the stairs to our part of the roof.

Interrupted, we walk down to the front door.

'I don't know what a beautiful young thing would want with an old bugger like me, but if you want to, we could meet up tonight.'

We arrange to meet again in the carpark behind Luna Park at 10 pm.

All that day I'm filled with shame about what I've done. I go back to Joanne's but tell her only about the conversation we'd had before the groping.

'Good on you, BB. I think you're very brave.'

If only she knew. I feel sick. I think about what Sue told me, about when she was pregnant and her dad tongue-kissed her at the train station and how she'd kissed him back. It's so deep and complicated, so real, that even hating it doesn't have enough power to make it go away.

Almost.

I don't meet him. But every day for months afterwards, I'm mortified and ashamed. In the deepest part of me, I know someone inside me wanted it.

Inside myself I'm honest. But I know that this is going to be a secret I'll never be able to admit to anyone.

NINE

CAUGHT IN A TIME WARP

Back in Adelaide I start uni again. It isn't a breeze but sticking with the nightmare of last year has paid off. Miraculously I've almost caught up with the rest of the students. I'm not drowning anymore. Mary Warneke plays me some pieces to learn that nearly break my heart. Debussy again, *Claire de Lune* and *Girl with the Flaxen Hair*, Ravel's *Sonatine* and a jazz piece, *Rhapsody in Blue* by Gershwin. Before the end of the degree I have to play a concerto too. There's the simplest falling melody in Ravel's concerto that puts me into a trance when I play it. I'm in love with the romantic composers but Mary insists I have a varied repertoire and gives me a modern Latin piece called *Minstrel Impressions* by a South American composer, Villa-Lôbos. I pour the deepest parts of myself into my playing. Parts I can't express with anyone.

At the end of first term my tribal singing class goes on a field trip to an Aboriginal community a couple of hundred kilometres west of Alice Springs. They've added the Pitjantjatjara language to the elective list too, which is perfect because there are so few I can choose that don't involve sight-reading. I still haven't caught up with that and don't think I ever will.

The field trip's two weeks and I'm allowed to bring Dan. Our teacher, Ian, brings his son too who's about the same age. Ian's divorced. He speaks Pitjantjatjara because he lived up there for a year when he was 21 as part of his honours year in ethnomusicology. That was 15 years ago. He talks to me about how lonely he was during that year and how no-one spoke to him until one day they told him to try to catch a baby joey.

'I knew there was no way I could catch it but I suddenly realised that everything else I'd tried to get them to accept me hadn't worked. So, I thought, what've I got to lose? It was like an initiation. They could see I wasn't too proud to make an idiot of myself in front of a bunch of black fellas.'

'What happened? Did you catch it?'

'No, but they thought it was a great joke. They called me brother and wanted to initiate me after that.' He laughs at himself and I like that.

The settlement's run by the government and there's no alcohol allowed. The Pitjantjatjara don't speak English and the old guy who owns the songs we'd been learning all last year, Sam, tells us how he remembers seeing his first white man when he was about 12. He thought the guy was the ghost of an ancestor. That was only 40 years ago and they were living like nomads then, the same way they'd lived for ten thousand years before we came.

We stay in Sam's camp and sleep on the ground. We dig for wichetty grubs with the women and hunt kangaroos with rifles and jeeps with the men. With one foot in their culture and another firmly planted in his own, Ian seems to know exactly where they're at in their evolution, or really, integration, into a white culture. He explains how he sees it when I ask why so many of the kids walk around with cans between their teeth.

'They're sniffing petrol to get high. It's a tragedy. It's mainly the kids about 12 who're about to get initiated. The worst one's Sam's grandson. My theory is that everywhere they look they see the people with power and influence are white. The nurse, the community adviser, the teachers, the storeowner. And they think, "There's no place here for me because I'm black".' He says all this in a humble kind of way. He's seems so intelligent.

'What about Sam's grandson? Won't he inherit the songs and be an elder one day?'

'Of course he will. But that's just the point. That's why he's the worst. He knows he should be a tribal leader, but he also sees that the role has no currency today. He looks at Sam and sees he doesn't have a car, doesn't have status, no-one wants to listen to the old lore anymore. Sam's been talking about it. They're all talking about it. They're at their wits end trying to work out what they can do to help the kids. The death rate with petrol sniffing's atrocious and if they don't die they're left with irreparable brain damage.'

We've all heard about the Aboriginal problem. There are a lot more in Adelaide than Melbourne, where you hardly ever see them. But people in Adelaide hate 'Abos'. Like most people, I feel guilty about them. Before Ian starts explaining,

I've never really known anything about their culture. How they think. What he says makes a lot of sense. But there must be something we can do to stop what's happening.

As he explains his theory to me, I try not to look at him as if he's God incarnate. Sagittarians do that. They put people on pedestals at the drop of a hat.

'If you look at the communities further away from Alice, that don't have schools yet, they also don't have petrol sniffing. You can almost trace the progress of sniffing if you follow when white schools opened in these places. About a year or two after the school starts, the petrol sniffing starts.'

'That doesn't make any sense. You'd think the more educated they are the less they'd want to get high.'

'When the schools come, the kids spend six hours a day learning that only white people are important. They're learning things that their elders don't know, like how to read and write and do arithmetic. They start to see their elders as having no important knowledge. As basically being obsolete old farts. Why would they be interested in inheriting a culture that they see has no value in the eyes of the dominant culture, which is white? They're caught in a time warp where they have no place in the future culture and their past one has no value.'

Wow. He's so passionate.

'But everything here's provided by the government. White folks. They all get pensions. Where would they be without that?'

There's something about Ian that reminds me of William. He's a good man, trying to help people. I've noticed how even though he's a uni teacher, he runs around for Sam like a messenger boy. He doesn't pull any superior white man bullshit.

'I don't know. I can't see a solution. It's too late to back up and there are too many obstacles to go forward. Our culture's come on them too fast. I'll never forget a couple of years ago driving up here in the middle of nowhere, like there wasn't even a settlement for maybe a hundred k's around, and I saw this glow up ahead. I couldn't for the life of me work out what it was. I drove for about ten minutes before I finally saw, when I got close up, it was the glow from a fucking television. Here these Pitjantjatjara were, in the middle of the desert with a generator, watching a James Bond movie. And they don't even understand English. It spoke volumes about the sudden merging of two cultures in a single lifetime. I mean, what would an Aboriginal person who'd never even seen a plane, let alone flown in one, who's never seen running water, possibly make of a James Bond movie for fuck sake? Except that maybe white men are Gods and they, the Pitjantjatjara, know nothing.'

I ask what he'd do about the petrol sniffing if he could.

'Sam's been getting in my ear about what can be done. He wants me to help get a tribal curriculum included in the school program where the lessons are outdoors and taught by elders. Namely him. So learning their own culture is part of what's seen to be valuable.'

So wise and smart.

We're in Mimili to sing the songs we learnt at uni. We're waiting for Pitjantjatjara to have their Inmas but trying to get one off the ground's a mystery even Ian doesn't understand.

Finally, after we've been here nearly two weeks, one's organised for the weekend, just before we have to go home.

The women paint our bodies and their own and the men light fires along the path of the dancers. We don't know how to dance but when the men come out it's like the night stops. They dance like the animals in their world. They like it when the white guys in our group make idiots of themselves by trying to dance like wallabies. Dancing and singing the songs under the stars like they've been doing for ten thousand years makes me think it should be part of our curriculum to have every white kid see this. See what we've cost them.

There seems to be a spark between Ian and me. But you never really know if it's just in your own head or not. When he's near me I'm aware of everything about him. The way he stands with his skinny arms dangling, his long, delicate pianist fingers hanging limp and relaxed by his sides. The way he sits cross-legged and stops himself from interrupting Sam when he's bursting to make a point. The way he seems to stand a little closer to me than he does to other people. Maybe it's my imagination. But maybe not. Already I can have simple conversations in Pitjantjatjara. He says he's impressed.

On our last night Ian and I sleep head to head in our sleeping bags between the two fires. You need one on either side because even though it's stinking hot in the day, desert nights can be bitter. We're talking long after everybody else goes to sleep. He's showing me some constellations and telling the Aboriginal lore about what they are and how they're made. I watch his long, thin hands pointing upwards and I can't stop myself anymore. I reach up and touch his fingers.

'You've got very nice hands you know.'

'Yours aren't too bad either,' he says and laughs because it's awkward. We stop talking and stroke each other's hands. We lock fingers lightly and bring our arms down together. He kisses my hand before saying goodnight.

I don't sleep for a long time because I'm in heaven.

The next morning there's a knowing between Ian and me. But again, I'm still not sure if it's just my imagination. Neither of us talk about the night before.

We pack up our camp and the two jeeps we'd hired for the trip. Everybody hugs each other before we say goodbye. We must stink and look like hobos. No-one's had a shower since we got here two weeks ago. Lucky when everyone stinks you can't smell anything.

It isn't until later that night when Ian's driving and Dan and Ian's son Ben are asleep in the back with one of the other students, that I'm sure it isn't my imagination. Ian puts his hand on my knee.

'That was pretty amazing last night,' he says.

'Which bit?'

'All of it.'

I put my hand over his and he turns his palm to face mine. He strokes the palm of my hand so gently I don't want to breathe in case it's all a mistake and he'll stop and wonder what he's doing.

On the two-day trip back, I tell him about my life. I don't tell everything.

Back in Adelaide, during the week Dan and I stay in a spare room at Jane and Dan Ranson's house in Goodwood. It's closer to uni and Jane says she likes the company. I hardly see Lindsay anymore.

Ian's helping me with orchestration, so we meet almost every day. When I finally tell him the difficult details of my life, he seems to like the fact that I've been a fallen woman. Didn't Jesus take Mary Magdalene under his wing? Ian tells me he was a preacher in some church or other when he was 16. He said he'd thought about becoming a man of God. Everything I find out about him makes me put him on a higher pedestal. We're becoming an item. What we're having is, like, a courtship. I've never had one of those before.

One day after I haven't seen Lindsay for a couple of months, he comes to visit at Jane's place down in Adelaide. It's the first time in my life anyone buys me flowers.

'I haven't seen ya for a while. You're never home. I just wondered if ya wanted to go out and get a feed somewhere one night? I've got a bit of work and I thought you might wanna go to, ya know, like a restaurant or somethin'?'

Suddenly he doesn't seem like a poet anymore. He seems like a country kid.

I put him off. I don't tell him about Ian. The flowers are like an accusing poem by my bedside. I never see him again.

Ian and I start having sex. It's not earth shattering but okay. He doesn't like to do it often.

'Sex is like a celebration of life. I think it should be a coming together physically and spiritually to celebrate important events. I think it drains your creative energy.'

Whatever. It suits me. I'm not interested in sex at all unless I get some pleasure out of it, and Ian's not hopeless, but a bit ordinary on that front.

Then one day I come into Ian's office at uni in high heels, black stockings and a short, pleated black skirt. I think I look sexy and I sit on his knee but he looks uncomfortable.

'I know what you're trying to do,' he says.

'What do you mean?'

'You don't have to try to please me. I like you anyway.'

'How am I trying to do that?' Now I'm the one to feel uncomfortable.

'The clothes. I know you're probably acting out your past but you don't have to do that with me. I don't actually like it.'

I don't say anything, but it's the first time I realise that whenever I get involved with a guy, an older one anyway, I didn't do it with Lindsay, some part of me goes into sex toy mode. My usual clothes are loose hippy numbers. I don't shave my legs or underarms because why should we when guys don't? But here I am with Ian, not even ten years older than me, and I'm already going into Pet mode. And I *was* like his pet. He could do anything to me he wanted and I'd accommodate him because I wanted him to love me. Just like I want Ian to love me. The revelation about my behaviour shocks me. I feel completely different now. I'm not that young girl who had no voice. I thought she was dead and buried. Now I'm not so sure. I decide not to let my past slip out like that again.

We've been going out together for six months when his ex-wife decides she's moving to Melbourne with Ben at the end of the year. She has family there. Ian decides he has to move too to be with his son.

'I know you've got one more year of your degree so it's up to you. We can try the long distance relationship or, if you don't want to wait a year, you can transfer the degree to Melbourne. Whatever you decide I'll try to make it as easy as possible. I don't expect you to give up anything on my account.'

I consider staying but don't want to risk losing him. I love Ian and he's the first normal boyfriend I've had. Also, even though I've made friends in Adelaide, I still have Joanne and some of the crèche mums in Melbourne.

Ian sells his house and I put mine on the market too.

With the money from our houses, we buy a Victorian mansion in Elwood, not far from Joanne's house in Elsternwick, with vaulted ceilings and two gigantic, adjoining living rooms for our two pianos. His is a full-size grand. I've traded mine in for a new upright. The house has deep, lush, front and back gardens with two street frontages. When we buy it at auction, Ian picks me up and swings me around while the crowd claps and cheers. It's better than Hollywood. I never dreamed I could be this happy.

Ian feels we've over-stretched ourselves financially and he's worried about the settlement and being able to make the repayments. Back in Adelaide, one night in bed, he asks me to hold him because he's feeling vulnerable and insecure. Neediness scares me. In our family people deal with fears and insecurities on their own. It's all I can do to help myself, let alone anyone else.

Ian introduces me to a family he knows who live in the Adelaide Hills. They've home schooled their cricket team of kids. The dad's director of the Flinders Street School of Music and the mum was a teacher. In their kitchen and lounge room there's kids' art work stuck like wallpaper to every inch of the wall and ceiling with flour and water glue. Every morning they get up at six to practise their instruments as a family orchestra. They each have jobs, milking cows, feeding chooks. After dinner they play a game where you can't answer yes or no. The first one who loses has to stack the dishes, the second wash, the third dry, fourth sweep the floor. Halfway through making their family, they decided to go on a trip to Europe. The mum got everyone picking wild flowers that grow already dried and selling the bunches at fairs on weekends. With this money they paid for everybody's ticket. What a family. Through them, Ian and I talk about home schooling our kids.

Just before we leave Adelaide I have to go to jail for parking fines again. Just a few days this time. Fines can take ages to get to the jail stage. Some are three years old. There's more in the pipeline but at least this will take care of some. Dan stays with Jane. Ian thinks my way of dealing with the fines is creative and eccentric. My friends think it's quite exciting and can't understand why I'm so blasé about it. They get a kick out of telling their other friends I'm going to jail. They think I'm brave because jail's a place where you get bashed up and the girls are rough as guts. At least that's what they think. Most folks don't know anything about girls on the other side of the fence. They're just people like everybody else. In fact the prison girls are quite nice. It's the power hungry screws that are tough as nails.

When I'm in there, I have an argument with one who's horrible to the prisoners for no reason. She just wants to belittle them and let them know who's boss. I stand up to her because I figure I'm out of here in a few days so what the hell.

When I go home, a friend holds a 'Getting Out' dinner party for me. What a hoot.

We move into the Melbourne house. Ben stays with us and goes to his mum's on weekends. We're prepared to teach the kids ourselves, but after talking to the Adelaide family and other home schoolers, we decide two kids isn't enough to make a school community. Ian's been teaching Dan and Ben violin. As well as piano, Ian also plays cello. He continues teaching the kids violin at home, but for the rest, we find a tiny parent-run school in Malvern. Ian, who isn't studying but giving a few private music lessons, does the required half-day roster at the school every week.

Continuing my music degree in Melbourne's out of the question because of the sight-reading test here. I'm a bit devastated while it sinks in but my hands are tied. In the end I console myself with the knowledge that a degree can only lead to teaching which I'm hopeless at. I don't have the patience.

Ian had a tradition of putting on music evenings once a month in Adelaide and he starts them in our new house. We find a network of quartets, trios, singers and pianists to play to and for each other.

The first music evening we have, I invite William, Joanne and Bear and the old mums from the crèche, some who've gone on to be parents at Dan and Ben's school. I play my Villa-Lôbos piece because it's showy and exciting. People whistle and clap. I walk on air.

'You should've seen Bear's face when you started playing,'

Joanne says in the kitchen later. 'His little mouth fell open and it didn't close again until you'd finished. He keeps saying, "Where did she learn to play like that?"'

'What did he think I'd been doing in Adelaide all this time?'

'I don't know. He just thought you were tinkering away. I think Bear's always thought of you as a bit of a silly person. I kept telling him how amazing you were but he never believed me. I'm so proud of you, BB.'

William hovers, too. He tries to catch my eye but I'm too busy playing charming hostess.

These soirees help me decide what I like about piano is playing, so I forget the music degree altogether and enrol instead in arts at Melbourne University.

At uni I do Women's Studies, English Literature and Social Theory. I wade through Dante's Inferno and float through the dreamy romance of Shelley, Byron and Wordsworth. I become an informed and piqued feminist. I have my first story published in the uni rag, *Farago*. *First Love* is about my date with Fabian at the end of my Sydney Tech year. I sit at big tables where someone's reading the magazine. Some smile to themselves and others laugh out loud. I nearly choke on my pride before moving off to another table.

After a few months of living together, Ian begins to drive me crazy. He wants to be good all the time. It's what I admired so much about him when we'd first met but now it makes me want to strangle him. He can't own up to being angry or pissed off. If he can't own his dark side, he can't see the dark side of other people, including me. I need him to see all of me, not pretend I'm Mary Magdalene.

As I become more disillusioned with Ian, I gravitate more towards Joanne. Soon we're seeing each other every day. Now I have my own garden, she and I go foraging for mulch and fertiliser. We go to the beach and return with mountains of seaweed in plastic garbage bags and pile up autumn leaves from the plane trees in our respective streets. Joanne finds an old house with a decades-old compost heap that we begin to raid. The soil I lay down is deep and rich and smells like sweet rust.

During the year I meet our neighbours across the road, Sally Gibson, Bruce Partland and their new daughter Ruby. Bruce looks like Harrison Ford dusting himself off after jumping the abyss. Sal has her own cool style. She's got long hair when everyone else's is short and she wears retro orange and purple clothes with a black and white scarf thrown on top 60s style with sensible shoes and Clark Kent glasses. Very intellectual. She'd been a journalist on the *Age* newspaper for ten years but left to write the *Dismissal* mini series. Old George Miller, from Robert and Joanne's film processing lab, the one who made *Mad Max*, produced it. Then she had Ruby and became a mum.

She comes to a couple of music evenings and I give her one of my short stories to read the next day. I don't know what I'm going to do when I finish my degree. Sal likes the story and says I should become a journalist.

As soon as she says it the short circuits running riot in my head close and I know that's what I'm meant to be. I've been interviewing people since I was a kid. I can get people talking about almost anything. Where did you get that scar? What's it like being in a wheelchair? How do you cope with men staring at you all the time with those big breasts? Have you ever been sexually abused? What was it like when your father ran off with your best friend? Tell me the story of when you first met? Joanne's always been amazed that I can ask the most outrageously personal questions and people actually answer me.

'I don't know how you get away with it, BB.'

But I know why. I'm asking because I'm genuinely interested, not because I'm being a smart-arse.

But still, being a journalist seems like something other people do. It's competitive and everyone says I'm too old. But just imagine. Me? A journalist? That's really in the heart of things. I still see myself as a nobody hanging around the fringes of society.

'It's not that hard, Babsie. Anyone can do it. You wouldn't get a cadetship but if I were you I'd start writing features. Just have a go. If you became a news reporter you'd lose all your style anyway and it'd take you two years to get it back. Just write,' Sal tells me.

Easy for her. I'm intimidated and don't know how to start. I know it's so perfect for me but inside myself I don't know how committed to get about the idea. When I really decide to do something I can move mountains, learn anything, do anything. But what if I try and they're right, I really am too old and it really is just too competitive. Scarey, but I'll just do a course and think about it at the end of next year.

Sal finds out about a professional writing course at Holmesglen College. I send away for course information for the following year. I can do it concurrently with the last year of my B.A.

Dan and Ben love their new school. Ian plans a children's opera for the end of the year. He swears it's all fair and above board but after auditioning the kids, Dan and Ben get two of the leading parts. Soon I'm doing a day a week at the school taking the kids on excursions. There are only 20 kids and one teacher, Marion. It's on one excursion I decide to give Dan a birthday he'll never forget.

WENDY'S HAVING A BIRTHDAY PARTY. She's going to be eight. I've never been to a friend's party. I know I'm not really her friend but I want to go to a birthday party more than anything. I ask her if I can come and she and her two best friends laugh and laugh. Then she says I can come. Part of me knows she doesn't mean it because I haven't got the invitation with my name on it but she does say it so I go home and tell Mum.

All the time until the day of the party I'm excited because it's my first party but scared too because I don't know what Wendy and her two friends are going to say when I come. It's a big party and I hope no-one will even notice that I'm there. Mum buys me a doll to give her and a card.

I get dressed up, take my present and walk from home to Wendy's house. I walk up to the front door and I know I'm late. I want to be late because then maybe no-one will notice when I get there because there'll be too many kids. She invited almost the whole of grade three! I knock quietly at the door. No-one answers, so I knock again. A mother answers and it must be Wendy's. She says to come in and calls Wendy to look at her present but I say don't worry I'll just leave it here on the chair by the front door but she ignores me and keeps calling. Wendy comes and when she sees me she calls out to her friends. The whole party turns up at the front door.

'Look who's here! She came! I can't believe she actually came. She wasn't invited, Mum. She invited herself. She can't come in.'

'Wendy! Stop that. Of course she can stay!' says Wendy's mum.

I want to disappear because it's only now I realise what a very terrible mistake it was to think Wendy wouldn't notice me. I want to run home but Wendy's mum has me by the arm.

'Don't take any notice. Come into the kitchen dear and we'll get you some cake.'

I don't want any cake. I want to go home. But she's got me by the hand and stroking it. She's being really nice. I wish she was my mum but more than that I wish she'd let me go home. I have to stay in the kitchen and lots of girls come and sneak a look at me and whisper and giggle because I've come to the party without getting a proper invitation. It seems to take forever for Wendy's mum to have to do something else before I can sneak away.

Someone calls her out and I start to leave but everyone notices and they all come out to the front garden where I'm walking out the gate and they call out things to me.

'All dressed up and nowhere to go! I thought she'd never leave. What a dag!' They laugh and laugh. I can still hear them laughing even on Monday when the whole school knows what a terrible thing I did and I decide I'm never going to another party in my life.

For Dan's birthday I decide on a treasure hunt. I go to op-shops and buy mounds of showy-looking costume jewellery and a small tin sea chest. I load the chest with the jewellery, perfume in old bottles and pieces of silk. I put a heavy chain and padlock around it. I tell William about the plan. He's being positively accommodating these days. We drive down the coast to Mornington and pace out steps between forked trees and giant rocks, and bury the chest deep in the ground. I give the information to Joanne and she draws a replica of a pirate map, complete with the puffy-cheeked North Wind and skull and crossbones. She spills coffee on it, burns around the edges, dries, irons and crushes it three times and then folds it in four. Marion gives it to Dan as a birthday present. She tells him she'd found it cleaning her house which is crammed with old books.

'Now don't get your hopes up. I'm sure someone's already found the treasure years ago but we can go there for our excursion next week just to see where pirates might have buried their treasure in the olden days.'

We drive down in the school bus the next Wednesday and find our way to the spot marked X on the map. William comes too. Conveniently, it's rained the night before so the ground is authentically packed hard. We dig and dig.

'Don't get too excited guys. The chances of it being undiscovered after all this time are practically none at all,' Marion warns them with a wink at me.

Then the spade hits metal. Kids squeal and turn into little Eveready batteries bouncing up and down. 'That's it! It's real. Did you hear that? There really is treasure! William, quick, keep digging. Look, everyone, come and listen, it's metal. It must be the treasure.'

The older kids who've lost interest rush over. Soon the chest is uncovered and hauled up. We've bought a hacksaw, just in case, and saw a link in the chain. Dan opens the box.

'Real treasure! It's real.' They pull out the pearls and earrings, necklaces, perfume and silk. Dan lets kids choose something and then dishes out the rest of the booty.

He's eight. He thinks the treasure map's real until he's 15.

Ian and I are not getting on. He drives me more crazy with his goodness. He's not in tune with anything. Not himself, this city environment and least of all me. I tell him in winter that I want to split up but he talks me out of it.

When we moved into the house, Ian invited his Adelaide friend, Annie, to share with us. Ian thought it would help with the mortgage. Annie's angry because, since she'd changed state and moved in, Ian's ignored her.

'If he didn't want to put some time into the friendship, why invite me? If all he wanted was help with the mortgage, why didn't he just advertise?'

Annie's living away from home with no support around her. She's as disillusioned with Ian as I am and daily we workshop his shortcomings with gusto. Joanne doesn't like him either. We all think he's emotionally stunted and so obsessed about being good he isn't capable of seeing anything. The man I met up in the bush, isn't this one I'm living with in Elwood.

I treat Ian worse and worse. The more he mopes around the house wanting sympathy, the more he repulses me. I want him to express anger, something negative, something real, anything. I want him to tell me to pull my head in and cut out the off-hand way I treat him. The more he doesn't, the more callous I become. In the end, I don't know who I despise most, him or myself. Who am I kidding? Him! Hands down. At the end of the year he finally puts an end to it. He's in the bath and I come in.

'I think we should call it quits,' he says.

'Okay. Fine with me.' I walk out. Relieved.

But within a couple of weeks he has another lover. What! A single mother at the school who's been playing piano with him for the children's opera. It's never a walk in the park to be replaced so soon. I fall apart. I can barely believe the torrent of feelings this brings on. Desperate to avoid the emptiness, looming like a black hole, I pack up my life and move back to Adelaide.

I cry for days. Jane and I have an argument and I slap her face. I've never slapped anyone's face before in my life. I'm out of control. The worst part is she'd had a car accident recently and her cheekbone has a fracture. It isn't a very hard hit but it was a very bad thing to do. She gets hysterical and so do I. I rush out, leaving Dan with her. I have to get out and find some help for myself. Jane comes screaming out after me.

'I'm not looking after him.'

She's at her front gate, with her husband Dan Ranson looking totally overwhelmed and not knowing what to do. Ollie's there and the baby's in Jane's arms. Just before I drive away I see Dan standing there outside the gate with Jane and her family on the inside. His lips are quivering. I can't go back. I can't be with anyone. I feel like I'm really going crazy. Even in this state I figure Jane's hardly going to close the gate and leave Dan Biggs in the street.

I drive to a nearby psychiatric hospital. I wait hours before seeing a psychiatrist. I tell him what happened and he phones Jane's place and tells me Dan's fine and asleep at her house. They keep me overnight and put me on medication.

The next day a mutual friend of mine and Jane's, a French

girl, says I can stay with her. I'm still not coping after a few days, so I ring William and ask if he'll look after Dan for a few days. It's the weekend and he agrees. I put him on a plane and William picks him up at the other end. Poor Dan.

I finally realise there's nothing left for me in Adelaide. After just a year away, friendships have changed. Everybody else's life, and mine, has moved on.

I pack up again and return to Melbourne.

I get Dan and go to stay with Joanne.

'You look like a bird. You're so thin. Poor baby.'

She sits me on her knee and rocks me while I sob. Even though I'd wanted to break up with Ian in the first place, it's the first time I've committed myself to a relationship. I feel like I've failed.

Ian draws a hand-painted For Sale sign and puts it on a stick in the front garden of our small mansion.

Despite Ian's ideological disapproval of real estate agents, when the house sells, a week after the sign goes up, we make $25,000 profit on the house. I know we've sold it too cheap. We're in the middle of a real estate boom. Still, Ian gives me all the profit and my share of the deposit I've put in. Guilt money. I'm onto him. He expects me to feel grateful but I don't.

I start looking to buy a flat. After just two weeks I see one advertised in Hawsleigh Avenue, the same street Dan's crèche was in all those years ago. My heart leaps. There're only two blocks of flats in that street. Maybe it'll be one the ones I knocked on a door years ago to ask if they ever came up for rent. In those days I could only dream about owning my own place.

It *is* the same one.

Inside's like a *Home Beautiful* magazine article. There are two north-facing bay windows with sun streaming onto honey-coloured Baltic pine floorboards. The kitchen has a real pantry and there's a Juliet balcony overlooking a courtyard garden with a liquidamber tree. My own tree house. Woodwork and ornate plaster ceilings are painted white and the walls are light butter yellow. From my share of the Elwood house, I have $80,000, exactly enough money to buy it without a loan. Because of Ian's ideological objection to banks, he's given me the deposit I need in cash. After the auction, I sign the papers and hand over $8000 deposit in a brown paper bag.

TEN

A DOUBLE WHAMMY

I get over Ian quickly, but still wallow in grief at being alone and the knowledge that I'm a relationship dunce. This is when William, who's been a regular visitor to our house for the past year, decides I need a distraction. When he invites me on a car trip to Adelaide, Dan goes to stay at Beacon's house.

I discover that William has a couple who are staying with

him and they're coming too. The guy, Madu, is Indian and grew up with William in the ashram. His wife, Helga, is German. Madu sits in the front seat with William. Helga and I sit behind our men. The feminist in me fumes sullenly in the back seat. Being stuck in a confined space with two tourists when all I want is to cry all day isn't my idea of fun. It takes a long while to work out that William has to entertain these people for three weeks and is running out of activities and things to say. He wants me along to grease the social wheels. He seems to reserve all his humanity and vulnerability for animals. With people he likes to play the guru, socially removed, the one who knows it all. This makes for an atmosphere about as unrelaxed as you can get without actually lying on a bed of nails. I sit in the back wanting to throw myself out the door while having polite conversations with Helga about how to make Peach Melba. I've tried her upside-down cake and I have to give her credit, she's a good cook. But right now I have other things on my mind. Between Madu's self-opinionated chatter to William and his patriarchal mumblings to Madu's wife, it's all I can do to stop myself leaning forward and strangling him.

Under these circumstances it puzzles me why I let William seduce me one night in a hotel room. I think I feel guilty that he's paying for me. I've always been financially independent of men. They say not to pray for what you want because you might get it.

After all the years of pining for William, finally we're an item. He comes over to my new flat for dinner a couple of times a week. He arrives and oscillates between telling me fascinating facts about the world and not saying anything. He doesn't ask me about what I think or like. In fact, questions aren't in William's repertoire. When you're a calm, spiritual person you don't need to talk all the time. Only chatterboxes have to talk. But when someone's sitting in your kitchen and you don't talk, after an alarmingly short time you start to wonder what the hell you're both doing there. So, when William's in his silent, pleased with himself mode, I chatter on about my day, gossip, anything that keeps the heavy silence from settling over the room like oppressive incense. Between topics, I ask questions.

'And how's your week been?'

'Same as usual. Nothing out of the ordinary.'

'Doing anything on the weekend?'

'Oh, not much. A bit of this and that.'

The first hour or two goes thus. In bed there's even less. Ironing board sex and roll over. There has to be more than this.

Then, one night, William surprises me. He asks why I love him.

'I can't remember.'

'Thanks very much.'

'No. I didn't mean that. I just do. But I fell in love with you when you changed my life. Remember?'

'In what way?'

'You know. When you came up with that brilliant idea of not stealing and seeing what that felt like. You were very intuitive. You seemed to understand me at a time when I really needed it. All that.'

'Is that the only reason?'

'No. There's a connection between you and me. Maybe it's got to do with the small person in the other room. I don't know.'

William doesn't like talking about feelings. He's being very odd.

'Sometimes I feel like I should've been born in another century.'

'Which one?'

'Oh, I think about two hundred years ago would do quite nicely.'

'Why?'

'I don't know. I seem old-fashioned somehow. I don't fit in. If someone told me I'd been transported in a time machine I wouldn't be the least surprised. If I suddenly learned I'd been a colonel in the British Army in a past life I'd almost believe it.'

Most people understand at least something about themselves by looking at their parents and the way they were raised. The things that influence their attitudes. Poor William got a double whammy on the repression front. He had a British Army dad and was raised from the age of five in a religious community that believed expressing feelings was a sign you weren't on the right spiritual track. Equilibrium was the thing. And he had it drummed into him until he left the ashram at 35 to come here. His feelings are squashed down so low he doesn't even know he's got them. He doesn't seem to get even these basic clues about what makes a person tick. He doesn't think there's anything wrong with feeling like a fish out of water, or that you can learn and change. So he doesn't see that the very quality about his father he despised, that he played the guru and raced-off young girls with spiritual stars in their eyes, has any bearing on his life at all. He doesn't seem to have ever thought about the fact that I'm 18 years younger than him and, even though the gloss is fading, see him as some kind of guru.

I look at William and hold him. He's right. He doesn't fit in. Not socially, not with me who he says he loves, not even with his own son.

William needs me to be a buffer zone between himself and Dan. When he's not visiting us, he plays uncle to Russian Steve's now four kids and they adore him. He makes a much better uncle than he does a father. He takes Dan snorkelling on his own a couple of times, but all other Dan Activities have to include me. I'm bored with William's outings. Once he takes us to a theme park in the middle of nowhere and we eat greasy hamburgers on plastic plates and laminex tables with thousands of other fun-lovers. Give me razor blades or a crowd and I'll take razors any day. Years of hanging out with Joanne has turned me into a gourmet cook and the worst kind of food snob. I can't understand why I have to be there when William could take Dan on his own. He doesn't seem to care what I like.

After we've been together a year, I decide to play him at his own game. While Dan's awake he chatters away so William's quiet routine is muffled. When Dan goes to bed, silence hovers. I sit in one corner of the lounge room and he sits in another. Boxers squaring off. If he thinks chatter's verbal masturbation he can hardly accuse me of not being deep if *I* don't talk. When two people are in a room not talking it's not easy knowing where to look. He casts his eyes around the room, which I find unnerving. What if our eyes connect? Fortunately my lounge has a fake Persian rug with an intricate pattern that I've never found quite so fascinating. After 20 minutes, William takes his tea cup to the kitchen.

'Well, I suppose I'd better be off then.'

Thank God.

The thought of another visit makes me want to faint.

I'm surprised one day to get a letter from my oldest sister, Jenny. Ma's told me the youngest of her four kids found her drugged on the kitchen floor. He couldn't wake her and ran to a neighbour's house. It turned out she'd been hooked on valium for years. She was admitted to a drug rehabilitation centre and is there now having counselling.

Dear Barbara and Daniel,

How are you? I am going quite well here. I am doing something about myself at last. I feel good about it. I'm finding out a lot about myself being here. You would probably be the most likely to understand how I really feel. I've never really been myself. I've always been here for somebody else, never me. Now I'm getting down to myself and it's really hard trying to get in touch with Jenny. Not a mother, a daughter, a wife or a girlfriend. There's just me. I don't know who the real me is yet but I'm working on it. It might take a while but I will get there eventually.

I don't have anyone but family to turn to and I feel guilty about not keeping in touch with you since I've been in Sydney. I never felt as if I was part of the family for a long time when we were all growing up. It's probably because Dad molested me when I was young, seven I think. That's one reason I felt different. I think Mum picked on me because of it.

Anyway, it's good to be here and Shane loves it. We went to Canberra a few weeks ago and it was good to get out of here for the day. We don't go out very often.

I had better go now. It's after house-to-bed and as we work all day I'm really tired.

Hope to hear from you soon.

Love Jenny

I remember back to a story Jenny told me last time I'd seen her, about when she was 16. She was working in a milk bar and Neville's brother, who she'd had sex with, came in and told her he had something to show her. She went out and there were two other Mount Gravatt boys in the car. They told her to get in. When she did, they drove her to the sticks and raped her. All of them. She lost her job and, now I think, a lot more as well. Her letter, the memory of that time, makes me squirm. I'm so far away from those days and don't want to go anywhere near it. I send a short, letter wishing her well. I don't visit and am relieved when she doesn't write again.

One day the phone rings. It's Jacqui. She says Christian, now 14, is living with her. He'd been getting more and more rebellious with Bloss. I'm a bit surprised, but I guess Jacqui has been like Christian's second mother since he was two. In fact she really did more of the mothering with Christian than Pommy when they moved in together.

I haven't heard from her since Japan. She tells me she's worked her way to a high level in the public service, is in a women's theatre group and has a lesbian band called the Mogadonnas. She invites me to play pool with them the next night.

Although we don't see each other much now, Jacqui's my oldest friend. In fact, because we moved around so often, she's my only school friend. I met her in first year high school. I didn't find out until years later when she started going out with Pommy that she was a lesbian. That's when all the massages she used to give me and her trudging all the way, miles, from her house to mine on weekends started to make sense. We had an intense friendship before she met Pommy. Well, more on her side than mine, but still, I loved her in my way. Then everything changed. Once she even threatened to physically manhandle me out of their house one day when Pommy and I had a fight. Things were never the same again between us after that. But I like Jacqui. She makes me laugh. Also, she's known me longer than anyone else in my life, apart from family.

When I get there, I see Christian's dyed his hair green. It's also cut in a Mohawk. There's a row of earrings lining one ear. I haven't seen him this happy since before Pommy went off the rails.

'When did you change your hair? Looks great.' He really does look great, but it's not because of the hair.

'As soon as I got here. Jac said I could. She bought me my own telly and video too.'

'What about Bloss? I thought you two really loved each other.'

'We did until bloody Bernie came along. He's such a bastard, Barb, and Bloss always took his side.'

I ask Jacqui how she feels about having Christian back after four years.

'You know I love him. And he loves it here. He's become like the band mascot. The girls think he's great. He comes to all the gigs.'

Although she has a new girlfriend, I ask her if she misses Pommy. She gets a faraway look in her eye and says, 'Not much'.

We play pool until after midnight. I wonder how Christian will get up for school in the morning.

Near the end of the year, I try to encourage William to express his feelings. He finds these attempts distasteful. I ask how he feels about me.

'I visit all the way from Brunswick don't I?'

This gigantic bubble I've blown air into for eight years, William, is leaking at a rate of knots.

It's not long before the balloon's not much more than a used condom in the corner. I'm not sure he notices. We're sitting on the Juliet balcony of my flat when I break the news.

'It's not really working with us, is it?' I ask.

'If that's how you feel, I suppose it can't be.' He's sitting ramrod straight. Not giving an inch.

'I think we should split up.' He stops to look at me intently for a second. Is he sizing me up, trying to work out what I'm playing at, if I mean it?

'If that's what you want.' He's infuriating. Whatever he thinks I might be wanting, he sure as hell isn't going to give it to me.

'It is.'

'Fine.'

No hesitation. No burning questions, like, for example, why. So as not to seem offended by my decision, he sits for a couple of minutes before standing up.

'Well, I suppose I'd better be off.'

'Okay then.'

'Cheerio.' Iron Lips kisses my cheek.

'Cheerio.' I say.

Five years? I'd pined for five years? What was I thinking? I know why he doesn't fit in. The man needs to cry all that stiffness out of his body.

It isn't long after Christian comes back to Melbourne that I first meet David.

Every month I suffer from premenstrual tension and end up at Joanne's house in tears.

'I'll never find a partner. I've never had a relationship longer than a year. What's wrong with me?'

'Listen BB, I'm sure there's someone out there for you. It's just a matter of time. There's got to be someone who'll love you for exactly who you are.'

I never thought she'd be the one to find him.

Joanne's new friend Robyn lives in St Kilda. She's an exotic-looking hairdresser who fries your brain in a batter of trivia while you're trapped with colour in your hair. Robyn does hair on the side but her big money comes from cleaning jobs. She rides a bicycle around and spends almost

$1000 a week on antique furniture, objet d'arts and teddy bears. The first time she cuts my hair I meet her house mate David. He's handsome but seems, at first, a bore.

'What do you think of him?' Robyn asks the next time she sees me.

'He's all right.'

'He hasn't slept with anyone for five years. He's really very sweet.'

Essential information. Must be a nerd.

A month later, I'm eating a pear at their kitchen table and David starts telling me about his previous girlfriend and how he'd gone to Perth after she'd cheated on him in Tasmania. He'd been devastated and that's why he hasn't had sex for so long. It's one of the qualities that attracts me most, a man who isn't driven by sex. When William and I first met he'd been celibate for years. I also like the fact that David can be vulnerable and honest. The antithesis of William.

'You're really enjoying that pear, aren't you?'

I eat with gusto. He smiles charmingly and watches me cut off pieces and pop them dripping into my mouth as if I'm the most fascinating creature this side of the Yarra River. How can someone so enjoy the way I eat a pear?

A few weeks later, on New Year's Eve, I'm tipsy at a party with Joanne and Robyn. I lean over from behind David and whisper in his ear.

'What you need is an older woman.' He's 27 and I have just turned 30. I'd meant it as a joke. Half.

I leave and drive around looking for some other action. I go to four other friends' houses but they're all out. I drive back to the party to go dancing with Robyn, but she's already gone home, or so I'm told. I arrive at her house and David answers the door.

'Is Robyn back yet?'

'No, but she should be soon. Why don't you come in and wait?' He's shy but pretty damn pleased to see me.

We sit in the kitchen chatting. I'm wearing an elegant black dress that's become too small at the waist. It's tight so I undo the back zip and collapse forward like an expired bag.

'Are you tired, Barb?'

'Fucking exhausted, but I wouldn't mind going out dancing. Do you want to come?'

'Not really. Anyway, why do you want to go out? You look so tired.'

'I am.'

'Would you like a back rub?' He furrows his brow like he's offering me some much needed medication.

Hmmm.

'Everyone likes a massage,' I say.

'It'd probably be easier in the bedroom.'

I think David's a little backward, being Tasmanian. They have a reputation for inbreeding. I decide if he has enough wherewithal to seduce me, I'll sleep with him. If he doesn't, I'm not helping him out.

We go into the bedroom.

'It'd be easier if you slipped that old thing off.' He points to my dress.

Fair enough. Looking good. I take my dress off and lie on my tummy in bra and undies.

He starts massaging me in the most sensual way. What a surprise. He knows exactly how to touch. In fact, I can't remember when I've been touched like that. What a wild card.

It doesn't take long before his full, Turkish delight lips are shooting me into outer space. With kissing like that he could do anything with me. In fact, he does. He's the best lover I've had in recent memory. Or maybe it's just the comparison with William.

When he comes, he hovers above me and grunts.

'Man.' Neanderthal.

'Woman.' I grunt back. He laughs.

The next morning, I wake up and know straightaway I'm in love.

He comes to my house for breakfast. We have a bath together and make love again.

He doesn't call the next day and I'm panic-stricken. The following day I ask him over for dinner. I've marked my man and he isn't getting away.

David has other ideas.

Sometimes I go to his place in the middle of the night and he doesn't answer the door. His bedroom window's never locked so I go around the side and open it.

'Barb, what are you doing here?'

'Can I come in? I just wanted to see you.'

I climb in and we make love.

It goes on for three months until one day I climb in and he says he doesn't want to see me anymore.

'You're too intense, Barb.'

I go home sobbing. At the crack of dawn I arrive on Joanne's doorstep.

'I feel like my left arm's been cut off.'

'Did he say why?'

When I tell her, she looks at me like someone's just died.

'BB, I don't know how to say this, but he's right. You are pretty intense. You're like silly Sally dachshund.'

'What do you mean?'

'You know that look she gets when she wants the slab of butter on the table so badly you just know the second you walk out of the room she'll take a flying leap and ravage it until there's nothing left? You get the same look when you're interested in a guy. You can't do that with men. They like to chase us, not have someone climbing in their window every five minutes when they won't answer the door. You gotta chill out, honey chile.'

I don't enjoy having a friend who knows that in the core of my being I'm a sausage-dog.

'I don't know how to chill out. I don't do chill. It's not that I don't want to, I can't. Are you sure that's how I come across?'

'Would I lie?'

I decide to work on chilling out. I take up ice-skating to keep my mind off David. I go every day for three hours and skate furiously. I learn jumps and spins, fall and scrape my knees and bruise my bum. After a couple of months skating becomes like playing the piano, sensual flying. My teacher, a world champion, choreographs a dance for me to one of my favourite pieces of classical music, Pachelbel's *Canon*.

But when I dance to it, it makes me sad. I think of David. The more I think of him, the more I skate.

It's one day after I come home from skating that I get a call from Bloss. She hardly ever calls.

'It's me. Has anyone told you yet?' She's always one to get straight to the point.

'Told me what?'

'That Jacqui's gone and killed herself.'

I close my eyes and swear under my breath.

'How?'

'She gassed herself in the car.'

'Have you talked to Christian?'

'Yeah. I told him he could come back and live here but I don't really want him to and he doesn't either.' Miss Matter-of-fact incarnate.

'How is he?'

'He seems all right … under the circumstances.'

We talk for a few more minutes. She says she's not

coming to the funeral. Why would she? She hardly knows Jacqui. She says Christian doesn't want to go either.

How could Jacqui do that to Christian? She's my oldest friend but I'm angry. Just a couple of months ago, even though we'd grown apart she'd come around and bought me a lovely bowl from an exhibition for my birthday. But how could she take Christian from Bloss's house and then six months later go and kill herself on him?

I phone Christian and he says he's fine. He tells me too that he doesn't want to go to the funeral. He says he's read Jacqui's diaries and that she did it because she missed his mum so much. This seems to give him some comfort.

I go over to his place the next night and still he doesn't cry. He has a been-there-done-that attitude.

We talk about where he's going to live. I tell him he's welcome to come with me but he isn't sure. He wants to think about it.

When I go to the funeral everyone's in shock.

The service is too religious and formal. If Jacqui was alive she'd hate it. Friends are told we can't come to her final resting place. Girls from her band wander round trying to find the crematorium so they can let off some white doves. I follow them trying to find somewhere to put my grief. We meet at the pub later and even Jacqui's lover says she's more angry with Jacqui than sad. No-one can believe she's done this.

Christian comes over to stay with me for a few days but he's really horrible to Dan. I'm relieved when he says he's decided to live with a couple of lesbian women from Jacqui's band. He likes them and they want him to live with them. Good. It seems like the best solution. The band has decided to put on a benefit concert to raise some money for him. He can also get money from the government which should be enough for him to support himself.

I'm studying a professional writing course at Holmesglen College and writing short stories. At Melbourne University I read all Shakespeare's sonnets and write one of my own to David.

A week later, one day at the rink, I call him. He's been missing me and asks me over.

When I arrive I look like a sleek cat burglar in black wool leggings, skivvy and gloves. After skating three hours a day for months, my body's taut and ready. I have champagne.

'Did you like the sonnet?'

'Nnnn.' David's cuddling and kissing Brie, one of Robyn's whippets.

'What do you mean, nnn?'

'I didn't get it.' Brie's shivering while David pats her. 'Did I, Brieby? Who's a good girl? David loves Brieby, yes he does.'

'Nothing?'

'No, and I wasn't sure if you were saying I'd been bad or good.' He kisses Brie over and over while looking at me.

'And what did you decide?'

'Good.'

Neanderthal Man.

He'd passed his exams. He's a carpenter but after he first met me he began a preparatory year for adult entry to university. He wants to study English. He says I inspire him.

After another three months, at the end of the year, David breaks off with me again. Devastated, I decide to forget about him. During the school break I rent out my flat and move to the country for three months to get him out of my hair.

Back in Melbourne, I try to become a journalist. During the past year I've become committed to the idea. I decide I'm going to keep trying forever until it happens. I'm 30. Everyone, except Sal, says it's too competitive and I'm too old, that you have to be 18 to get a job as a journalist. But when I get an idea into my head, I'm like a dog with a bone. I sit for a cadet exam and hear nothing back. I answer an ad for a journalist on *Viva la Vie*, a shiny advertorial magazine disguising itself as a women's rag. 'Do you want to write for a prestigious glossy magazine and travel the world interviewing the rich and famous?' I don't get the job but they give me a tape-recorded interview of a Persian carpet importer. I write the article from the interview and they publish it as a double-page glossy colour spread. I race over to Sal's.

'At least it's got my name on it.'

'I know it's only one article but you've gotta start somewhere, Babsie. It's great because you can use it to show a prospective employer. It gives you cred. They're not to know it's a rag.'

I see another ad in the *Toorak Times* suburban newspaper. It wants people to invest in the paper. If I can't be a journalist I might as well own part of a paper, the next best thing. Now I'm not paying off a mortgage I've saved some money. I ring the number.

'I'm just looking at the ad about investing in the newspaper.'

'How much do you want to invest?' says the gravelling voice on the other end of the line.

'About $1500.'

'Is that all?' He's very short. Reminds me of Bloss.

'How much would I need?'

'A lot more than that.' He's losing interest fast.

'But that's all I've got.'

'Maybe we can work something out.'

I decide to come clean. What have I got to lose.

'Look, the real reason I want to invest in it is because I want to be a journalist and since I'm not having any luck there, owning a share in a newspaper is better than nothing.'

'So you want to be a journo?' He's interested again.

'More than anything.'

'Can you start work at 9 o'clock tomorrow morning?'

This can't be happening. Is he an idiot or something? Who is this guy?

'Doing what?'

'You said you wanted to be a journo, didn't you?'

Maybe he's a Walter Mitty.

'Where?'

'Well, you're talking to the *Toorak Times* aren't you? Where else?'

'But how can you do that? Do you know someone who works there?'

'Yeah me. I own the bloody thing.'

When I hang up I run around the flat a couple of times before I ring Joanne.

'You'll never guess in a million years what just happened.'

I start work the next day.

The office in South Melbourne's grotty but that's what newspaper offices are supposed to be like isn't it? I'm introduced to the other two journos, both old guys, who are working on typewriters.

'How can you write on those? I can't believe they haven't got computers. It's 1988. We're nearly at the end of the millennium.'

'You'll find out about this place soon enough,' says Max. He says he's an actor and works here because he can go to auditions during the day and not be missed.

'Is that because you're out on interviews most of the day?'

Max looks at the other guy and smirks.

'You can call it that.'

I bring my own word processor in the next day. I soon find out what an interview is. I have to go to a small business, that's been signed up for six months worth of advertising, and collect money from them. If they give me the money, I ask them about their business and write a story about it. It might be used tyres, a hairdresser or a sausage factory. Sometimes the clients abuse me and refuse to pay because they say they've been tricked into signing the contract. But I write the stories and they're printed in the *Toorak Times*. They don't have by-lines, but I'm still a journo. Of sorts.

After three weeks the boss walks past the door and stares at me typing on my word processor. I'm pretty fast because of having played piano.

'You touch-type?'

'Yep,' I say, proud of my speed.

The next day he says he has a special job for me. They have a new computer system installed in the accounts department and he wants me to work there for a couple of weeks. He's singled me out because I'm fast. I think.

I don't mind typing names and addresses for the first two days. I think then I'll be going back to the journo's room. After two weeks, I go to see him before I leave one Friday.

'I'm just wondering when I might be going back to writing?'

'Look, there just isn't any work at the moment. It's dead as a doornail. If there's no work, there's no work. As soon as it comes back though, you'll be the first to know.'

I'm vaguely placated.

The next Monday I arrive at work and see two young, gorgeous things swanning around.

'Who are they?' I ask the woman in accounts.

'They're the new journos.'

'What?'

'He hired them.' And he nods towards the boss's end of the corridor.

I don't believe her so go to ask them myself.

'Hi. My name's Barbara. You've just started. What will you be doing?'

'We're the new journos.'

I look at Max. He gives me a what-do-you-expect shrug.

I tear down to the boss's office and barely knock before barging in.

'What's going on with those two new girls?' Tact isn't my strong point. I know I've come on too strong before the words are out of my mouth.

'Get out of here. Who do you think you're talking to?'

'You said as soon as things picked up I'd go back to writing. You said there wasn't enough work. Now there are two new writers. What's going on?'

'Get out! You're fired!'

No, no, no. Even I couldn't blow it that fast.

'Just a minute. I don't mean ...'

'Out. Get out of my office.'

Back down? Me? I'll do anything to keep this job. I don't move.

'I want to talk about it. I don't think it's unreasonable to ask when I'll be doing the work you employed me to do.'

He starts coming out from behind his big desk.

'Just get the hell out of my office.'

He grabs hold of my arm and manhandles me out of the chair.

I haven't done kung fu and women's studies for nothing. I aim a knee at his balls but in the struggle he turns aside and I miss. I can't believe I'm having a physical wrangle with the owner of a newspaper. He pulls me out of his office, pushes me into the hallway and closes the door as fast as he can.

I haven't had a physical run in with anyone since Pommy and I nearly killed each other over a suitcase when I was 15. I go to the journo's room, pack up my word processor, say goodbye to Max and leave in a flood of tears.

I go straight to Joanne's.

'I heard he's got his dog registered on his board of directors. I don't know if it's just rumour or what, but no matter which way you look at it he sounds crazy to me, BB. You're better off out of there.'

'But I might never get another job. Now I'll never be a journo.'

Joanne makes me a cup of tea and we chain-smoke while workshopping my bleak future and her latest drama with Bear. She asks me over for dinner that night but I'm going to see Christian. She says to come for a cuppa in the morning.

When I arrive the next day, she shouts at me when she answers the door and points to a note on the ground that must have blown off her door, saying she doesn't want to be disturbed.

I'm so angry. How dare she invite me around and then shout at me when I come. While it's fine for her to change her mind, she doesn't seem to think that even though I'll drop just about anything I can to come and visit her, I might actually be busy myself. She could have phoned when she put the note on the door and I could have gone skating.

I'm sick of my visits being a burden to her. I'm sick of her never being vulnerable. And I'm sick most of all of giving her the emotional power over me to annihilate me by telling me she's sick of me just when she knows I'm more sick of myself than anyone else could ever be! I don't want to be friends anymore – it's not good for me and it's obviously a big fat drag for her. I can't stand it anymore. I write her a goodbye letter and drop it under her door.

She phones the next day. Dan's been sick and I've woken up with the same bug. We're both in bed. As a peace offering, she comes around with a gourmet omelette she's made and brings it in on a tray. Then she stacks up all my washing in her cane laundry basket to wash in her machine at home. She knows nurture is the thing I want most. Joanne has a knack for knowing exactly how to worm her way past resistance.

'There's some clothes in my room too, Jewanne.' She hates Dan calling her 'Jewanne'. We're both sitting up in my bed feasting on her omelettes. Joanne stops in her tracks. She doesn't like Dan. To her he's a spoilt brat.

'Who do you think I am, the bloody cleaning woman?' She suddenly tips the washing on the floor. 'You can do your own bloody washing.'

And with that, she storms off.

I think she made up with me just so she could break up the friendship instead of the other way around. She's a bit like that, Joanne.

I think we've paid a lot for that omelette. Why do I have such an unpredictable best friend? I'm very pissed off that she spoke to Dan like that. She doesn't even try to get to know him.

She rings to apologise the next day. I'm premenstrual and feeling lonely again and depressed about not having a man.

'What's wrong with me? Is having a normal relationship so much to ask?'

'Have you ever thought about counselling, BB?'

Counselling? Does she think I'm a nut case or something? For some reason that I don't stop to think about, this sends me into a huge spin. Everything I've been trying to control in my life seems to bubble out and spew into my brain.

'Me? At least I'm *trying* to fix myself up. You don't even *pretend* to try with getting a job, with your agoraphobia ...'

'It's just a suggestion BB. And you did ask. I just ...'

But the idea fries my brain. I feel like exploding.

'You're the one who needs a fucking counsellor,' I say.

I've been trying so hard to grow up, be in control, work

out my life, get a job, get a stable relationship, be a good mother. I try like a maniac and then she comes along and tells me I'm failing?

I go around the flat gathering a bag full of presents she's given me over the years. Mainly art work she's made, but also a beautiful glass ball I couldn't afford that she'd pushed me into buying for the vicarious pleasure of it. I take them around and knock on her door. When she answers I don't say anything. I smash the whole bag at her feet and storm off.

I think about my record with guys. It isn't good. But it's one thing for me to harp on about what a failure I am, another thing entirely for Joanne to do it.

We stop seeing each other.

Again.

ELEVEN

NOT A SHEEP

Finding a journalist job through the paper's never going to work. I start writing to editors. In November, after almost a year of looking for a job, I ring one at the Southern Division of Leader Newspapers to ask for a job. He calls me in for an interview. I show him my impressive-looking *Viva la Vie*

piece and say I've been working at the *Toorak Times*. I don't say for how long and he doesn't ask. I hope he won't ring and find out I'd worked there for less than a month. I also hope he doesn't know that it's not a newspaper going on over there, but a circus.

He says a journo on one of the papers, the *Malvern Caulfield Progress*, hasn't turned up for work and no-one knows where she is.

'If you don't mind working as a casual until she comes back, that's about all I can offer you at the moment I'm afraid.'

'That's fine. Some work's better than none.'

I'm so cool, even though I can't believe it. He says to start Monday.

I find out the reporter who hadn't turned up was the boss's daughter and that's why they don't want to sack her. She never comes back to work. They say she's run off to Adelaide. After a month they give me a full-time job. I'm a real journalist at last. The newspaper chain's owned by Rupert Murdoch's News Corporation. It's the bottom of the dung pile because it's small, but it is News Corporation. A serious journalist job.

When I first start I'm so desperate to experience everything that I'd accept an invitation to the 'opening of an envelope'. I hear the other journos talk about politicians like that but I can understand perfectly.

My first assignment outside the office is to cover a 20-year high school reunion. I mingle with the early guests and tell them I'm from the local paper. They give me cheap red wine. As the night wears on and they keep plying me with more, I start pretending to be one of the old students.

'I can't believe you don't remember me. That kiss we had behind the sheltersheds. And he said I was the girl of his dreams,' I say to a man in a large group of graduates.

'No, look, I do remember. You look familiar. Just tell me your name and I'll get it. It's on the tip of my tongue.'

The last thing I remember is being introduced to someone and as I put my hand out to shake his, my knees collapse under me for a second. I'm kneeling on both knees when he shakes my hand but in a split second; I've leaped backwards to my feet like a film scene run backwards. I convince myself no-one notices.

With my first pay packet I buy $100 worth of underwear for Dan and me. We prance around the house together showing them off.

After I've been there six months, I ring Robyn and make an appointment for her to cut my hair. When I arrive the first thing she talks about is David.

'He asked when you were coming. I think he wanted to be here,' she says, waiting for the perming solution to set. That girl can always talk me into more than I ask for.

'Yeah, like I'll want to see him after nine months while I look like a drowned rat.'

'He's making sets at the Melbourne Theatre Company. You should drop in and see him sometime.'

It seems like fate that a couple of weeks later my car's automatic transmission needs work and the repair place is in South Melbourne, right around the corner from the theatre company. I'm still big on signs.

'David, it's Barb. My car's getting fixed around the corner. Do you want to have a coffee?'

'Barb.' He sounds surprised and happy for an unchecked moment before he turns serious. 'What's wrong with the car?'

'Transmission. Do you want to have a coffee?'

'Yeah. What's wrong with it?'

David knows about cars but he's enjoying dangling me on a rope.

He and I have a damaged childhood in common. He'd been raped when he was 12. When it happened he was still grieving because his father had died from Parkinson's disease 18 months earlier. His mother had a hole in the heart and couldn't even make it to the letterbox and back without getting exhausted. David's sister was 13 years older so he grew up like an only child, bored and always wanting more from his mother than she was able to give. She spent most of her day lying on the couch while David teased the cat. When David was ten, his mum had an operation to repair her heart and in the same year, his father became sick and languished at home for a year before he died.

That's when David stepped up his teasing. First of the cat and then his mother. He tells me he was so ashamed of what he used to do to the cat that he's blocked it out of his mind. I wonder if maybe he's also blocked out what he used to do to his mother as well. He's teased me since the day we first slept together. I find it charming and cute. Very strange when it usually makes me feel terrible about myself. This should be some kind of warning but when you're blissed out on new love, who's got their eyes open?

We start trying to be friends.

At the paper I cover my first federal election.

I meet the local member for Higgins which is the electorate of my paper, the *Malvern Caulfield Progress*. He's tipped to be a future Prime Minister.

We have a policy to give equal coverage to each candidate in each electorate we cover. The Labor guy for the Melbourne Ports electorate, Clyde Holding, invites me and the other reporter, Al, to an Indian curry night at someone's house. We get pissed and dance on the tables and have a great time.

The Liberal Higgins member, Peter Costello, invites me

to lunch on my own. It's at a posh restaurant in Glenferrie Road. I haven't been to a posh restaurant since before Dan was born and I was a working girl.

He knows my name from the tram strike and thinks I'm a right wing, union-hating kind of gal. I don't actually have any views at all because I don't read newspapers or watch telly. He was a lawyer before he became a politician and he talks about some union ball-breaking case a few years ago that he calls Dollar Sweets. I think it's the name of the company, but this guy has no idea how little I know about news. I bluff my way through the lunch and have a fine old time drinking expensive wine and eating lots of nouvelle cuisine courses. We stay in that old restaurant for hours.

A couple of weeks later he rings and asks me to do a story on the fact that his office has moved. I tell him I've already done the story on the interview in the restaurant on the feature page, like I'd done with Holding, and that an office moving wasn't really newsworthy.

Then he gets nasty and tells me he'd spent a fortune on our lunch. I point out that if he'd had to pay for the feature story he would have paid a lot more than the price of a lunch. The conversation doesn't end on a happy note.

I only go to his office once on election night. Over in the other electorate, Clyde Holding's office is buzzing, so Al and I spend most of our time there.

It's my first election and I'm full of feeling part of the great big machinery of government.

We've held the front page for an interview with the winner and I line up with old Clyde to meet him in his office for the chat the next morning.

When I arrive, he keeps me waiting for half an hour while my editor's screaming for copy. Then when he finally sees me, he only gives me five minutes. He says he's promised to have breakfast with his wife.

The campaign gives me my first lesson about life at the top. There's a lot of free grog and politicians are best mates with journos only while they need them.

It isn't long before David moves into my flat in Hawsleigh Avenue. The day he moves his few clothes in, he rides me around the courtyard while I sit on the handlebars of his bike. It seems so romantic. I'm happy.

The first thing he buys is a goldfish. He puts it in my hand basin. It dies the next day.

A week later I come home and there are two budgerigars in a cage.

'They're for you, Barb.'

'That's lovely, sweetheart.' He trains them to come out of the cage and sit on our shoulders and fingers.

After a few weeks someone leaves the cage door open and they escape.

David is upset.

We visit Al, who I've become friends with. She's a big girl who reminds me of photos I've seen of Ma when she was her age. She's quite beautiful and has a fantastic laugh. She comes from Griffith and we go for Christmas to visit. When David and I go walking, a small stray kitten follows us home to Al's place. David talks me into bringing her back to Melbourne.

I've never been an animal person.

The night we get it home it shits on my pillow and the diarrhoea dribbles down onto the bottom sheet and the doona cover. I change everything. The next day she does the same thing four times. I have to change the entire bed linen four times. I shout at Dan and David, demanding to know who left the bedroom door open. The final time, when I see her about to squat on my pillows again, I grab her and bowl her across the floorboards. She skids, unhurt, but the next day she disappears and never comes back.

This year seems like a time of death and endings.

I get a call from my 'husband' Steven's friend. I might not think of Steven as a husband, but certainly as a friend. He'd moved from Adelaide to Sydney to live with his new lover there. He'd visited me six months earlier with this Melbourne friend now on the line. Steven had given me a Roget's Thesaurus as a present because I told him I was writing. He was always spot on with his presents. He'd also transposed a Poulenc orchestral piece to piano for me.

Now, the voice on the end of the phone is telling me that Steven had died several months ago and that he had only just found out. I felt cold. And cheated. How could Steven have been dead for months and no-one had bothered to tell me? All our friends in Adelaide, someone in Sydney, his lover there?

After the call, I phone the Sydney lover. He's apologetic about not getting in touch. He'd been in shock and didn't have my number. He tells me the whole story. Steven had got a boil on his bum and had it lanced in a hospital. He spent the next month unable to get out of bed. Doctors kept telling him there was nothing wrong even though he was sleeping 16 hours a day. Finally, one morning he was taken to hospital in an ambulance. They did tests for AIDS, glandular fever and golden staph, a deadly disease you get from unclean needles in hospital. They found golden staph and immediately pumped him full of antibiotics. He recovered enough to get up and have a shower but died a few hours later.

What a waste. He was just 22. Talented, kind, sensitive, so much life ahead of him. And I couldn't even go to his funeral. Through Pommy's and Jacqui's deaths I'd learnt that funerals are important. It's somewhere to put your grief and come to terms with the death. I still haven't grieved for Pommy.

Now, technically anyway, I'm a widow.

David's home the night I get the call. He sits me on his knee and strokes my hair.

Not long after I hear about Steven's death, I'm playing the piano-one night and David wants to talk. When we first met I invited him to music soirees I had at my flat every month. He seemed to like the fact that I played piano, but now when I play, he interrupts. He reminds me of Dan when he was little. He wants attention and will talk about anything, or ask lots of questions just so he'll be my focus for a while.

Tonight, I don't know why he gets it into his head, but he want to know about Vernon. I've told him the bones but now he wants me to tell him the story from beginning to end. I'm glad. I want him to understand who I am. What makes me tick. To see me. Why I'm a bit obsessive and crazy.

I tell him about the suicide attempts, the psych hospital, a little about the weird sexual stuff Vernon did. I tell him everything except the most important stuff. The hard bits.

He sits on the floor listening, with a look of innocent interest, as though he's a child hearing a bedtime story about some stranger. If I had to choose one quality I like best about David, it's this. An innocence, a boyish guileless quality that makes him seem like the guy in the movie *Being There*. Someone who wanders through life simply as an observer, never judging, never really participating. That's why, when I finish, I'm so stunned when he cocks his head to the side and says: 'It sounds to me like you brought it on yourself, Barb.'

I blink. Now it's my turn to cock my head. I can't believe he's saying this. Because he's someone who doesn't judge, this is all the more devastating. Is he simply stating an irrefutable fact?

'It wasn't like that.'

'You could've left but you didn't. It seems to me Barb, like you wanted it.'

Although I know I didn't 'bring it on myself' as David

put it, hearing him say this is like being stabbed in the chest. Not because it isn't true, but because the part about how I could have left *is* true. And people think if you could have left and you didn't, it's like you were asking for it. But it's so much more complicated than that.

For months after I met Vernon at the sea baths in St Kilda three years before, I thought about what went on between us. I'd realised that the sex wasn't the worst part, it was all the other stuff. He'd got into my psyche through the strongest door, the sex door, and I might never be able to dig him out. I've got over wanting to cry when I have sex, but there are still things in my life that come from him that I don't want or understand.

In the face of David's questioning, I feel like a simpleton who can't work out why he doesn't want to even try to understand. Wasn't he raped as a kid, too?

'I had nowhere else to go,' I say, crying. It's the best I can do.

What I want to explain about the reason I'd stayed, is that I really thought Vernon was eventually going to love me. At 14 I was hormonally ready to have sex and babies. And to fall in love. I can see now that with my emotional naivety, if I was having sex with anyone often enough, my hormones would have made me fall in love with them.

What happened with Vernon messed with my head. Is still messing with my head. Isn't that why we have laws to protect kids who haven't yet worked out what the hell's going on? Because it messes with their heads? Because my hormones were running riot, the love I felt then was bound to be more obsessive, manic and passionate than it was ever going to be again. I wonder if the mix of passion and mess that seems to surface in my relationships will ever go away.

I sob more while David says again, 'You could've just left if you'd really wanted to get away, Barb.'

I want to scream. Instead I feel trapped by the jumble of

thoughts and feelings that I'd rather had stayed where they'd always been. Way down where I don't have to think about them. One thing I do know, is that for me, the confused kid I was then, Vernon seemed like my romantic rescuer.

But there's more than that. And the confusion of *all* my feelings threatens to boil over in my brain. On some subterranean level, I also know that I was Vernon's dirty secret that he hid from the real people who were important in his life. While the certainty of this pushes up through layers of time, I realise I must have always known it and wonder at the desperation that enabled me to push that away while I was living there. Vernon could fulfil any sexual fantasy with me because my feelings didn't matter. *I* didn't exist. And now, here with David, I feel emotionally invisible again. I want to scream. To show him that I'm here. I do exist. But I do nothing. Say nothing.

I sit on the piano stool and David sits on the floor. He's looking up at me. Accusing. My thoughts jumble around like water in a dishwasher, my feelings threaten to short circuit and tip me over the edge. I can only cry.

I get up to clean my teeth, get ready for bed.

In bed, I'm shocked when David wants sex. I feel he's betrayed me. But he strokes my back tenderly, knowing all my weaknesses. He's so gentle it's impossible not to believe he does care about me. I have great orgasms with David and tonight is no exception. With him I've learned to like sex and see it as a playful part of life. Usually it relaxes me, but now I can't sleep. For years I've been training myself not to be transported back to my first seductive orgasm. To Vernon. But tonight, it doesn't work. I'm hot and restless.

I get up for a drink of water. When I come back to bed, David's awake.

For the first time he starts telling me how he feels about

his own experience. He says he hadn't thought about it for years.

'I'm sorry I said all that about Vernon, Barb. The second time the guy tried it on, I said "no" and he let me go. All I had to do was say 'no'. That's when I realised that the first time was all my fault.'

'You don't think that now though do you?'

'No. Yes. I don't know. I'd just like to get the guy, Barb.'

'Why don't you report him?'

'I don't even know who he is. He was just some old guy who used to hang around where we lived.'

'Can't you find him?'

'Barb, if I found the bastard I wouldn't be able to stop myself from killing him.'

On weekends, David likes to get out of Melbourne. He has a stiff back and likes to walk, sometimes for hours.

'Come on Barb, let's go to Venus Bay.'

'Dan doesn't like walks.'

'What else is he going to do? Watch television?'

'I can't leave him here on his own. He's only ten.'

'Barb, I'm working all week and it's the only day we can do something together. Make him come or leave him here. He'll be all right. He's not a baby.'

'I can't force him to come. And I can't leave him here, either.'

'Yes, you can. He'll just plant himself in front of the telly. Come on Barb. You'll do it for your man, won't you? Or don't you love your sweetheart?'

I don't approve of television but Dan bought an old black and white one from a garage sale. I keep it at work during the week. Lucky I've started bringing it home on weekends. I'm torn between my man and my son. I agree to go.

We set off at midday and arrive at Venus Bay at one o'clock. On the way, choosing David over Dan is a jagged piece of tin I scrape along behind me. It catches on everything. I'm not a happy girl. We walk up the deserted stretch of beach for two hours before cutting inland. The summer day is hot and exhausting.

'Hurry up. What's wrong with you? You're not an invalid.'

'David. Why do you talk to me like that? We're supposed to be having a nice day together.'

'Barb. Just shut your little trap and come on.'

'Arsehole.'

I seethe but, like a good romantic junkie, I tell myself he doesn't mean it.

We lose our way and climb through wallaby highways, paths through the ti-tree growth just tall enough for us to crawl through on our hands and knees. We climb fences, one turns out to be electric and we go round through a paddock of menacing bulls. We don't stop arguing until we get back to the car at midnight. It's a horrible day but I bloat with the pride of a soldier after battle. I discover two things. David drives me crazy. And I love walking.

Similar commando walks follow. He manages to coax Dan along with us on the same walk a month later.

When we come to a particular fence I'm not sure if it's the electric one or not.

'Is this it?'

'No, that's further on.'

I start to climb through and get a shock.

'Bastard.'

David thinks it's the funniest thing.

He's put one of Dan's wet socks on the top wire. We'd been swimming in soggy paddocks.

'What did you do that for? Doesn't electricity conduct when something's wet?' I ask.

'Don't be silly Barb. Putting something wet on it earths the current. Like if you're wearing rubber shoes and you're standing in water. That earths it. You've heard of that before. Why do you think I put it there?'

I'd heard you could earth a current with something. I start to climb through and am shocked again.

'You fucking bastard.'

Now David *and* Dan think it's the funniest thing.

I hit David.

'Barb! It was just a joke. Look, we'll go around. Come on. Don't forget the sock.'

He starts walking off. I grab the sock and get shocked a third time. I swear and cry and hit David again. Dan thinks that's funnier than anything.

'It's not my fault you're so stupid Barb. Is it, Dan?'

'That was pretty silly, Mum. I mean, you did touch it three times.'

'Neither of you give a fuck about me.' I sit on the ground and bury my head in my arms and knees and cry. Dan sits down and puts his arm around me. A little parcel of concern.

'Why did you do it, Barb, when you knew it was electric?' Dan says softly.

'Because I'm so fucking gullible I don't think people who are supposed to care about me would want to electrocute me three times. Call me stupid, but that's what I thought.'

David can't stop laughing.

I've been at the *Malvern Caulfield Progress* for a year. I've learnt how to write and put a community newspaper together from the What's On column to lead news stories and editorials. I've interviewed the current Prime Minister Bob Hawke twice, and a former one, Gough Whitlam, who was famous for being sacked by the Governor-General. Even I remember that! Well, just. But the main reason Gough's my hero is because he made uni free and introduced the single parent pension, both of which helped get me to where I am now. One of the photographers takes pictures of me and the PMs and I put them away to get framed one day. I haven't been big on photos since a suitcase of them, with all the pictures of us kids as we were growing up, got lost in one of the millions of moves we made when I was small. But I'm a bit proud of these ones. I've also written a couple of stories for the *Age* newspaper as a freelancer which was very exciting and made me think that maybe one day I could really work on a metro paper. I cover council elections too. Nothing of importance happens in this community without me knowing about it and meeting the players. I feel for the first time that I'm part of the big, wide world. After being on the fringes for so long, I feel that I'm part of it. That I belong.

It's in my first year as a journo that I fall out with Malvern Community School and learn a big lesson. They keep wanting me to do a half day roster and it's tricky because of work. The school mix has changed. It used to be single parents, now it's mainly married couples, often with more than one child at the school. The school was a 1970s creation. Formed by mainly left-wing parents who believed, despite their economic disadvantage, that they could give their kids a quality low adult/child ratio education without having to pay private school fees. Now, a lot of the new parents have been paying private schools fees but have switched because they like our homey, friendly atmosphere.

I start talking around the school about how it isn't fair for a single parent with one kid to have the same roster as a married couple with a few kids. Some parents agree with me. The wealthier parents and those with a few kids close their minds like cupboards. The day I list the motion on our agenda, it's those parents who hijack the meeting. They get the only loudmouth father in the school to chair the meeting and he won't let me talk. Where we'd normally spend hours to get consensus over who should take the garbage out, now, when there is something of real moment to discuss, a point of social equity and school policy, the agenda is suddenly too full to spend time even discussing it. A hasty unanimous vote is taken against my suggestion and the subject is closed.

I announce that if they're not prepared to discuss or consider my point, I'll have to take it to the Equal Opportunity Commission.

Three parents, a diehard Labor voter, an anarchist and a lapsed member of the Liberal Party, the powerbrokers of the school, lead the campaign against me. They convince others that if they side with me, they too will be responsible for 'ruining the school'. The phrase gets repeated to me over and over. Nobody explains exactly how the school will be ruined. A couple of parents sit on the fence. They're invited on camping trips by one of the campaign leaders and when they come back, they don't want to talk to me anymore.

I don't like being an outsider but I've been one all my life. I've never liked it, but for me it's normal. It gives me perspective. Standing back from the group, I see how people can manipulate their beliefs to suit their own agenda. Like, if you asked the Labor guy how he could object to anyone using the Commission, a left-wing invention, to arbitrate the case, he'd say 'but this is different'. It's just like the tram strike all over again.

As quick as wildfire, I'm a pariah. People whose houses I've stayed at, who I've been friends with for three years, phone to abuse me.

I have enough of it one day when a new parent, who's never discussed the issue with me, abuses me in the street when I drop Dan off one morning. I find out later he's a conflict resolution counsellor. That's when I tell Dan if he wants to keep going to the school he'll have to catch the tram on his own.

I think a lot about whether I'm doing the wrong thing by Dan. I'm letting my own ideas get in the way of his life. He's been here for four years and loves it. All his friends are at the school.

I think about how years ago I decided I didn't want to be a sheep. The mob behaviour of these ordinarily perfectly nice people reminds me all over again about the reasons for that decision. For me, taking a stand isn't so much about winning as about honouring my own point of view. Before these loud parents made their feelings known, some of the others had agreed with me. Now here they are doing an about-face. But I can see it's because they don't want to be made outsiders like me just for the sake of having their own opinion. In the end I decide that kids learn a lot from their parents, but most of what they take in, they learn not by being told, but by example. I don't want Dan to be a sheep either.

When the full case comes before the Commission some months later, I have my argument ready. The roster system in its present form discriminates against single parents because it prevents them from taking full-time work and advantages families with two parents who are able to bring in an income and easily do their roster. Simple.

One of the wealthy parents engages a QC who digs through the rules and finds the school is exempt from Equal Opportunity legislation because it's a cooperative.

The Tribunal members adjourn to discuss this surprising find and during the recess I realise I've lost before I've even begun.

When they come back to tell us this, I'm overwhelmed with relief. I just want the whole thing over.

Riding my bike on the way home, I realise something

important about myself. Morals, beliefs, personal opinions and friendships mean nothing in the face of having a group turn on you. Ian once told me that's how Aboriginals used to kill people, by 'pointing the bone'. When the bone is pointed at someone, the tribe behaves as if that person is already dead. The victim walks around like a living ghost and dies shortly after. People can die without a sense of belonging. I don't enjoy being an outsider, but for the first time I realise I've got a strength most people lack. I don't need to be liked.

Dan goes to the local primary school for his last year. Throughout the year-long saga, even though he's only 11, he knows what's been going on and never once complains.

TWELVE

IDIOTICALLY POSITIVE

After Joanne and I haven't seen each other for more than 12 months, we cauterise the wound and make up. Again. We take a car trip and discover Daylesford, a forgotten little town an hour from Melbourne. It had been a honeymoon spot at the turn of the century because of the mineral spa baths there, but after the Second World War the population was siphoned away to places with supermarket chains. It's 15 minutes drive from each of the two main arteries heading west out of Melbourne. It's on the way to nowhere, nestled at the bottom of a hill in the Wombat State Forest. We're enchanted by the gold rush architecture. The town is an intact Sleeping Beauty. Progress has passed it by. Half the main street shops are empty and the small miners cottages are a dime a dozen. A month after we first see the place, I mortgage my flat for the deposit and buy a run-down place for $42,000 in both our names. Joanne and Bear start doing it up. It's the year interest rates explode to 20 per cent. Joanne and Bear are nesting away and I can't afford the mortgage, so I tell them they can have the cottage if they keep up the payments. They renovate and put a shingle out saying 'Lavender Cottage' and rent it to weekend tourists. It's Daylesford's second such house. The first, Dulwich Cottage, belongs to Carol White, a local woman we meet who has a crazy idea to open a lavender farm miles out of town. She's originally from one of Melbourne's snooty suburbs, so Joanne dubs her Lady Carol.

Bear's nursery business has been losing money since he began it ten years ago with money he got from mortgaging Joanne's house. It isn't through not working hard enough. He works like a dog 16 hours a day. If you ask me, he just isn't a good businessman. And Joanne doesn't help by hemorrhaging money. Any knick-knack, Persian carpet, antique gold ring or piece of stair for the dolls house she's building is snapped up or put on lay-by because, 'BB, if Bear can lose all that money in the nursery, I deserve a few measly trinkets for all the worry he puts me through'.

One day all the stress and worry over money comes to a head. In a monumental act of love, Joanne says she'll sell her Melbourne house and buy another one for half the price in Daylesford. The condition is, they have to pay cash for the new house so they won't be in debt anymore. Bear doesn't keep his side of the bargain and they end up with an $80,000 mortgage on the Daylesford place, just down the road from Lavender Cottage. He puts the rest into his business and loses it within a year.

Joanne's a hoarder. The move to Daylesford takes 55 tea-chests. They pack up 15 years worth of collected junk, treasured possessions and a small shop full of potted plants and move in a bustle of excitement. Quaintly, she keeps in touch through letters.

I'm covering the opening of a gigantic extension to the Chadstone Shopping Centre when I slip over outside an ice-cream shop and my knee goes on me. They cart me off to hospital and someone puts a note under David's door to ask him to bring a change of undies. He comes in looking as if he thinks I'm about to die.

'Barb. Are you okay? What's happened?' He looks stricken. He sits by my bed and strokes my hand. It's the first time he's been affectionate with me since a music evening at my flat about two weeks after we got together the first time. I still remember how he held my big toe between his index finger and thumb. Very strange form of affection but it was pretty damned sensual alright. This hand stroking though, is just tender. I'm amazed. If only I could break my leg every week.

It doesn't last long. The doctor comes while David's there and wants to examine my leg. I tell him it'll hurt too much and I won't let him touch me.

'Someone else has already done that,' I say and immediately faint. David drops my hand like a hot potato. I only stay out for a couple of seconds.

'Barb! He didn't even touch you and you fainted!' He keeps laughing to himself. 'I can't believe what a wimp you are!'

At least my leg gets me out of the commando walks. We visit Joanne and Bear in Daylesford every other weekend.

Months after I throw away my crutches I decide to resign from work. Someone at the newspaper told me when I first started that if you stay on suburbans more than two years you get stuck for life. Two years is coming up. Even though I've done some freelance articles for the metro papers, there's no chance of working on one because dozens of journos lost their jobs when the main daily and afternoon papers merged.

Dan's turning 12 at the end of the year and we haven't been overseas since India when he was two. I decide to go on a round-the-world trip with him. Without the Daylesford mortgage payments and no rent to pay, I've saved thousands. I tell David about my plans. He says I'm 'being brave'. He has microscopic horizons, my man.

Dan and I leave on our trip a few days before his birthday in December. David gives me a pair of earrings for my birthday. I want to attach some mystical importance to the fact that I love them then lose them before I get off the plane in New Zealand. I decide it means deep down I know he doesn't love me. It's a tricky interpretation when you're abandoning your man for a world trip.

Ma's been living in Christchurch for five years. She'd started Australia's first fantasy phone call business in Sydney but given it to some boyfriend I'd never met to get him off her back. She'd moved to Christchurch to get as far away from him as possible. And because she heard they didn't have a fantasy line in NZ yet. They're new everywhere. Ma puts an ad in the paper for girls to work for her and another one for the service. I haven't seen Ma for years.

She picks us up at the airport. She was 12 stone at the wedding eight years ago. Now she's huge again.

'Hi Dannell, aren't you a big boy now?' I don't know why

she doesn't like calling Dan by his name, but I don't care. She always says Dan's her favourite grandson. And if Ma doesn't like someone, even family, she feels no compulsion to hide it. She'll say it not with venom, simply as a statement of fact. Ma doesn't have a bitter or venomous vein in her body.

'Gran, how's things?' He gives her a big, charming smile and disappears into her pillow bosoms. David sees people like characters in a book, and he loves Ma's funny ways. Fortunately, Dan takes his cue from David and treats her like the eccentric old granny she is.

'Oh, not too bad. And how are you Barb? Good?'

We kiss and give each other a short, restrained little hug. Ma's become more affectionate in her old age. I know she's trying to make up for when we were little. I want to help her feel better but it's awkward.

'What happened to the svelte Ma?'

'Oh, it's just me metabolism. But I'm a lot less than I used to be.'

She tells me she's 20 stone now and it has nothing to do with what she eats. But I know Ma and the tail end of chops – 'Just the fat please, don't worry about the meat' orders.

We drive home to her unit. Inside, she has ornaments on every surface and every wall. They're displayed in cabinets. Dolls in wedding dresses, crystal animals, painted plates. Most of it I haven't seen before. It's kitsch but seeing her surrounded by these homey, grandmumsy things makes me happy. One room with a huge table with a working train set on it is like Toy Town.

I can't remember having seen Ma doing nice things for herself.

'How's the fantasy line going?' I've heard from my brother Peter and Jenny how she's got right into it. Peter says she'll do the phone calls anywhere. If one comes when she's walking down a supermarket aisle she'll do it there. Peter told me she'd done it once when he was with her and he shuffled off in the other direction and pretended he didn't know her. I can see Peter rolling his eyes asking himself if Ma will ever be embarrassed about anything.

'Great. But I'm making more money out of the physicals at the moment. New Zealand guys just love fat old ladies.'

That night Ma has a client and Dan and I have to wait in the kitchen while he comes in. Then she goes to a bedroom for an hour while we watch telly. Quietly. We hear Ma shouting at him. Dan and I look at each other.

'What's Granny doing, Mum?'

'She's just got a friend in there. She'll be out soon.'

'Granny's funny.'

'What do you mean, sweetheart? She is a little bit funny but what bit do *you* think's funny?'

'Well, like I went to find a video in the cupboard and saw all these ones with willies and girls with no clothes on and stuff? So then I found one with a picture of a policewoman with a gun on the cover and I thought it was one I could watch? But then I put it on and there were all these people with no clothes on?' Dan's started to do that annoying inflection of turning statements into questions. It drives me crazy.

'So what did you do then?'

'I put it back, of course.' He screws up his face. 'But then I found this big plastic willy in the cupboard? There was a button on the side so I turned it on to see what it did? And it started shaking and it nearly scared me to death. It was gross. Why does Granny have all that stuff?'

'She needs it for her work darling. She's not like other grannies. She's a sex worker. She's a little bit of a funny one, your Gran.'

'What's a sex worker?'

'Well, there are people in the world who can't have sex

easily, so they pay people like Granny to help them. Anyway, sweetheart, I think it's time you went to bed.'

How much do you tell your little boy about his granny when she's a sex worker?

Dan goes to bed.

Soon Ma takes her client to the door and as she goes past the lounge room she introduces us.

'This is my daughter, Barbara. She's a journalist in Melbourne. She's on her way 'round the world with my grandson.'

She might be a sex-working mum, but she's a proud sex-working mum. I'm glad we're in Christchurch and not Melbourne. The guy's very young, maybe 25. I find it hard to imagine him having sex with my mother. When he's gone I ask what he wanted.

'He's a regular. He likes me to smack his bottom with me slipper.'

'Why?'

'Oh, I don't know Barbara, why does anyone like anything?'

Ma doesn't like to analyse things too deeply.

'Dan found your blue videos in the cupboard.'

'What was he doing in there?'

'Looking for a kiddies' video to put on. You might have put them away somewhere when you knew we were coming. It isn't easy explaining why his Granny keeps sex videos lying around.'

'They weren't exactly lying around, Barbara. I did put them away. Anyway, I'll put 'em in me room next time.' I know she really is trying.

We stay with Ma for a week. Now I'm a mother myself, I'm curious about why she's so emotionally removed. About her life before she became a mother. She's watching telly while Dan's out riding Ma's bike.

'Do you know anything about your father Ma?' I ask.

'Not really.'

'Ma. You must know something.' She lifts her chin to the ceiling and puckers her lips in concentration. Maybe I finally have her attention.

'Well, all I know is that Mum told me she married a bigamist. She said she found out he was already married after I was born and she left him. But I think she said that so I wouldn't feel like a bastard.'

'What makes you think that?'

'Well, if she really married him I wouldn't have the same surname as Poppy and Lizzy would I?' They're her mother's parents.

'Is that the name on your birth certificate?'

'Yeees.' Her voice goes up and down, like she's been trying to get this simple point through my thick head for hours.

'Who were you closest to of the four adults?' Ma lived with her mother, uncle, Poppy and Lizzy.

'Oh, I don't know. Why do you ask so many questions?'

'Ma, that's my job. I'm a journo remember?'

'Well, I pity the poor sods you interview at work then.'

'So, who did you love most?'

'It's hard to say. I loved Lizzy. She was a great cook. She used to make all me favourite things. Poppy was a lovely old man too. He worked on the trams and used to bring me things passengers lost or left behind. I remember once he brought this gorgeous umbrella with a Japanese geisha girl on it and he was always bringing me embroidered hankies and stuff. But Uncle Bill, he was a great character. I think he was me favourite.'

'Why?'

'Oh, he was just such a character that's all. And he really loved me. He was into the black market and all that carry on, you know. There were always people at the kitchen door with parcels and whispering and the money changing hands! You wouldn't dream about it. The war was on when I was a kid and that's when he was a real wheeler-dealer but even after that he was still a bit of a Steptoe.' I'd seen *Steptoe and Son* in the 1960s when I was in primary school.

'What about Gran?' Her chubby hands are clasped on her tummy, fingers laced together while her thumbs circle each other in time with her circling foot.

'Oh, she just worked in a munitions factory when the war was on. After that she worked as a cook.'

'Did you love her?'

'I s'pose I must've. She was me mother.' She raises her eyes to the ceiling and looks a bit disgusted. I'm not sure whether with herself or Gran.

The shopping channel's on telly and her eyes keep wandering to it.

Then I remember a photo of Ma I'd seen once as a little girl. She was about nine or ten. She had ponytail ringlets and a white lacey baby doll dress. I remember she looked happy. She was beaming with a naughty sweet smile that, remembering back through adult eyes, reflected that moment in childhood between innocence and knowledge. She wasn't grossly fat, but pudgy and pretty. I ask if she remembers it.

'Which one?'

I describe it, telling her she looked pretty and innocent, a nice kid. She looks horrified. Like I've told a huge lie.

'Oh, I was not! I was the kind of kid that if I met one as selfish as I was then, I'd think she was a real little so-and-so. I get embarrassed just thinkin' about how awful I was.'

'How awful?'

'*Real* awful.' So there. Take that.

'But in what way?'

'Well, I remember one Christmas the girl next door didn't get many presents. Her family was dirt poor and I had more presents than you could poke a stick at and I put on such a show because she was playing with me new bike.'

'What about bad memories of your childhood?'

'That's not a good memory.'

'But you only felt bad later. Do you remember feeling bad as a kid?'

'Only when Poppy died. I was about nine at the time. He had a heart attack. I found out when I came home from school one day. I was heartbroken and cried for days.'

'What about the incident with the grocer?' I knew Ma had been 'interfered with' when she was a kid. I wondered why that wasn't her first bad recollection.

'Oh, well, yeah. There was that too.' She starts getting interested in the telly again.

'Maaa, we're talking! Why don't you turn it off?' She turns the sound down instead.

'So, what happened exactly?'

'I used to go and play with the grocer's niece and this day I walked in but Polly wasn't there. I went to leave but he called me over and asked if I wanted a lolly and he took me behind the counter and told me to choose one. While I was lookin' he went and pulled the blinds down and closed the shop door.' She stops while the TV beckons.

'Ma?' I call her attention back. 'So what happened then?'

Her left foot, with its missing small toe, continues to circle. Now she stares at a spot between ceiling and wall. Her brow furrows, assisting in the search for that point in history. She loosens her bottom dentures, rolling them around in her mouth to help her think.

'Well, he just put me on the counter while I sucked the lollypop and started strokin' me hair. I remember I could feel me bare legs and part of me bum stickin' to the wooden counter and I wanted to get down but he wouldn't let me. The old bastard kept saying "I bet that feels nice".'

'And what did you say?'

'Oh, I don't remember!' She's exasperated. 'Does it matter?'

'Not really. Anyway, what happened next?'

'He swung me legs around and laid me down on the counter and started rubbing me thighs and kept saying "I bet that feels nice". Then he took me pants off and started feeling me up and I just thought righto. I started countin' the jars and boxes on the top shelf. I counted 'em about 100 bloody times.' She laughs.

I imagine her eyes drifting up through the dusky light to the jars and boxes on the high wooden shelves that go right up to the ceiling so far above.

'Was there penetration?'

'Barbara, how would I bloody well remember? It was more than 50 years ago.'

'But it must have been pretty traumatic if there was penetration.'

'Well I don't know. I didn't think about it, I thought it was just part of life. You didn't worry about it like people do these days.'

'Well, I was thinking if there was, it would've hurt. Surely you'd remember that.'

'No. I don't think there was. In fact there couldn't have been because when I had sex with a sailor a few years later I bled like a stuck pig, so there couldn't have been.'

In my mind I can see a photo of Ma as a teenager.

'Remember that brown suitcase of photos we used to have?'

When we were kids we'd pore over the case when we were left alone in the house. A delicious pleasure. Me and Pommy used to ferret out the brown case and, daringly, pour the photos on the floor – a carpet of clues about Ma. There were old birthday cards to us as babies and from old friends (men!!) to Ma. There were photos of her holding us, of Lizzy who died just after I was born, and ribald and romantic handwritten poems which revealed a life inconceivably different to the one we considered should belong to 'Mum'.

'Oh yeah. The little leather one?'

'Whatever happened to it?'

'God knows. Lost in one of the moves I s'pose.'

The photo I remember is of Ma and a blonde girlfriend wearing sailor hats leaning rakishly against a berthed ship. Ma, Pat, was dressed in a white navy-style dress standing with one leg bent coquettishly leaning against the ship. The other girl is falling over Pat giggling. There are two men off to the side, eyeing them. When I first saw the photo, I thought Ma was beautiful. I ask if she remembers it.

'Hmm. Vaguely.'

'There's a couple of sailors in the photo.'

'Oh yeah. That was a sheila I used to work with at the exchange. We used to ring ships arriving in Melbourne and organise dates with sailors visiting port.'

'Had you had sex yet? When was the first time you had sex?' Ever the journo.

'Oh, some sailor. It happened when I was 14.'

'Where?'

'In the summer we used to go to the Trocadero on Saturd'y nights. It was on St Kilda Road where the Concert Hall is now. I was a pretty good dancer because I'd been having dance classes for years, mainly tap but I was pretty good at rock 'n roll as well.'

'I didn't know you learnt dance.' I can't imagine it. Ma?

'I wanted to be a tap dancer when I was a kid.'

'Why?'

'There was a famous tapper I liked and I wanted to be

like her. Eleanor Powell. I did all kinds o' things when I was a kid. That was just one of 'em.'

'What else?'

'Oh banjo, piano, guitar, all kinds of dance lessons, even deportment classes.' So that explains all the classes she sent us to as kids.

'So anyway, what about this guy?'

'Which guy?'

'The one you first had sex with. After the dance.'

'I just met the bloke there and he took me across the road to the Alexandra Gardens after.' I hadn't even registered the fun in her voice before. I do now only because of the irritated drawl that's replaced it.

'Was it romantic?'

'Hardly.' She picks up a crossword puzzle and pen sitting by her chair.

'Well, did you like him?'

'Who?'

'The guy you had sex with after the dance.'

She's concentrating on the puzzle. I try to stay patient.

'Ma?'

'What?'

'The guy after the dance. What was he like?'

'Oh, he was alright I s'pose.' She's puckering her lips and pointing her chin to the ceiling so she can see the crossword puzzle better.

'Well, what happened?'

'Not much.'

'Ma.' Now it's my turn for my voice to go up and down. 'What do you mean not much?' She looks up at the wall.

'He just got me up against a tree and rammed it in.' I'm shocked. I've heard this story a few times before, not in this detail, but she'd never said it was rape.

'Didn't he kiss you first?'

'Oh, for about 30 seconds.' She rolls her eyes at the gullible girl she was back then.

'Did you want to have sex?'

'Not really.'

'So it *was* rape, then.' I can't believe this isn't obvious to her.

'Depends what you mean by rape. He didn't beat me up.'

'But you didn't want to have sex?'

'Not like that.' She's not involved in the story. It's like it happened to someone else.

'So it was rape.'

'Barbara, I don't know. Why do you ask so many questions?' Total exasperation.

She picks up the remote and scrolls through to see what's on the other stations. The sound is mute.

'So what happened afterwards?'

'I went home of course.'

'How did you get there?'

Her voice is with me but she's distracted by the telly. 'On the tram. Actually it was pretty embarrassing because I was bleeding like a stuck pig. I thought I was dying.' She laughs.

'What did he say before you went home?'

'He said he'd call me the next day, I think.'

'And did he?'

'Course not.'

'Why do you say of course not?'

'That's just what guys are like.' She says it as though I'm a simpleton who hasn't yet grasped life's basics.

'Weren't you a bit devastated or something?'

'No. I felt a bit hurt at the time but I didn't think about it.'

The next day I find out Ma's already made front page of the Christchurch newspaper. It's in the odd spot column.

'Who is the large elderly lady who rides around Christchurch on a bicycle in the dead of night and falls off when she stops at a red traffic light? She has been spotted regularly in the pre-dawn hours toppling off the bicycle, crawling on all-fours to get up, mounting her transport again and continuing down the road as though nothing has happened. The unfortunate accident seems to occur at every red light. Can anyone explain?'

'Ma, can you explain? What were you doing riding around in the middle of the night? And why do you do it if you fall off all the time?'

'Well, I started riding the bike about a year ago and I really loved it, you know. I'd go to my mailbox at the post office. The only problem was that 'cause one of me legs is shorter than the other, since the accident, whenever I stopped and put me short leg down, I'd fall off.'

'Why don't you put your long leg down instead?'

'Because I can't get off on the other side.' The whiney tone again. Like it should be obvious to blind Freddie. 'I've tried and I fall off anyway.'

'So why in the middle of the night.'

'Because when I went in the day I got sick of people rushing out of their cars to help me up. It's very embarrassing. You know? The only way I can get up when I fall down is on all fours and there's nothing anyone can do to help. If they just left me alone I'd be fine.' Ma rolls her eyes at the general imbecility in the world.

'But doesn't it hurt falling off? I can't imagine you'd like it.'

'It doesn't hurt that much actually. Me fat protects me when I fall. Naturally I'd prefer not to fall but it doesn't really worry me. Anyway, I still wanted to ride so I took to doing it in the middle of the night. Until that bloody article came out anyway. Now I'm too embarrassed and haven't ridden anywhere for about six months.'

The next day I find out how right Peter is about her work ethic. She does fantasy phone calls anywhere. I've already told her I don't want her doing them in front of Dan. She's very good about it. Or tries to be. If we're at home she takes the phone to her room. But if we're out, she does them in such a loud whisper everyone can hear. I take Peter's advice and find some vitally interesting potato peelers in a distant aisle from Ma, or, if we're in a shopping centre, I whisk Dan off to the boys wear section. 'A boy can never have too many socks Dan Biggs.'

While we're here, Ma wants to show me a house she's buying. Well, as it turns out, she's not actually buying it.

'This lovely lady's got behind in her mortgage payments and the bank's going to repossess it. And if they do that she'll get nothing back in a mortgagee auction. So she said if I pay the bank what's owed I can have the house.'

'What does she mean by "have" it?'

'Well, I'll own it. All I'll have to do is keep making the payments.'

'Have you got all that in writing?'

'No, but look, she's a *lovely* lady and honest as the day's long.'

'But Ma, how many times have you trusted people and been burned. In fact, with your record, the more you trust someone, the more I'd guarantee they're about to rip you off. They can see you coming a mile off.'

'Don't be so cynical, Barbara. There are some people in the world who are just plain good people.' She says this as though she's the model of sensible behaviour and that I should be ashamed of myself for being so mistrustful.

'Well, if you pay to have a solicitor's letter drawn up, there really isn't any reason why she wouldn't sign it is there? If she really is going to give you the house and she's such a lovely lady and all. I mean, it is $5000. It's not peanuts.'

'Well, I'm sure she'd sign it. She's a real salt of the earth type lady. Wait 'til you meet her. She's just lovely.'

We go the next day and meet the woman at the house and she shows us around.

'What do you think? Isn't it great?' Ma whispers to me.

'Perfect. Just make sure she knows she isn't getting any money until your name's on the title.' I whisper back.

In the lounge room we sit down over a cuppa.

'They'll be repossessing it in two weeks,' the woman says to Ma. 'So, we'll have to have the money before then. We don't want to cut it too fine.'

'Well, me daughter here says I shouldn't hand over any money until we put the agreement in writing and put my name on the house. I don't s'pose that'd be a problem, would it?'

The lovely lady glares at me. She has all kinds of reasons for not doing it.

When we leave, Mrs Salt of the Earth swears at Ma in the foulest language and looks as though she's restraining herself from kicking the tyre as we drive off.

On the way back to Christchurch Ma's bewildered and has the wherewithal to be just a little sheepish.

'She seemed like such a lovely lady.'

Ma's the most gullible person I've ever met. For such a schemer, she has great belief in people's goodness. On this trip it occurs to me more than ever how similar we are. My friends think I'm gullible but you wouldn't know the meaning of the word until you'd heard some of the lines Ma's fallen for. But not only do we both have an idiotically positive outlook in situations that would make others down tools and go home, we've also followed a certain pattern. It can't be coincidence that we were both raped and left home at 14 and that we are both single parents. Even my foot goes round and round like hers.

While we stay with Ma, I catch up on what she's been up to in the last few years. I've hardly seen her since the wedding. Even then I didn't spend enough time with her to ask about her two and a half years in jail. She'd been put in for defrauding the government in hundreds of names. For sickness benefits when she broke her leg. She makes jail sounds like ClubMed.

'When I got moved from Silverwater to Cessnock jail it was great. We had a swimming pool and the food was pretty good too. There'd be cake and tea for supper and videos sometimes. I had me own room. It wasn't too bad at all actually.'

'Is that when you got into knitting?'

'Hmmm. I thought a lot about you kids too and what kind of a mother I'd been. I think maybe I worried too much about material things when I should've spent more time with yous kids. That's when I tried to kill meself.'

This is news to me.

'When? What happened?' Visits with Ma are never dull.

'Well, nothin' really. I just took an overdose and they found me. That's all. That's why I had the stomach stapling. I told them about how upset I'd been when those Japanese tourists'd laughed at Betty and me at the airport.'

When Ma was going off to jail the second time, she was waiting at Canberra airport with Betty who was almost as fat as her but shorter and these Japanese tourists, all men, had stopped in their tracks and pointed and laughed at them. They stood there for about five minutes according to Ma.

I think they thought Ma and Betty had been provided as entertainment.

'But you've told me that story a million times as though

it was the funniest thing that's ever happened to you. Betty says you laughed and laughed.'

'Course I laughed.' Is that hurt scratched all over her face? Ma would admit to anything but that. 'What else can you do when you've got bloody 20 Japanese guys standin' there laughin' at ya in a public place.'

'They probably just thought you were lady sumo wrestlers. Anyway, you always say your weight doesn't bother you. When I ask, you say you don't think about it.'

'Well, I don't most of the time. But it still hurts when someone laughs at ya.' So there, take that if you want to drag it out of me. 'Anyway, that's why they gave me the stomach stapling.'

'But how come you've put the weight back on?'

'I don't know. It's just the kind of metabolism I've got I think. Anyway, I nearly died and lost half me stomach so now I can only eat little bits at a time. Otherwise I'd probably be back to 30 stone again.'

I look closely to see if she's going anywhere with her hurt, but she's picked up a Nintendo and her eyes have already glazed over. ·

THIRTEEN

BROWN FLANNELETTE PYJAMAS

After leaving Ma's place, Dan and I travel around New Zealand. While Dan's off black-water rafting, I abseil in a wet suit down a hundred metre cliff to spend the day walking and swimming through an underground cave system. In Hawaii I watch Dan feeding rainbows of fish with bread and see a surfer walk out of the sea with his board broken in two. In San Francisco, Dan and I can't stop laughing at our giant's breakfast in Haight Ashbury and I feel lucky, listening to the recorded tour of Alcatraz, that I only had a barbed wire fence to scale when I escaped from the convent. In Los Angeles, when I go to pay at the youth hostel, I discover the bum bag's missing. Dan had asked if he could carry it, and, still a continuum concept mum, I'd too-hastily agreed on the grounds that it would make him feel grown-up and responsible. We work out he went to the toilet at a Taco Bill's two hours down the highway and left the bag, containing all our travellers cheques, cash and passports, in there. I sob for an embarrassingly long time before changing my entire pre-conceived notion about Americans when the desk clerk phones and finds the bag's been handed in by a customer. In the hostel we find a lift with a school teacher down through Mexico to Central America.

In Guatemala, we go to an ancient town with cobbled streets called Antigua. We move in with a local family and Dan and I have private Spanish lessons every day. After a week, Dan gets jealous because I start to spend time with the daughter of the house. She's the same age as Dan but he never wants to come with us when she takes me to look at ruins. He moves in with the family next door where we'd first stayed for a couple of days. He's 12 so I figure it'll be good for his language and independence.

After a month, thanks to the unending patience of my host family who don't understand a word of English, I learn enough Spanish to find out about the whole history of their marriage.

I go out alone one night and meet Emilio, a Canadian guy who was born in Hungary. We play chess and I win. We play again and he wins.

'One more,' I say.

'I think it would save face if we don't play again.' I think his accent is suave and sophisticated.

'Whose? Yours or mine?' I challenge.

'Mine, of course.'

'You're such a gentleman.'

'Well, in fact, I am really a chauvinist,' he tells me candidly.

'That's okay, don't feel bad,' I tell him. 'I'm a feminist.'

We talk about our lives. Emilio owns a restaurant in Alberta that his business partner looks after during the coldest three months of the northern winter which he spends in Central America each year. For seven years he's been with a woman who loves him who he's considering marrying. Or leaving. He can't decide but is leaning towards marriage. She knows he isn't faithful when he's away but doesn't want to know the details. He doesn't want to marry her or anyone but since he'd given her a ring for her birthday he can't forget the look of disappointment on her face when he explained that it was only a friendship ring. I tell him about David. That I have been, and plan to continue to be, faithful. When he walks me home and, at the door, tries to kiss me on the mouth, I turn my cheek.

'Why not come with me to a place by the sea on Friday. It is very beautiful. You have not seen anything of Guatemala yet. No?'

'I don't want to sleep with you, Emilio.'

'I respect your decision. We can go simply as friends. I like your company.'

He tells me where the bus leaves from and the time. He says to think about it.

Emilio's intelligent, interesting, handsome, respectful and honest about his situation.

Dan and I turn up at the bus stop two days later.

After talking for hours, when we arrive at the beach, Emilio casually puts his arm around my shoulder. An interesting trick, he manages humility and confidence at the same time. It's charming. I'm also a sucker for romance and he's good at it. I've been starved of it for so long.

The three of us spend four days together. Emilio is great with Dan and plays and swims and talks with him. I'm in a blissful daze.

To be economical, or so we say, the three of us share a room. When Dan's asleep we don't exactly have full on sex but I discover Emilio has the touch of a butterfly. He doesn't want me to break my vow to David so there's no penetration. Seems silly to me, especially since I have exquisite orgasms all over the place and he doesn't. It never fails to open my heart.

I decide to go on to see a volcano with someone else in our hotel since Emilio is going to Belize the next day. When Dan and I leave at dawn I can barely look at Emilio because I know I'll cry. As I settle onto the boat, although I feel a bit silly because holiday romances are cliches, I feel special. Sitting here, with the boat taking me far away from this experience, with a gently intense sunrise in front of me and Emilio, who I know I'll never see again, behind me, an acceptance of life exactly as it is settles over me. I let go of my longing that this romance will continue and fulfil me. The freedom in it exhilarates me and I know I'll never forget this moment. I'm alive in a way that I've only felt once before when Dan was born. There's a vivid awareness of the mossy forest, flocks of birds careening through the sunrise, the sound of the motorboat in a deafening silence. This acceptance is like a crack opening up in the world. Through it I glimpse a more lasting peace that seems, just for that half-hour boat journey, as familiar as home.

When we get back to Guatemala City I phone David. I hadn't planned to hit David with the Emilio story, but I don't get a chance to tell him anything, even about our trip.

He tells me Joanne's had a suicide attempt. Slit her wrists in the bath. Bear's left her and taken up with another woman. She has no prospects of work and a mortgage to pay. The nursery, and, really, I suppose Joanne's excess as well, has eaten more than $200,000, virtually all the money she'd got when she sold her Melbourne house and moved to Daylesford. David's amused that Russell has stopped trying to make the nursery work now the money's gone and is becoming a masseur like his new girlfriend.

David tells me Joanne's been in a psych hospital for a few weeks but now she's out.

'She's trying to get in touch with you to sell Lavender Cottage, Barb. They need your signature for the sale. If you don't do something and she knocks herself off, it'll be on your head.'

Thanks, David.

I phone Joanne and, as usual, she manages to tell the suicide attempt as a funny story.

I continue travelling around Guatemala, to the Mayan ruins of Tikal and then to Belize, where I tell myself I'm not going in the hope of running into Emilio. I don't.

Every time I call Joanne she's crying. Not when she finds out it's me, but when she picks up the phone. I'm worried and think I should go home. She'd cradled me in her arms and rocked me on her knee when I'd been devastated about Ian and David. She's been like a mother to me. Joanne can be manipulative and a drama queen, but there's no getting away from it, I owe her.

'Do you want me to come home?'

'BB, I can't answer that. What do you expect me to say? You're on your big trip. I can't ask you to drop that and come home.'

'But how are you going? Will you be all right?'

'Of course I'm not okay. Every day I feel like I can't go on. But I don't want you cancelling your trip on my account.'

We can't go home straightaway but I ring every day to let her know where we are and when we'll be back.

'Don't do anything. I have to go to Disneyland. Dan's been looking forward to it since we left. But hang on. Okay? I'll be back in a few days.'

'I'm drowning, BB. Hurry.'

We're held up with flights in Zurich. I have to continue clockwise around the world according to my ticket.

'Are you sure you want to cancel all these,' the Qantas ticket officer asks in Zurich.

He tears them off one by one. I watch while Egypt, India, Thailand and Indonesia are torn from the ticket stub and thrown like confetti into the bin.

I arrive at Joanne's house in Daylesford late one autumn afternoon. Dan knows why we've come home. He's never liked Joanne much on account of her not liking him. But when we arrive he's the first to put his arms around her. It's a long hug.

'Dan Biggs. You're so tall. It's *so* good to see you.'

I wait patiently for my turn.

'BB, thanks for coming home.' She gives me a long hug, too.

I've never seen Joanne humble.

She tells me about Bear. He and the new woman have been staying at Lavender Cottage. Joanne went to the tip one day to drop off some rubbish and saw her artwork and precious pieces from the cottage dumped there by the new girlfriend. She went to the local market and saw pieces she'd made and collected for Lavender Cottage being sold on stalls. The stall owners found them at the tip. Joanne had been to confront the woman and had been kicked out of her own house by this stranger.

David knows I'm back but he waits a week before coming to see me. When we finally meet in Daylesford, we're shy like new lovers.

'If you hadn't come back, Barb, I wouldn't have been here in a year. It's too long to wait.'

I knew that and never tell anyone that was part of my decision to come back. Though Emilio had been constantly in my thoughts for weeks after we separated, that reality has faded. There's a soft elusiveness about David that makes me want to climb inside that dreamer's cloud with him. It bedevils me that there's something unutterably romantic about him despite the fact that he makes not the smallest attempt to actually *be* romantic. Unlike my good self who starts sending him a poem a day, some my own creations and others from famous romantic poets, in the hope of awakening in him the idea that one needs food for the soul. I don't succeed. He says he feels harassed and that he'll send me a poem called *The Swarm*. This, his saving grace. He has wit.

Joanne stews pears from her tree on the slow combustion stove. It's a witches' brew we have every morning for breakfast and every night after dinner. They're always on the stove. As the perpetual pears simmer, so does Joanne's depression. It's like another person in the house. I walk on eggshells.

She makes her artwork and sells it through the Convent Gallery. Dan starts high school at Daylesford Technical

College. I find a job on the local rag, the *Midland Express*. Every morning before work Joanne brings me toast and tea in bed. At night she arrives in our room smelling of lavender with a tray of hot chocolate for Dan and champagne for me. She lies in bed with us and reads aloud from *The House at Pooh Corner*. Afterwards, when Dan goes to sleep, she and I retire to her boudoir, flounces of white spilling over the four-poster bed, and whisper and laugh about her drive-by intimacies (not literally, but she did get her licence) with locals. How she woos and then drops them. I judge Joanne shamelessly and admire her tremendously. That she can elicit loyalty and love from adoring fans who want only to be in her company is a quality that makes me just a little envious. Even if she doesn't really like them.

Over the first months Joanne washes and irons our clothes and cooks gourmet meals with vegies from the garden. A fire glows in the kitchen grate and her latest art-naive ceramic piece, a toppling but jolly, fat fisherman, mouth a perfect O of surprise that his row boat has broken in two, is the centrepiece of the kitchen table. Above, the light is draped in a colourful scarf, tangerine and lime distilled from an oil burner and the sounds of Enya wraps all in a cosiness so thick you have to elbow through to the sink. The living room too is a womb with tangible tentacles. Chock full of paintings, camellias floating in water on the table, more lamps draped in silk, a couch so low and luxurious you have to wrestle your way out of it. Not a spare surface or wall unadorned by knick-knacks and artworks collected from antique and junk shops since Joanne was a girl. Her camel, kangaroo and emu carousel dotted with fairy lights goes round and round.

Most afternoons we walk around the lake together with the dogs. She wistfully eyes possible drowning spots in moments of melancholy, drawing my attention to them to claw at my ebbing compassion, but after a few months Joanne's depression peters out. At least until another season.

On weekends David visits from his student house near La Trobe University. We go for marathon bush walks and argue about everything. He puts me down constantly, but because he does it with humour it's hard to protest effectively. Because he's funny, I wonder if I'm the problem when I don't laugh. I'm always wondering if the relationship is a good idea. Good for me, anyway. David seems to be thriving. He, Dan and I learn to ride a unicycle, something they delight in doing better than me. My bum and thighs swell and I walk like John Wayne.

Dan doesn't make friends. Always a popular boy at school, now he escapes into the television at home. Kids call him Skippy. He's suspicious about what kind of insult it can be if it isn't a term of endearment, which he strongly suspects it isn't. At school he hangs around with kids he doesn't even like so he won't be lonely. After school Joanne tries to cheer him up with strawberry jam toast and hot chocolate with maple syrup. She brings it on a tray while he mopes in front of the telly.

I talk to him but nothing helps.

'I hate this place. I wish we'd never come.'

Six months after we've been living here, I see a house for sale a block down the road from Joanne. She's number 78 Raglan Street and this old miner's cottage is 91. Unlike her gracious old home, mine has aluminium windows and doors stuck on like cancers. The original features have been efficiently, thoughtlessly removed but I can perform major surgery to restore them. Settlement has come through on Lavender Cottage and instead of paying back the bank for the mortgage on my Melbourne flat, I pay a big deposit on the new house and still have enough left to give Joanne $5000 to help with her mortgage. She's, ostensibly, living like a dormouse on the dole and struggling with house payments. She thinks I don't know she continues to lay-by rings, tulip bulbs, the dearest little corkscrew you ever did see that folds down to nothing ...

David won't leave me alone about buying the new house. He drives me to distraction.

'You've already got a flat in Melbourne, Barb. What if you can't pay the mortgage. And it's in such bad condition you know you'll have to pull it down.'

Not a week goes by when I don't think about leaving him. We fight over everything. He's negative about every plan and idea I have. Do I really think I can survive this for decades? If not, isn't it sensible to get out now?

I stay because, despite all appearances, I believe he loves me. Should this be enough? No, Goddamn, it isn't! Then I remember his creampuff eyes, his grown-up gruff, and, like a million women before me, I'm trapped by the little boy inside whose dad died when he was ten. I see in him the utter fear of the impermanence of life and I want to save him. I understand it's why he takes up his post to ward off any stray sparks of enthusiasm that pass his way.

Also, though he will attempt to block me to the bitter end, I know he's attracted by my blind faith in the future and belief that things will work out. And, if I don't let my frustrations get the better of me, like a frog in hot water, he acclimatises to my plans as he finally does with the house.

After a couple of months I get appendicitis and have to be rushed to hospital in the middle of the night after blacking out and wetting the bed. Joanne visits with Dan. I ask why David hasn't come. She rings him again and finally, on the third day, he turns up.

He brings flowers so begrudgingly I wish he hadn't bothered. I wish he could be sincere, vulnerable, real. I long for it.

Because I talk about getting out of hospital the next day, four days after they've gutted me instead of three, he tells me I'm becoming institutionalised. This is complex. It sounds like a joke, but there's the catch; it is and it isn't. He thinks like that. He hates every illness like it's the plague.

The visit makes me feel worse, not better. When he leaves, I brood.

I wish I knew what to expect from life. Is it enough not to be in pain or is it just a big joke to believe we should be happy, have our heart's desires fulfilled in this life and be loved the way we want?

For the first two years when we made love he laughed straight afterwards, as though he was watching how ridiculous he looked. He doesn't do that anymore. Another hopeful sign – he can change.

An unhopeful sign; now he rolls over to read after sex. I know he can be utterly tender; once he kissed the tips of my fingers like they were some rare-tasting Turkish delight. Because then I felt cherished and I know it's in his repertoire, I keep fantasising that it will happen again. On brisk, cutting, clean days, like now, after his visit, I know that's all in the past.

Are the mysteries we women hang out for just gossamer veils flying through the air, that upon touch, turn to brown flannelette pyjamas? And is that so bad? That's what I want to know. Should I settle for brown flannelette pyjamas?

By the time I take possession of my Raglan Street house, David has accepted the purchase and starts coming up every weekend and during uni holidays to work on the renovation. He does it on condition that I climb under the house with him and dig stump holes in the dead of a freezing winter. There's nothing I hate more than cold. But in David's mind doing the renovations earns him the right to move in with me because he won't accept charity from anyone. When uni finishes, that's what he does.

Though he's graduated, he says nobody can get a job with just an arts degree.

'What I really need is a degree that uses the carpentry skills I've already got. There's a project management course in Newcastle that I can do part-time. It's six years. I'm enrolling in that.'

Inside, I groan. Six more years of procrastinating with assignments, and migraines when they're handed in late.

David likes the new house but it isn't big enough.

'You can't keep a dog and chooks on a block this size, Barb.'

Six months later another house comes up for sale a couple of streets away in Western Avenue. It's on a huge acre block with Crown land on three sides.

I increase the mortgage on the newly renovated Raglan Street place for the deposit on the new one and mortgage the new one to the hilt. I can afford the repayments with rent from Raglan Street. We move in together in December. The house breathes cold air through cracked and sagging corners, an old black telephone sits crookedly disconnected on the hallway wall and a cast iron tub crouches in a corner of the gigantic, billowing bathroom. All the rooms are big and dim. Three have fireplaces. There's front to back door lino and newspapers from the First World War underneath.

I buy Dan a black furry handful of collie-kelpie cross for the first Christmas in the new house. We call her Sigi. She becomes David's shadow from the first night when she sleeps between us in our bed.

The second year in Daylesford Dan joins the chess club. Through kids there he meets Toni Tori. Toni's dad's the town Chief Executive Officer, basketball and netball coach, the taxi to and from games and president of the high school council. He has two other kids, both girls younger than Toni. Jude, the mum, has half the street at her house after school, a pikelet and scone-making mum, a drive-the-kids-around-the-corner-to-school kind of mum. Toni and his friends are the uncool school brains. The other boys, 'footies', trip them in the corridor. They defend each other but they're not a big enough group to stand up to the thugs. At least they have each other and nothing bonds like being underdogs together. Shannon, with a personality like a labrador pup, Chris whose parents are both teachers at the school and - the only uncossetted boy in the group - freckle-faced Matthew, who comes from a single-mum home and knows how to take care of himself. Toni's parents are both third generation Daylesford but the others have moved from Melbourne a decade or two ago.

Dan slides into that family as easy as a puppy being born. He teases Toni's sisters, Jacinta and Kelly, and chases them around the house. Like David's, Dan's teases uncannily hit the mark, but he has nothing corroding inside to make his barbs dirty. They're like shiny pins, an ouch with a tickle bubbling after. Kelly, five years younger than Dan, forgives his baiting and watches telly with her head on his lap. Soon he's almost living at the Tori's, which is just as well because as the year goes on, there's less and less to come home to as our new house is being painstakingly dismantled. It's like ripping a bandaid off. Slowly.

At the beginning of the year, David brings the rest of his tools up from Melbourne and starts work. I know by now if he's going to feel at home he'll need to contribute. Make his mark. He gets serious and goes off Austudy, his government living allowance.

'I don't feel right about taking money from the government, Barb.'

He keeps studying and I begin supporting the three of us.

He wants to continue earning his keep by renovating.

The first thing David sharpens his teeth on, is restumping. I've all but ground mine (teeth that is) to stumps doing Raglan Street and never want to see the underside of a house again.

I suggest we pay someone and get it done in two weeks, but he's adamant about making his mark. David's way takes a year. It's dark and near zero degrees when I return weary from working on the paper that winter. Restumping goes at the rate of a few posts a day. On the way home, ever the optimist, I imagine dinner cooking, a row of stumps dug in, a fire in the grate. Instead the cupboards are bare, the stove cold and the floor missing, mysteriously leaving no wood for a fire. Perhaps David burned it to keep warm in the day. I scream at him, put the electric blanket on and stump off to bed.

It takes me a while to realise that one reason the restumping's going so slowly, is that where regulations say stumps have to be a metre or whatever apart, David makes them 70cm; where holes have to be so deep, David digs deeper, then cements the posts in. He spends energy ensuring against possible dangers, leaks, collapses. David's inner world is fragile. I wonder if these house-building rituals are his way of shoring himself up too.

The next addition to our farm menagerie is Roostie, who comes from a battery hen farm after being mis-sexed. He wanders in and out of the house as if he owns the place until David turns him upside down on his knee and makes him stay there. Roostie's eyes look wildly for escape.

Then come chooks and guinea fowl, all of which David raises to be fat, healthy and fertile. Goatie follows. David knows exactly what to feed her, how to cut her toenails and how to wrestle her to the ground, close her eyes and make her nap on the grass next to him in the sun.

While David and I fight, he and Dan develop an easiness that eludes me. I'm not sure if I don't know how to relate to Dan because he's a teenager or because I'm his mother. To me he grunts or gives monosyllabic answers. David doesn't make a home for Dan while I'm away, but he does elicit all kinds of information about his friends, girls, school, parents of friends. Instead of being a surrogate father, David's the naughty big brother Dan can confide in. Dan's the same with Judy Tori. He prattles away telling her all kinds of things. I worry about not connecting.

I'm not a snooper by nature but with contraband, when it's lying about, I'm not going to goody-two-shoes the other way and pretend I don't see it. So it is with the essay Dan wrote on his first kiss. He's a maths boy so I'm tickled at his ability to set a scene. He and ice queen stunner Katy Donald were in her backyard having an afternoon picnic when it happened. They were talking, goblets of wine almost touching, heads close together; he could feel her breath on his cheek before the kiss arrived. In the essay, he claimed it was the most exciting moment of his life.

I show the potential short story to Joanne and other girlfriends who have to coo over how romantic Dan Biggs is without letting on they've been privy to the most intimate moment of his small life. It whets my appetite for more and I'm not proud, but not ashamed either, that I do spend a couple of months snooping around his room for more vicarious tastes of his private world. I find treasures. I have a ball. The best is Katy's *One Hundred Things I Love About You*, over which I glow with satisfaction at The Way You Love Your Mum, even though it's buried at number 78. And yes, I love them all too. The way you eat ice-cream, The way you walk, The way you smile your crooked smile, The way your lips go sloppy under mine, even though I can't completely attest to that one.

I think about getting him a double bed.

But that's down the track. The doors and windows stay off that winter while David handcrafts new ones. He's a good carpenter and wants to make the double-hung sash windows work perfectly and the French doors solid and beautiful. He has a vision for the house. He wants it to look like the American timber houses in upstate New York we've seen in movies. It takes time. Oh, how it takes time.

It's freezing and Dan spends more nights at the Toris'.

I have another Equal Opportunity wrangle because my boss on the paper keeps harassing me. It starts when I write a front page article to which he adds a small paragraph at the end and puts his by-line up there with mine. Sigh. I also write a great article when I find out about a Daylesford accountant who's ripped off the ANZ bank to the tune of more than a million dollars. He's already been on telly but when I write the story for our paper the editor won't publish it.

Well, as luck would have it, every cloud has a silver lining and mine is getting that story published in the *Sunday Herald Sun* as a contributor piece.

After it comes out, I ask if they have any jobs going to let me know. Two weeks later a call comes. I ring Sal Gibson.

'You'll never believe it, they've asked me to do a Saturday casual shift on the Sunday paper.'

'That's fantastic, Babsie. Show 'em what you're made of. Get a few good stories and they'll want you back. Go get 'em girl.'

David puts in his two bob's worth one day in Melbourne when we're driving past the Herald and Weekly Times building where the *Sunday Herald Sun* office is.

'That's great about the job, Barb. I guess little Dan's already got another family so he won't miss his mummy not being home on Saturdays. Look, here we are, do you want me to stop so you can kiss the ground?'

My first story as a casual runs big on page five. Sal's right. They ask me to come back. Soon I give up my job on the country paper and take the gamble to work as a casual four days a week. I start staying in Melbourne three nights a week with Sal and Bruce and their now two girls. Melbourne's too far to commute every day and the rest from David's as refreshing as sleep. It's one of the reasons we survive. Trying to do anything around my love—cook, garden, read—is like walking in gumboots full of mud. He interrupts everything and harasses me until I stop.

Dan's 14 now and I keep joking that he'll be moving out soon. I'm not serious, but David pulls me up one day.

'I know you left home at 14 Barb, but that doesn't make it okay.'

'It's just a joke. I don't mean he should leave now.'

'When then? When he's 15? Or 16?'

'The earlier they're independent the better.'

'Barb, he's just a kid. Think about what you're saying.'

Joke or not, I really think Dan will be independent before he finishes high school. It shocks me that my roots have such an insidious hold on my thinking. I look at David. Maybe he isn't the devil incarnate after all.

But he still drives me to distraction. The rate of our renovation makes the pyramids look thrown together like a Lego set. I berate him constantly. He thinks my anger's cute. His smile would charm spots off a leopard.

When the charm wears thin, I try to stab him with a chopping knife. Usually when I'm cooking in the bedroom that's serving as a kitchen while the back of the house comes off. He pokes me in the ribs while I chop vegies. Not once but over and over like Chinese water torture. We bicker until I snap and go for him with the knife.

David laughs and runs with a wild, excited look in his eye while I chase him around the kitchen table.

'You're an arsehole, David.'

'Barb, you can't stab your man. Think of little Dan having no mummy because she's in jail for manslaughter. Barb! Barb!'

Then he runs out the door and leaves me to calm down. I've read *The Man Who Loved Children* by Christina Stead and I understand exactly what that man was made of.

These scenes make dinner party fodder for our friends. My girlfriends love David. At least they behave as if they do. Some say he's sweet and charming and that I'm a mean, nagging witch. Others, like Joanne, treat us as if we were an eccentric, entertaining couple. Either way, we're a real life comedy skit of marital unsuitability. We play our roles to a tee.

Unsuccessful at mastering my home front, in Melbourne I take up a more realistic challenge. I learn to rollerblade. Ice-skating has prepared me but learning to control speed is slow in coming. The elusive art of stopping I only master after countless humiliations.

It's eight kilometres along the beachfront from Sal's house to the Herald and Weekly Times building in Flinders Street. I manage for many weeks with the snowplough – inclining my skates inwards and spreading my legs to slow down. I get by until the day after work when I have a blustery tailwind coupled with a slight decline, which hurtles me towards one of Melbourne's busiest streets at an alarming speed. It's peak hour. The traffic light facing me is red. I spread my legs to slow down, hoping it'll be green by the time I arrive at the intersection. I'm almost doing the splits and still travelling at a frightening speed by the time I'm metres from the intersection, not even an amber light in sight. I have to choose quickly: (a) risk killing myself, possibly taking a pedestrian or two with me into the Swanston Street traffic, or (b) crash into a steel lamp post before I get there. A second before the post whishes past, I change direction suddenly and slam head-on into it. I slide down the pole like a Disney cartoon character, winded, but unfortunately not unconscious. Instead, I'm so mortified (cars are tooting at the spectacle) I pick myself up as if it wasn't a minor miscalculation and skate off with stars in my eyes.

I blade everywhere, drunk, sober, rain, shine, midnight or dawn, but it takes more and severe accidents, one where I can't sit down for a week, before I finally have the T-stop under control. Meanwhile I'm skating a hundred kilometres a week from Sal's place in Elwood to work and back every day and to visit friends in Preston, Canterbury, Brunswick, out to theatre reviews wearing sweaty long johns for warmth or ungraceful raincoats to keep dry. I feel like superwoman.

My two or three nights a week in Melbourne are like blood transfusions. I get David out of my hair by going to bed when I want and reading without being harassed. When I start reviewing for the paper I go out to dinner and fringe theatre plays with friends. When I'm not staying at Sal's I spend nights at their houses revelling in the easiness of barbless chat late into the night and over morning cups of tea: Formosan at my Jewish friend Lissa's colour palate of minimalistic mess; camomile after a Thai massage at Annie's, who I've kept in touch with since she shared with Ian and me; and beer and cigarettes, late night dancing and laughing until it hurts at Beacon's.

I'm staying at work 12 hours a day and love it. At Sal's, we spend our time workshopping her and Bruce and then my battlefront.

'We've found a great counsellor, Babsie. He's at the

Catholic Family Welfare Centre but you don't have to be Catholic to go. He's fan-bloody-tastic. You've gotta get David along. You can't go on like this.'

On weekends I see Joanne. When we aren't scouring the countryside for abandoned houses to raid, we also workshop me and David. Then we move on to her and her latest boarder who she's usually seduced within a fortnight of them moving in. One Joanne dubs The Futon on the grounds that he's very tall and broad and has no brain. The current one, Little Tim, just down from Queensland, lent Joanne $6000 which she has no intention of paying back because she's looked after him and tried to love him even though he has poppy eyes and the personality of a gnat. All are not much more than half Joanne's age. She has a very big problem about getting old and says she has to get in as much action as she can before she gets so saggy and wrinkly she has to wear a paper bag over her head. It does no good telling her she looks ten years younger and can still hold a torch to most women in town, which admittedly only has a population of four thousand without the weekend tourists who have started flocking in like flies. But better to keep the comparison in mind than living in a paper bag no matter which way you look at it.

Before Bear left, Joanne couldn't share a bottle of champagne at Christmas without getting drunk. Now she's hiding the number of bottles outside her house in plastic bags and stuffing them with paper so the garbage men won't hear the tinkle as they fall.

Daylesford's a gossipy town. It's also one of the coldest places on earth outside Siberia. A lot of talented, unemployed, masochistic artists who hate the cold live here and hibernate during winter with fires and cask wine that can put normal people under under the table in five minutes.

These days despite the wine, Joanne can also still give good advice. At least on a good day.

I tell Joanne about Sal's counsellor and that David won't have a bar of it. 'No, Barb,' he'd said in no uncertain terms. David's being unequivocal in a way he never comprehends when I try it.

'What are you going to do, BB?' Joanne asks. 'You can't go on like this. He's very sweet but he'll drive you to drink. What did you say?'

'He's got me over a barrel. I can't leave him because the house isn't finished and we can't sell it in the state it's in. My only bargaining power is sex. I said I'm moving out to live with you. I said I'd still come and help with the house so he'll keep going but he won't have me around which he seems to want more than anything.'

'What did he say to that?'

'He said he doesn't care, but we'll see.'

'BB, BB, BB. You've got it all wrong. It's not you being around he wants so much as you being around to help him. I bet if you said you were moving in with me *and* downing tools he'd be off to the counsellor so fast he wouldn't even have time for a migraine.'

She's a genius.

David and I start counselling a week later.

FOURTEEN

LEMONADE BUBBLING UP

'Now, can you tell me why you're here?' says Fernando, our handsome Latino counsellor. A smile that's up to no good hangs around his mouth. Like we're playing at being grown-ups and any minute now the cover will blow, like he isn't really a counsellor and we aren't people who want to blow each other's brains out, or, at least, get a good night's sleep.

Nevertheless, a very good question indeed. How to explain David? The sweet impish smile over which only I can see the pique and terror at what might be about to occur. The mild, polite, charm oozing out of him like sticky honey. I don't have a hope.

'I came because Barb says I have to,' David volunteers cheerily.

'And you don't really want to be here?' A different smirk kicks in. A boy's smirk. Haven't they all done things because their girlfriends or wives said they had to? David's got him already. Or am I imagining it?

'No!' David laughs nervously at the ridiculous suggestion. Why would anybody want to be here?

'And Barbara, can you tell me why you're here?' He has a slight accent, which I find familiar from my short time in Latin America. And he talks slowly so he pronounces the words right. It's charming.

'David drives me crazy and I can't stand it anymore.'

'What can't you stand anymore?'

I tell him everything in a gabble.

'So why are you together?'

'I love him.'

'And David?'

'Hmm. I love Barb too.'

David and I look at each other, bewilderment clouding our wan, warm smiles.

'So you don't want to separate?'

We nod instant agreement.

'How long have you been together?'

'Six years off and on,' I say.

'And you see yourselves as committed?'

We nod again, in unison. A pantomime of mutual satisfaction.

We spend the next few sessions filling Fernando in on our backgrounds.

Within a few months Fernando gets David to stop poking me in the ribs every time he comes near me. I'd started to flinch whenever David was in close to me. It's a good change that gives me hope, but the essence of the relationship stays stuck.

After six months of driving to Melbourne for counselling every week, David decides to stop coming.

I continue on my own.

I go right back. Fernando's interested in the connection between David and my family.

'You seem very committed in your relationship. There's something powerful that binds you two together. Do you know what it is?' Fernando always asks questions. He doesn't tell you what he thinks is wrong. It's laborious but saves you hating him for pointing out things you're not ready to hear.

'What do you mean?'

'Every time I skirt around the possibility of separating you're both very certain that's not an option.'

'David was on his own for a long time when we met. And before William and Ian, so was I. In fact, apart from David, I've never lasted with a man longer than 18 months. I think we're both afraid of being alone again.'

'Anything else? Does David remind you of anyone in your family?'

'Not really. Maybe my sister Pommy. She put me down a lot and I always felt never quite good enough. And he doesn't hear me. He doesn't listen. That's like my mother, I suppose, and like Vernon too. It's like I'm invisible for him as well. Emotionally, I mean.'

'Can you think back and remember the first time you felt invisible? That you weren't being listened to?'

'I don't know. It's just something I've always felt without thinking about.'

'No incidents that you remember? With your mother for example? Or your grandmother?'

'M IN THE GARAGE with Pommy and Jenny and Mick. I haven't started school yet. Mum wants us to clean the garage but I feel sick. I tell Mum and she says I'm just trying to get out of cleaning the garage which is a huge mess. I don't know what to do with all these things and it's dark and cold in here and smells like soggy leaves and pooh. The mess makes me feel more sick and I know I have to get out of the garage somehow. I see a piece of wood with a nail sticking out of it. It's a big fat rusty nail. I know if I stand on it I'll be allowed to go inside and lie down. I know it will hurt but it's the only way I know how to get out of the garage and into my bed where I'll be warm and the sheets are clean and there's no cobwebs and broken things. I put my foot over the nail and play with it, jumping over it with my foot on it but with most of my weight on the other foot. I think about jumping on the bit of wood. I know I have to do it hard or it won't work. I just have to decide and I know it will go right through my shoe and into my foot. I stand around looking at the piece of wood. I think about taking my shoe off and doing it that way but the thought of that makes me feel more sick. It takes me a long time to work up to it. Then, the moment comes and I decide it's now or never. I lift up my leg and jump with all my weight onto the nail. I scream in pain and feel wetness in my shoe.

'What did you do that for?' shouts Pommy.

'Go and get Mum!' Jenny calls.

'You meant to do it! You just wanted to get out of doing the garage,' yells Pommy.

Mum comes and she doesn't believe I stood on the nail deliberately. She carries me in her arms to the bathroom and carefully takes off my shoe. She bandages my foot and carries me to the bedroom and puts me in my clean white sheets. My foot hurts a lot but I'm happy again.

'That's pretty extreme behaviour to get someone to listen. Do you remember ever deciding or knowing that telling people how you felt wouldn't get you anywhere?'

'No. I've hardly got any memories of my childhood. I have no memories at all of Bloss or Mick or Peter. Jenny features a tiny bit. Pommy's the star, if there is one, but really it's like a wasteland out there when I think about growing up.'

'Okay, that's your homework for this week. When you go

to bed or on the train on the way home, at some quiet time, I want you to try to remember anything you can.'

'Maybe I don't want to remember.'

'Maybe you don't.'

WE'RE PLAYING CRICKET outside the house. Pommy's bowling. The Cleary kids are all here. They live around the corner and they're always playing with us because for every one of us there's one the same age of them. Cathy's the same age as me and we just started school together. We're both being fielders. Pommy's bowling and she's the boss. I've only had one go at batting and everybody else has had more goes than me. Pommy says I can have a go soon but every time I think it's my turn someone else gets the bat first. I know if I don't have my turn soon we'll have to go inside because it's getting dark. Anne Cleary is Jenny's age and she's having her bat. Then it's my turn. Pommy says so. But when she finishes, Maureen - she's Pommy's age - grabs the bat and says it's her turn.

'No it's not. It's my turn. Pommy said so and she's the boss. Ask Pommy. It's my turn isn't it?'

'Maureen came late and she hasn't even had a turn yet so she can bat.'

'But I've been here for hours and I've only had one turn ...'

Then Gran yells out from the front verandah.

'Come on you brats. Dinner's ready. Inside now if you know what's good for you.'

'Just throw one ball and then we'll go,' says Maureen.

'Make it two and I can have a go too.'

Pommy throws one ball to Maureen and then everybody scatters.

I call out that it's my turn. I'm mad and I start to cry but everybody's running inside. Pommy turns around just before she goes in the front door and looks at me still standing in the street. She laughs and says better hurry up or I'll get it.

I start walking inside but I only get to the grass along the footpath and then my legs collapse under me and I fall down. I can't move anything. I can't move my head or my arms or legs. I can see a dog coming down the street and he's getting closer. I want to get up and run inside in case the dog bites me but I can't move. He's getting closer and he's big. He stops at all the trees and there's a tree near me. He's close to my tree now and I'm scared. He's coming right towards me and I start to cry. He sniffs me but doesn't bite and then walks away. I lie there crying wondering when someone will come and find me. I can hear a Mister Whippy van playing *Greensleeves* getting closer and I think it might turn into our street and see me lying here. Mum plays *Greensleeves* on the record player and she says it's one of her favourite songs but she's not home. Maybe when she comes home from work she'll find me but by then it will be very dark and anyway that's a long time away.

Then Jenny comes out and I'm so glad to see her I start to cry more. Jenny pats me and asks what's wrong. I tell her I can't move. She says she'll go and get Gran but I don't want her to leave me in case another dog comes. She says she'll come straight back and I make her promise.

Gran comes out and I tell her I can't move.

'What do you mean you can't bloody move?'

'I don't know. I can't move anything.'

Gran and Jenny carry me inside. Gran calls Mum at work and when she gets home she calls a doctor who comes to the house. He can't find anything wrong with me but I still can't move.

After that I'm allowed to lie on the couch all day and night and when the others come I keep the couch while we watch *The Jetsons*, *Gilligans Island*, *Lost in Space*, all my favourite programs. I watch telly there until I fall asleep because I'm allowed to sleep in the lounge while I can't move because no-one wants to carry me to bed. Everyone has to be nice to me. After a couple of days I can move my neck again then my arms and then my legs. I'm all better after a few days. Mum keeps saying I was bunging it on so no-one believed that I couldn't move. I don't know how to tell them it was real.

I'm in Fernando's office again and he's finishing taking notes on my story. He looks up. There's no desk between us like Dr Hammersmith used to have. The only other time I've seen a professional about stuff like this is when I put myself in a psych hospital at 16. I'd had two suicide attempts then, four in all before I was 20. But even then Dr Hammersmith didn't go into things like Fernando does. She didn't ask what I thought about anything.

We sit on chairs facing each other in the middle of his office, which is a little confronting, but when I'm telling my stories I look out the window as if the view stretches for miles. Out there in the street I don't see cars coming out of the Coles carpark, I see my stories happening as though they were yesterday. I'm surprised at the clarity of my memories.

'And what do you think that's all about? Do you have any ideas?'

'None. Your guess is as good as mine.'

'Do you think maybe your unconscious was working to help you get what you wanted?'

'I didn't get my bat.'

'No, but you got some attention. You got the whole household to listen to you all at once.' He laughs at my ingenuity.

'And how's David? You haven't mentioned him for a while.'

'He's still driving me crazy. All I really want from him is to be left alone.'

'That's it?' He gives me a wan kind of smile like he doesn't really believe me.

'Of course I'd *like* more but if he just left me alone life would be bliss.'

'There's something very strong binding you two together.'

'You've said that before. Weird isn't it.'

'I'm still wondering if David reminds you of anyone.'

'Not in the slightest.'

'Didn't you say once before that he was similar in some ways to your mother?'

MUM'S HOME BUT SHE'S IN BED. I want her to wake up but I know if I make her Gran will say she'll beat me until I'm black and blue. Even though I know because I've just had a birthday and I'm nine now, that she won't really, I still know I'll get it somehow. The other kids are outside playing loud outside Mum's window hoping she'll wake up but I know she can sleep through a war if she wants to. So I sneak inside and go to the bedroom door and turn the handle slow so Gran won't hear the squeak in it. She's got big ears when it comes to Mum's bedroom door. I go in and close it, being as quiet as a mouse, and sneak as slow as I can to the other side of the bed where Mum is facing the window. She's got one arm up under the pillow and the other on top of the bed clothes. I sit down quietly on the floor next to the bed and stare at her face. If I think hard enough about her waking up she will and I won't get into trouble because I haven't made a noise or anything. She'll just be ready to wake up. So I sit here and concentrate as hard as I can on her eyes and wish them to open. I half believe if she knows how much I want her to wake up she will. Half of me believes that and the other half of me knows that's stupid. I sit here imagining her waking up and seeing me and asking if I want a cuddle and saying, 'Hop into bed and have a sleep with me'. But I know that won't happen even if she does wake up because once when I did the same thing she really did open her eyes and she got the fright of her life and yelled at me. I sit here for a long time until I hear the other kids and Gran all asking where I am. I wait until I hear their voices in another part of the house and I sneak out of the room again so no-one will know I've been sitting by Mum's bed being with her. Although she doesn't wake up I feel like I've had some of Mum and the others haven't even though my insides ache because I didn't get the cuddle.

'It doesn't sound like you were angry with her. While you were sitting there looking at your mother, do you remember how you felt.'

'I ached.'

'With what?'

'With wanting her to wake up.'

'You didn't feel angry?'

'No, can't say I did.'

WE'RE IN THE LOUNGE and Mum's got her shoes off. She's teaching us the charleston. She used to be a good dancer when she was little and you can see she is because her feet are moving like the twin tub in the washhouse. It's very hard but I go slow and concentrate. I love dancing. Mum loves music because she can play *Tales of the Vienna Woods* on the piano. That and one other piece I don't know the name of that she sits down and plays sometimes. We love dancing with Mum and we fight to have turns. Pommy and Jenny and me are learning because Bloss is too small. Mum tells me to practise the steps while she teaches Jenny again because I'm faster at learning the steps than her. She has to do it all over even though she's older.

Mum says it's not the real charleston music but we can dance to *Oo Ee Oo Ah Ah Ching Chang Walla Walla Bing Bang, I tell the witch doctor I'm in love with you, and then the witch doctor he tells me what to do.* And the *Big Rock Candy Mountain* which is supposed to be a place in Canada on top of America with lemonade springs and rock lollies and bluebirds singing all over the place. I imagine going there with Mum and dancing our feet off like there's no tomorrow but I know I'd never want to come back.

After we learn the charleston, Mum dances the cha cha with us because we learnt that one last time and we have to practise otherwise we'll forget. It's easier than the charleston and more fun too because Mum holds us and we can do it together. She puts one arm around my waist and holds my other hand and I pretend there's lemonade bubbling up out of the ground around my feet.

We do the waltz last and that's the easiest of all because Mum holds you the closest in that one and you feel her moving and showing you which way to go if you forget. My favourite song is *My Blue Heaven*.

At home, sometimes I catch David watching me from the house. I tense, thinking he's about to interrupt, but he leaves me in peace to finish his own work. He's like an artist working on his masterpiece. Often he looks over his work and shakes his head, sure something will sooner or later not hold up, and complain that it'll have to do. Less often I catch him admiring his work.

Spring's nearly over and sometimes we have warm days. In the late afternoons, when we're both finished our work, we walk in the bush, Sigi running along beside in doggy heaven. Sometimes we end up at Lady Carol's lavender farm, now a tourist gold mine. She looks up from under her sunhat as we arrive sweaty, with scratches on our legs, 'You two look like fresh-faced young lovers. Who'd think you were pushing forty.' She's right. We're disgustingly healthy.

David never asks about counselling when I get home from Melbourne. He knows I'm going on my own but is relieved I'm not coercing him to come. There's no point dragging him there. Mostly I think that. But then some bad incident happens and I tell him if he doesn't come he'll have to prise my legs open with a crowbar. Already we're hardly having sex. He's so good at seducing me by stroking my back. Sometimes it works even when I'm angry. But an orgasm makes me open my heart and the next day when he's torturing me or putting me down, I feel angry and betrayed. I can't believe at night he expects me to pretend he hasn't enjoyed seeing me cry or knotted up with frustration in the day time. That I'll put all that aside and open my legs and heart again.

The first time I make him come back we have a fight about the light in our room. David and I both read in bed but he falls asleep with the light on and I wake up with it in my face and have to get up and turn it off before I can go back to sleep. I nag but David takes no notice and continues to do it almost every night. But after the night that lands us back in counselling he never does it again.

I'd said to him the night before, 'It's not fair. I'm sick of it. If you fall asleep with the light on again something very bad's going to happen.' The next night something very bad happens.

'David, remember what I said yesterday about the light? *Please* turn it off when you finish reading.'

'Yes, yes. Close your little eyes and mouth and go to sleep.'

Half an hour later the light is still on and I turn around to see David asleep. I shake him awake.

'David, turn the light off.'

'I'm a sleepy boy, Barb.'

I know no matter what I say he's never going to do it.

In one rush, boiling oil erupts and, without thinking, I throw the covers off, stand up on the bed, take hold of the light shade and yank the whole thing off the ceiling. The glass shade smashes into the bed end and glass shards scatter over the covers. David leaps up and starts shouting.

'Barb, what did you do that for?' He's incredulous.

'Now we don't have to argue about the light anymore.'

'You could have killed us.'

'Then we wouldn't have to argue about the light anymore.'

We hear a banging on the wall.

'Will you two shut up and let me get some sleep!' Dan calls from his bedroom.

David and I look sheepishly at each other. We start laughing, quietly, at how ludicrous things have become. We're the naughty kids and Dan, at 15, has become the parent. So accustomed has he become to our antics that he doesn't even come rushing in when he hears the smash.

Neither of us will clean up the glass, each saying the other should do it. Neither gives in so we sleep that night in a bed with broken glass on top of the doona and a live exposed, electrical wire above our heads. David cleans it up the next morning and comes to counselling for the next year under threat of death.

When we're at counselling together, Fernando talks mainly to David about his anxieties. Anxieties about studying and making phone calls, talking to strangers, getting a job, dying, finishing the house, getting sick and not dying, money. Sometimes I wonder why I'm here.

Fernando asks why I think David teases me.

'It's pretty obvious he's got low self-esteem and feels

powerless. It's his way of having some control. I think he has to put me down and torment me to feel okay about himself.'

'You've been giving this some thought.'

'Pop psychology. I've been reading, trying to work things out for years.'

Now Fernando, legs crossed, turns his body slightly to look at David.

'And do you torment Barb because it makes you feel better about yourself?'

'I do it because it's fun!' David looks incredulous that Fernando hasn't grasped this simple point.

'Fun?' Fernando is trying to be professional, but I can see that he's as surprised and amused by David's answer as I am. I get the feeling he finds our sessions entertaining. Compared to screaming, sulky or quietly desperate couples, ours must seem like a refreshingly charming kind of torture to witness. But him being so charmed by David makes me feel like he thinks I'm the problem.

'Yes! She's so gullible and so easy to upset. I don't know why she lets me do it.'

'What do you think would happen if you tried not tormenting her? Do you think your relationship would improve?' He's suppressing a smile, as though earnestly trying to teach an alien the elementary points of human interaction.

David furrows his brow for a moment, as if he's giving this novel idea some serious consideration, then responds with all the guilelessness of an innocent child. 'I don't know. Maybe.'

'I think this is a good point to finish. This week why don't you try not teasing Barb and see how that goes. You can report back next week.' No matter how much smiling he's been trying to hide during our sessions, he always ends with a serious, low key frown to let us know he really does take us seriously.

David and I look at each other and smile, pleased that someone has been so clever to find such a simple solution.

FIFTEEN

THE FM FACTOR

I cut down my work on the *Sunday Herald Sun* from four days a week to three so I can work on the garden. We live on crumbs, rarely go out, David and Dan aren't interested in clothes and I buy mine from the op shop and we drive a bombed out 1974 Honda Civic.

It's a Mickey Mouse car which David fixes the second he hears a suspicious noise. It never breaks down on our countless trips to Melbourne for counselling or on visits to wineries all over the state that I'm now doing for a fortnightly wine tourism column for the paper. The trips provide the only break we get from renovating, but they've

261

also had their humbling moments. After talking in a worldly fashion to the Melbourne journo, me, our hosts invariably walk us to our battered car. Having given us free accommodation or sample bottles of wine, they nervously glance from the car to us and back again, puzzled and piqued. It doesn't help that the passenger door handle is broken and I have to climb over the driver's seat to get in. I learned the hard way to park a long walk away.

We spend any spare money on building materials for the house. Anything else, holidays, other luxuries, mean nothing when home's like a war zone. As the waves of David lash at me, I shore up the damage in a frenzy of gardening.

I strike hundreds of cuttings to make hedges. English and French, white and pink lavender, rosemary, hydrangea, box and wormwood. I hack roots and cuttings from friends' gardens like a maniac. I borrow and paw over friends gardening books. I split old fence posts for garden bed borders until sweat stings my eyes and pours down my sides. For mulch Joanne and I gather bags of oak leaves in autumn like we did when I lived with Ian. I buy oceans of lakeweed from Ballarat in spring and small stadiums of peastraw from the local sewage farm. I start on the front and side gardens but the three-quarter acre paddock that looks onto state forest at the back is going to be the big job. For that I need to landscape, build retaining walls, paths and make a plan. It's the one part of home life where I have some control. The garden's my domain and David leaves me to it. When I'm in a fever about the garden I'm out there at dawn finishing what I'd started the day before when dark had grown around my silhouette. My fingernails eat dirt, hands grow calluses and my back aches. Like I'd brought myself up all over again through Dan when he was little, I know this gardening obsession is turning the clods inside in a way that I don't yet completely understand.

I'm still spending most of my spare time with Joanne. I prefer her company to being at home. She's in a man-eating phase.

'I don't know BB. I can't keep them away. They see me as some kind of femme fatale. Who would've thought in the autumn of my life ...'

Midlife crisis is making her more neurotic with every passing day. It's embarrassing. Often she'll be entertaining three or four guys in her kitchen at once, wearing a low-cut, white, Lady of the Lake nightgown, sometimes with a nipple artfully falling out. She sits on one's knee while blowing kisses to another over his shoulder. She gets them in by nurturing, doing things they only dream about. All kinds of sex things she'd never done with Bear.

'I thought you said all that sex stuff was "erky perky",' I ask her.

'I'm getting used to it. Sometimes I quite like it now.'

'But why bother. I'm sure he wouldn't care if you didn't.'

She replies as if I'm an imbecile who hasn't yet gleaned the elementary lessons of courting.

'BB, if you make yourself indispensable, do things no-one else will ... that's how to get them to fall in love with you.' I suddenly realise how she's kept *me* in over all these years. I can't dispute it. And anyway, I certainly have no tricks up my sleeve. Look at me and David. And adore her they do. Not just men but women as well. Her house is a vortex into which the town's misfits, artists, drunks, all the interesting, if troubled, people are sucked. Some by the small daily incidents which she, with all her art, turns into comedy skits. Whoever visits, Joanne holds court and is the undisputed social queen of our group. Others stay away on the grounds that they think she's crazy.

She might not be crazy but Joanne's going somewhere I don't want to go. The more she drinks, the more bizarre her house becomes. One night some guy's so drunk he pisses in the corner of her lounge room thinking it's the toilet.

It comes to a head for us one sunny spring morning when I come over for our morning fruit salad. The agreement is that she makes it and I buy the fruit the day before. We'd been doing it for five days in a bid to get healthy. I bounce in her open back door. She isn't in the kitchen, so I call out. No answer. When I appear at the foot of her bed she doesn't open her eyes.

'BB I'm in no state to be getting up.' She's annoyed. She keeps sighing, arm thrown over her forehead, part of her dying swan routine. My spirits sink. I'm supposed to coddle and stroke her hair like I did when Sally dachshund died, but I don't want to play the game anymore. She's a spider pulling me into her web and I want to smack her off me. I'm not going to say anything until she at least opens her eyes.

'Well, what do you want?' She's peeved, as though I've come unexpectedly, done something wrong.

'I guess we won't be doing the fruit salad today.'

No answer. Just more sighs. She closes her eyes again and leaves me standing there.

I've had enough. The game goes like this. She plays mum, offers to make fruit salad for breakfast. Then, when it comes time to pay, emotional blackmail sets in.

I go to the kitchen and make her a cup of tea, bring it in on a tray with biscuits, say, coldly, I hope she feels better soon. She opens one eye and watches me go. I've already decided I'm not coming back.

Despite Daylesford's size, incredibly, we don't see each other again for *another* two years.

Christian resurfaces after he disappeared from my radar for four years. He'd moved so many times I'd lost him. I knew he'd moved in with two of Jacqui's gay women friends who'd been taking care of him, but then he'd moved and nobody knew where. Now, miraculously, he's finished high school and found Ruthy Baby, a normal, intelligent, caring Virgo girl. They've been going out together for three years when we meet for the first time since his 16th birthday party at the lesbian's house.

The sweetest of kids, now, at 20, Christian has turned into a sullen bruiser of a man. Ruth tells me her middle-class parents tolerate him but think she's hanging about with scum.

After the reconnection, when we occasionally meet for dinner after work, Ruthy greases the social wheels while Christian chews gum, looking distracted and bored. I always pay because he's working as a kitchen hand and can't have much money. It's also guilt about letting him be lost for four years and wanting to look after Pommy's son. When they visit us in Daylesford, it's hawkeye David who notices the gold dripping off him. The watch and chains and expensive clothes. I'm very unobservant.

That's why it doesn't surprise me when I hear he's in jail for burglaries to support a heroin habit. Ruthy Baby calls to let me know.

'Barb. I can't take it anymore. He keeps saying he'll stop but it's just not going to happen. He's too far gone.'

'Save yourself, Ruthy Baby. There's nothing you can do until he hits rock bottom. I've been there. The only person who can help is himself and while you're picking up the pieces it delays the inevitable. He has to face his own demons.'

'I can't leave him, Barb. I love him. It's just the way it is.'

Sumo, Christian's five-year-old German Shepherd-mongrel cross, moves in with us.

At work I go to town on clothes. In the country I dag around in Blundstone boots and overalls. But at work I wear my mountain of op shop clothes. I like to experiment. Sometimes it's retro numbers or conservative white shirts and pleated skirts. Sometimes tight tops or dresses. Occasionally I notice the guys at work eyeing me off in a way I don't like and wonder if I'm dressed inappropriately. I think back to what Ian had said to me about living out my sex toy past. Then I thought Pet, the me of 20 years ago, was dead and gone. Now, again, I'm not so sure. There are fleeting moments, when I catch a look in some guy's eye, when I wonder if she's still there trying to get noticed in the only way she knows how. But I'm in such a different world now I don't stop to think about it. I don't *want* to think about it.

I meet a couple who want to buy a house in Daylesford. Like me they work part-time. Sue's a subeditor with the smile of an angel. She and Roger buy their house in Hepburn Springs over the back hill from ours and start renovating. David and I see them almost every weekend. I start doing freelance travel stories so Sue and I organise a trip together in Queensland. It's the first time she's spent more than a night away from Roger in 20 years. Sue seems suffocated by Roger's dependence but calls him, ecstatically, every day for the two weeks we're away. This is a love I don't understand.

I'm holding my own in the newsroom. The challenge of a Sunday newspaper is that dailies get the press releases and break obvious stories. We have to find our own. My day is spent on the phone talking to community groups, financial counsellors, local government councillors, libel lawyers, Equal Opportunity Board contacts, rape and drug squads, the Prostitutes Collective, Office of Fair Trading, anywhere I'm likely to find a story with the FM factor. A 'Fuck Me!' story. They're Melbourne's Sunday paper fare.

I go to the library and look up back issues for story ideas. It's the only time in my life when I know what's going on in the world. I read about Father Clep, a priest at my brother Mick's boarding school who was sent to jail for pedophilia. I wonder if he interfered with Mick and that's why Mick shot himself less than a year after he left school. I read about financial corruption in the psych hospital Mick had been working at as an orderly when he died and wonder if that had anything to do with his death. I ring Ma and she says Mick not only knew about the corruption but was about to make a report about fund mismanagement and patient mistreatment before he died. Mick was shot in the mouth at close range with his own .22 rifle in a room at the hospital. Even though everyone thought it was suicide, the coroner's finding was inconclusive. Ma always said he was murdered.

I read about Vernon defending some of Melbourne's most notorious criminals. The man accused of opening fire on Mercy Hospital patients and staff, another who shot motorists at peak hour in Hoddle Street and one accused of murdering two policemen in Walsh Street, South Yarra, right outside Pommy and Jacqui's old flat.

But I'm hardly a news freak like other journos. I have gaping holes in my knowledge of politics, world events, sport. And me and names? Forget it. Remembering them assumes we'll have a future together. For me people are passing parades. You learn early that knowledge about people isn't cumulative when you're a gypsy child. When you move as much as I did as a kid you learn to distinguish people by generalities, not names.

This has drawbacks in an industry run on famous incidents and personalities. When the editor or journos talk about events and people they assume I know, I fake it. Oh him! Yeah, that! Wasn't that amazing. I'm safe there. If it isn't amazing what's it doing in the paper? Nevertheless, I'm famous for bloopers. Someone might mention Pat in relation to tennis and I'll be so pleased with myself for knowing Pat Cash I'd throw his name into the next sentence. The sports journo stares like I'm an alien. I have to go to the library to find out he meant Rafter and that Cash was a 70s phenomenon. I take mild comfort from not being the only ill-informed worker at the rock pile. When the whole news-room flocks to the editor's office one Saturday to watch US police chasing OJ Simpson down the highway after his wife is found murdered, I go to the library and find two other journos at the 'S' file.

I hold my own only because, once onto something, I'm like a dog with a bone. Your stories only run if they're better than others'. Every week there are too many and some never see the light of day. My FM stories always have a look-in. I talk to a mother whose son's been tortured hideously to death, to a family who'd been made prisoners in their home for two years by a confidence trickster, a sister whose brother's slammed himself to death against cell walls while in police custody, women whose silicon breast implants have fallen out in the shower. I knock on doors of parents whose kids have died in car crashes hours before. I know how they feel being pestered by a journalist because I was on the other end during the tram strike all those years ago. It doesn't stop me. I like my work because it's on the edge. People talk to me because I know how they feel and what to say to make them open up to me.

My work gives me an engaging world to call my own while the home fires sizzle and burn.

In my early days at the metro paper, I get increasingly frequent notices from the Sheriff's Office about traffic offences that have accumulated from years ago. I haven't been parking illegally since they changed the law. Now they don't like you to serve the penalties concurrently in jail. Instead they prefer to confiscate property to pay the fines. It changed a few years ago because too many people were doing what I'd done and getting rid of dozens of offences with a short stint as Her Majesty's guests. While I think that's fair enough, I don't understand why the same logic isn't applied to serial murderers, pedophiles and crooks. When you can do the same amount of jail time for buggering or beating 50 children as one, well, where's the deterrent to curb your activities there?

In any case, although for the past ten years or so I've paid the odd parking fine I've incurred, because of the accumulated court and agency costs of the old ones, I now owe about $10,000 to the Sheriff's Office. I support three people and a house on a three-day-a-week salary. There's no way I want to be paying off these fines from another life for the next ten years.

I investigate through my now weighty contacts all the ins and outs of how the outstanding fines are recovered. I discover that although property can be confiscated, they can't take goods that will detrimentally affect children in a household. That means the only two items in our house of any value, the piano and TV, are safe. Jail, since it costs the Government money, is used only as a last resort if there are no goods to seize. When I visit Christian in prison, he tells me that jails have become overcrowded with drug-related crimes because heroin use has soared.

I'm still attached to the idea of getting rid of the fines in one fell swoop in jail. Even though I have the flat in St Kilda and the first house I bought in Daylesford, both with biggish mortgages, I also find out that seizing property with mortgages for parking fines is bad PR and too much trouble.

I make phone calls to try to deal with the problem quickly and easily, but it seems I have to wait until it goes through the system. They keep sending letters requesting payment. I keep sending letters saying I don't have funds to make a lump sum payment and don't want to be in bondage for a decade to pay them off. The process goes on for several years.

During my first two years on the *Sunday Herald Sun* I step up my efforts to push the process along to get it over with. But I'm repeatedly told I have to pay up or wait for the Sheriff to contact me. It gets to the point where every morning when I rollerblade into the grand, solid old building in Flinders Street and past the front security desk, I worry that one day soon, someone from the Sheriff's Office will come to that very desk and ask for Barbara Biggs. I imagine them leading the uniformed officers upstairs and them escorting me away in handcuffs through a growing throng of curious colleagues.

It's unnerving, but with a life like mine I've grown nerves of steel. I'm also, like Ma, hysterically optimistic by nature and always think everything will be okay. The funny thing in both our cases, is that they usually always are.

Finally someone from the Sheriff's Office in Ballarat contacts me and arranges a day to come to our home in Daylesford to check out what household goods I have. On D-day, the old Honda is practically in pieces out the front, half the floorboards are still missing, the back part of the house is off and the kitchen still in the bedroom. David hasn't quite finished making new windows and the old ones have already been taken out and big holes cut in the walls for the new ones. When the portly officer arrives I ask if he'd like a cup of tea. He can't believe what he's seeing but manages a nod as his eyes travel over the chaos.

'We're doing a bit of renovating,' I say as he continues to gaze.

'So I see,' he says.

'David isn't working so I have to buy the materials from my salary. I only work three days a week. It's taking a bit longer than we thought,' I say apologetically.

'How long's it been like this?'

David and I look at each other to try to work it out.

'Let's see. We've gone through what, two or is it three winters here?' I ask David.

'Three,' he says definitely and smiles as though he's very pleased with his calculation.

'Pretty cold up this way,' the Sheriff says.

'You're not wrong there,' I say.

We have a further pleasant and polite conversation about the weather before he tells me there's nothing worth confiscating. I tell him I'm more than happy to do my time in jail. He says they don't like cluttering them up with traffic offenders these days. We arrange for me to turn up in the Ballarat court the following week where he assures me a magistrate will order community work. I ask what kind. He says at the Salvation Army op shop for a couple of days or helping to drive Alzheimer patients around to therapy groups in a bus. This will get rid of all the fines.

The officer doffs his hat to us as he drives away with pity in his eyes. When he's gone I'm so relieved it feels like the weight of years has fallen from my shoulders. David laughs and shakes his head.

'I can't believe the luck of you Biggses.'

SIXTEEN

SHE TAKES A MILE

One day I see an ad on telly encouraging people to come forward with previously unreported sexual abuse. They want a better idea of the real extent of rapes and incest because they know the numbers reported are only the tip of the iceberg. Over the next weeks I see more ads on television, radio and in the papers. I've never reported my experiences to police. I've never considered it. I still don't, even when I'm bombarded with the campaign. It seems so irrelevant to who I am now.

'You should report Vernon, Babsie. Think of it as a social duty,' says Sal.

'It's so long ago. They'd never believe me anyway. You know, the big barrister and all that.'

'That's not the point. They don't have to believe you. They just have to have the statistics. Anyway, you've got nothing to lose. It's just a phone call.'

On the way home to Daylesford on the train that night I think about what Sal said. It's my social duty. I call myself a feminist, however dirty the word has become. I talk about Vernon to Fernando in the course of explaining my life, but it's an old life I've buried long ago. For that reason Sal's right, I have nothing to lose. That's why it comes as such a shock when I finally get around to the nitty-gritty of making a report.

At first I think I can make a quick phone call, let them know what happened, give them his name, my name, rough dates. It's only for statistics, right? Not so fast, they say.

'You'll have to come down to the station and make a statement.'

I rollerblade the eight or so k's through city traffic from Sal's place to the police station. When I blade I'm superwoman. My heart goes, my face flushes, endorphins ricochet, I'm strong, fast, invincible.

Most of my friends know the story. I've told it a million times. Just the bones. Enough for them to know who I am, where I've come from, my road. But they don't ask questions because they're too embarrassed or don't want to be voyeuristic. The dyke-looking policewoman isn't so shy. I'm sitting in her office with my blades still on and my legs crossed, one set of wheels dangling in the air. I figure I'll be out of here in five minutes flat. The Bull Dog had looked me up and down when I'd first arrived, bright red and sweating like a pig. But she doesn't hold my appearance against me. She takes notes and lets me tell the story in my own way before she goes to work on me.

'How often did you have sex with him?'

'I can't count. I lived with him. How often do you have sex? I can't say.'

'Would it have been every day, once a week, once a month?'

'Maybe every day, every other day. Depended.'

'Can you tell me some of the specific incidents so we can match his *modus operandi* with other reports? If he did this to you, you're probably not the only victim.'

I tell her in generalities. She doesn't stop there. She wants detail, more specifics, how I felt at the time, if I was in love with him, if he was in love with me, if I enjoyed the sex, if I'd encouraged him, if I'd seen him since. It only takes 20 minutes for Miss Invincible to slip over the edge to another me I thought I'd left far behind. By the time she's finished I'm such a mess I can't leave the office. She pats my shoulder and leaves me alone.

I don't want to know why I'm crying. I just let the tears fall freely because I know from the self-help books you're supposed to let it all out. The only surprise is that there's so much muck in there.

The Bull Dog comes to reclaim her office.

'We'll be interviewing Mr Vernon about the alleged incidents and we'll be in touch once that's occurred.'

'He'll just deny it. And there were no witnesses. That's why I've never reported it. Who'd believe me, right?'

'He might deny it but it'll give him a bit of a scare, I'm sure. Like I say, you're probably not the only one. If he is guilty I dare say the thought of more people coming forward will at the very least make him lose a bit of sleep.'

'And it'll be counted as a statistic, right?' I mop up and sit there with swollen eyes, a sniffing, heaving engine. I'm exhausted, like I've had a heavy night drinking. I could go to sleep right here on the floor.

Next time I see Fernando I tell him the saga.

'It's an important step for closure. You never really had closure about it, did you?'

Like my friends, Fernando doesn't ask any details and I'm glad. It's easier to leave it in the past, but now I can't. I imagine Vernon being interviewed. I know exactly what he'll say and how he'll say it. He'll do the uncle routine. She didn't have a job. She was a runaway, I took her in and helped her. It's nonsense. She was suicidal you know – unstable – and it didn't help that she was in love with me. He knows the drill. Cast me as hysterical. Get the suspicions going the other way.

About two weeks later, Bull Dog phones to let me know what happened.

'He denied everything as we expected.'

'Did you see him? Did you do the interview?'

'No, he's living in Brisbane now. He's semi-retired. We got our boys up there to go around.'

'So that's about it then?'

'I'm afraid so. The only thing you can hope for is that someone else comes forward. In that case we'd need to speak to you again, but for the time being, that's about all we can do.'

I've been around court reporting enough to know that's how it would be. I don't expect anything else but I feel better for having made the report. All those years of not being believed. For all the hard-nosed demeanour of the Bull Dog, it's a comfort to feel that she, at least, believes me.

I join a theatre group half an hour from Daylesford, in Castlemaine. They're doing a tap dancing play. I've never tapped or learnt to dance before but I'm keen to put time and effort into keeping the rest of the world at bay. Rehearsals are once during the week and on Sundays. In between, I tap around the house practising heel toe tap, heel

toe tap, heel toe heel toe heel toe tap. In the group is
Marlene, a tap teacher who never understands how someone
(me) can be so disorganised with their clothes during dress
rehearsals, and Dianne, a red-head drop-out hippie who
occasionally shoves me in the ribs when she doesn't catch my
cane when I throw it in the routine. I can't believe they give
us a cane-throwing routine. It's heady.

I get into the role practising my lines in the mirror and
escaping from home and the memories of Vernon that come
at me like sharks.

At home, if it's a warm night or a full moon on a freezing
one, David takes a foam mattress, our pillows and doona
down near the goat paddock and we sleep there covered in
a plastic tarpaulin. We wake at dawn with our hair covered in
dew. Sometimes, if he brings an extension cord and hooks up
the telly, Dan comes out too. Although David's jokes still
revolve around my shortcomings, his offbeat ways charm me
and his connection to nature opens me to a part of life that
I'd never had in my own childhood. I like it for Dan. And I
like it for me too.

The house is close to being finished. The night we move
into our new bedroom we buy champagne and invite friends
to toast the end of sweeping out the bed with a broom. We
sit in wicker chairs and on the bed with its crisp new damask
doona cover, fling open the French doors to the verandah
and laugh at the now quaint follies of renovating. The
verandah overlooks the chook shed and my garden which is
blossoming under the full moon. Earlier in the day I'd mown
the lawn and the sleepy smell of warm cut grass seduces us.

Always, after hours of weeding and mowing, happiness
seeps into me. Once, late afternoon sun is skimming lime
green new leaves. Everything is pleased with itself: weeded
beds, newly planted roses rescued from a demolished house,
silver snail trails tracing lines on the spinach leaves, shy rose

buds and open drunken floosies too, even sprinklers spout abandoned mist that makes everything glisten. Standing in my gumbies and overalls, drinking in the garden's wellbeing, I suddenly realise I don't want to die. Existentialism has been off the agenda for so long the thought hits me like an apple falling from a tree. Like Ma, I've always said if I died tomorrow, as long as there's no pain, *c'est la vie*. No hard feelings, you have to go sometime, see you in paradise. Now, desperately, I want to stay breathing. For a long time. I want to see Dan grow up, my garden in ten years or 50, wonder at the unlikely crossroads of the world and my friends. Life's exciting and I don't want to miss a beat. It's happened since I've been with David. Even though I'm so tormented by him, since we've been together, I've never suffered from the depression that dogged me before we met. I find this mystery deeply puzzling.

So many priests have been convicted of molesting kids and I'm trying to get together a story about another priest with the help of the Broken Rites victim support group which has gathered evidence against him. I work with them because I want to flush the bastards out. The Catholic Church is rigorously defending claims because of the magnitude of possible compensation involved. Often they stall a case so long the priest dies before a final hearing and their headache disappears. It leaves the victim with no closure, no resolution, nowhere to take their pain.

In the midst of this, one day, covering a court case about a priest, I stumble into the wrong courtroom and come across another pedophile case. Half a dozen girls are there to give evidence against a guy now in his 60s. One of them, a woman now in her early 20s, agrees to meet for an interview.

She tells me how the guy had abused her from the age of six. When she was 12 he told her he couldn't be with her anymore. He said she was too old and he had to find another little girl.

'You know, you wouldn't read about it, but I was that hurt,' she says with disgust. 'I actually felt, like, rejected. Can you believe that?' She doesn't have to explain. I can see her self-loathing. I know exactly how it is. Kids form attachments to guys who abuse them because the guys get into their heads and hearts through giving them attention. Then, as I'd already realised, into the deepest reaches of their psyche through the most sophisticated and mysterious route. Sex. In my travels, I'd seen how sex can be perverted into just about anything. These guys understand that, usually because it had happened to them. It gives them radar for emotionally needy kids like they once were and the know-how to manipulate that familiar emptiness. It's the worst part of the abuse that never goes away. And, if you can bear to admit it to yourself, like this woman's doing now, the guilt about wanting the attention adds vinegar to the wound every time you think about it.

Then she tells me how when the guy came back into her life as a family friend, she'd let him babysit her own kid when he was two. It wasn't until her son said the guy touched his willy that she was shocked enough to remember her own abuse and go to the police. I know she let him back into her life because, on the deepest unconscious level, she still wanted his approval. She wanted him to be like the dad she'd never had. And she wanted it so badly she blocked out the abuse.

Even though I write the story changing her name, I mention that and she decides it makes her look like a bad mother. Or worse, a knowing party to the abuse. She starts defamation proceedings against the Herald and Weekly Times. After endless discussions, our solicitors decide to pay her $25,000 because they can't guarantee if she breaks down in the witness box that a jury won't side with her, despite our watertight argument. The name change means the story can only identify her to people who already knew her story, therefore she can't be defamed.

Although in the discussions I do everything to help our lawyers build a winnable defence, including mentioning my own abuse – my reputation as a journo is at stake – secretly I'm glad when she gets her money. There's no way she's ever going to get a head start for her son or herself in any other way. She deserves every break she can get after what she's been through. And, I know, her pain is going to continue for a long time yet, with or without the money.

I'm sitting at Sal's kitchen table after dinner one night telling her about all the cases involving priests. And about the young woman, who'd used a *pro bono* solicitor.

'If it weren't for the no-win no-fee law firms that launch these cases there wouldn't be any convictions or any hope at all for people like her,' I say.

Sal looks at me in a quizzical kind of way.

'Have *you* thought about doing it?'

'Doing what?'

'Going? Vernon. Flick's done some *pro bono* abuse cases. You could ask her to take it on.' Her friend Felicity Broughton is on all the child protection boards and works in a small law firm.

The idea momentarily stuns me. It's one thing to empathise with other people's stories. Another entirely to dredge up your own.

'There's no way I'd win. There were no witnesses. The police said so and they'd know.' I've also covered enough legal cases to know what's what.

'But the proof in a criminal case is a lot more stringent than in a civil case. Anyway Babsie, it doesn't hurt to ask. Go see her. She'll tell you what's possible and what isn't. Maybe there's nothing she can do but if there is you might as well do it now. He'll die one day and then you might wish you'd moved before it was too late.'

Sal doesn't try to talk you into stuff. She just says what's on her mind and leaves it to you.

I find the idea scary. But just the thought of telling my story and being believed after all these years suddenly seems exciting. I imagine Vernon trapped in a courtroom having to listen to the whole story as seen through my eyes. Not being able to dismiss it as just some ramblings of a disgruntled girl, or being able to justify it by saying, 'If you'd only walked a mile in my shoes'. From the moment I first imagine that, I can't think of anything else.

I've met Flick at Sal's a couple of times. The next morning I phone to make an appointment. But as the days pass, my enthusiasm fades. I begin to think that after so many years, what happened way back then seems so much like another person's life. That stupid mixed-up kid that was me, is someone I'd run a mile from if I met her now.

And yet another part of me knows she's still here, somewhere inside me. The night before the appointment, there's a tennis match in my head. An argument about whether or not I should go. There's dread and excitement as well as a voice trying to tell me it's a waste of time. But it's the voice of the small mixed-up kid who wins out. I owe it to her to have a go.

The same thing happens as at the police station. I tell Felicity my story and cry a lot. You give that little kid inside you an inch and she takes a mile.

'The biggest problem we've got in cases like this is the time frame. There's a statute of limitations which this has clearly passed. But we can get over that by saying that post-traumatic stress has only just surfaced and that the injury itself is within the current time frame of the statutes.'

Felicity's a person who inspires confidence. She's got long blonde hair and is slim and attractive, but in every other way she's more like a man. Tough, no-nonsense, efficient, to the point. I like her.

'You're right that you wouldn't have a chance in a criminal trial without witnesses. And even if you had them, to prove beyond reasonable doubt's just too hard in cases like this. If he's got money you can go him in a civil suit. And if he hasn't you've always got the Crimes Compensation Tribunal. I'm prepared to take it on a *pro bono* basis. There's a certain amount of satisfaction in cases like this. I wouldn't mind seeing him squirm. Let's just hope he's loaded.'

Vernon turns out to be a serial bankrupt. Three times. I remember he was bankrupt and often got paid in cash when I worked for him. Ma said at the time it was his way of avoiding tax and hiding assets.

Flick puts the wheels in motion for a crimes comp case. She makes an appointment for me to have a psychiatric assessment to show the stress had surfaced only recently, then lists the case. It seems like a lot of legal bullshit to me. I'm not traumatised.

The law recently changed so that now the alleged perpetrator has to be informed if a case comes before the Crimes Compensation Tribunal. Since it means no legal penalty, most never contest the allegations. With no contest, when cases appear, they're usually over within half an hour.

That's our first blow.

When Vernon finds out I'm filing a case he writes announcing his intention to fight it.

'It's going to take longer and be more involved. You're going to have to get character witnesses, find people you've told the story to over the years. Have you told people other than Sal?' Flick asks.

'Most of my close friends know. I haven't hidden it. Lots

of people know.'

'The further back you go, the better it will be. We'll need people you told at the time and in the years since. Anything that will substantiate that this isn't something you've just concocted but something that's been talked about as part of your life for a long time. Let's just hope he doesn't hire a Queen's Counsel. It's on the cards. He'd have a lot of friends around town. That'd be a whole other ballgame.'

Then comes the second blow.

'I've got some bad news,' Flick tells me on the phone. 'Not only has he got a QC, he's got Hartog Berkeley, the ex-Solicitor General of Victoria. One of *the* most senior barristers in the state. I don't know why he's doing it because if he just let us go ahead without challenging it, chances are no-one would even hear of the case. This way the whole legal community'll be onto it.'

'I guess he's trying to protect his reputation. He always said no-one would believe the daughter of a prostitute over a barrister. But I can't afford a Queen's Counsel.'

'He actually said that?'

'Mmm hmm.'

'Arrogant bastard. Don't worry. I'll scout around. There's got to be someone who'll take it on. I'll get back to you. In the meantime, dig up some witnesses.' She doesn't sound defeated. More like this is an obstacle she's come across before, a routine hurdle that has to be dealt with.

I'd told Joanne about Vernon when I was 18. I haven't spoken to her since the Fruit Salad Fallout but my pride won't let me ring to ask a favour. Daylesford's a tiny town where you can run into people three times a day if you don't want to. I can't understand why I haven't seen her in the one-strip shopping street, in one of the two most delicious restaurants in town where we both eat or on our separate but regular walks around the lake.

There are still a couple of months to go before the case is listed to appear at the Tribunal. In the meantime I contact as many people as I can who I've told about Vernon. I track down Carol who I told when we were at Sydney Tech together when I was 17 and she writes a letter saying when and how she discovered I'd lived with Vernon when I was 14. I ring the psychiatric hospital I went into when I was 16, less than a year and one suicide attempt after I'd left Vernon's place. I want to get my file from Dr Hammersmith but find the hospital closed years ago.

I hunt down my medical file by sweet-talking someone in the Government records office and telling her why I need it.

'There's only about half a dozen pages I'm afraid,' says the voice on the other end of the line.

'But I was an inpatient for months and an outpatient for at least six. Dr Hammersmith used to take notes of our sessions. We had them once or twice a week. There must be something there about me. At least about why I was there.'

'There's only information about when you were admitted, when you were assessed, when you left. That kind of thing. But that's all, I'm afraid. I admit it does look a bit sparse.'

Unbelievable. All those sessions where I thought she was writing. I wonder if she'd listened to anything I'd said. The only option left is to find her. I can't believe she wouldn't remember my story. Even to me, as a seasoned Sunday paper journalist, my situation back then seems at least moderately interesting and unique. A 30-stone mother with six children to five different men would hardly have been a dime a dozen in those days. Not to mention an allegation about sexual abuse by a barrister in the days when most people thought that kind of thing was a sick lie kids made up to get adults into trouble.

I track her down to a private practice in Sydney through her membership of the Australian College of Psychiatrists.

'Dr Hammersmith, you may not remember me but my name's Barbara Biggs. I was a patient of yours about 25 years ago at Rydalmere Psychiatric Hospital.'

'Yes.'

'Do you remember my name?'

'No, I can't say I do. I treated hundreds of patients in the years I was there.'

'It's quite a famous name. You made a joke about me being a relative of Ronald Biggs, the great train robber.'

'No. It doesn't ring any bells. If I could see what your face …'

'I got my file from Rydalmere and there's nothing in it. No notes. Nothing. You must remember something. I saw you for at least nine months.' I'm breaking the first rule of journalism. Don't alienate the source. I'm pissed off and I know my voice isn't hiding it.

'I've seen hundreds if not thousands of patients over the years. And it's two decades ago. I'm afraid I just can't help you.'

I start to back track.

'What if I came up to Sydney and told you more about what I told you back then.'

'It's possible. But I really can't guarantee anything. Certainly if you come to Sydney seeing you might jog my memory but I won't be held responsible if nothing comes of it.'

I suddenly realise she'll make a terrible witness even if she does remember. I wonder how someone can get a medical degree and be so vague. I tell her I'll send her a photo but I know I never will. I have to find stronger witnesses than that if the case is to have any chance at all.

As the house continues to go at a snail's pace, David and I argue more and end up back in counselling together. I see similarities, not between David and my mother or my sister or anyone else in my family. The similarities are with Vernon. On the surface you can't find two men more dissimilar. But in ways that count for me, they're the same. For both, what I think and feel has always been irrelevant. Their motivations are different, but I experience them in the same way. Yes, David loves me alright. But what use is that if I feel invisible?

SEVENTEEN

A DAMN GOOD GARDEN

Felicity assigns my case to a colleague, Melanie Eagle, who'd been Lord Mayor of St Kilda during my time as a suburban newspaper journo. They work in the same law office, Howie and Maher. They're friends but so completely different from each other. Melanie's soft and feminine. She's got a head of unruly, curly hair, a vague air about her and an unhurried, leisurely way of talking, almost country. When I worked on the suburban paper I'd met her a few times. She never got ruffled about anything, never judged anyone or took sides. I like her demeanour.

'Last time I saw you, you were collecting signatures to stop that old house in Mitford Street from being torn down and trying to save the old Stokehouse from getting a revamp,' she says, and gives me one of her crooked smiles.

'We lost the Stokehouse. But the house is still standing.' Both were Joanne's idea. She got bees in her bonnet to keep her amused between creative bouts. Back then I got the feeling Melanie thought I was a bit of a nutter, but she treated me with respect and tried to give helpful advice all the same.

'Well, let's hope that's a portent for what we've got to do here. Now, let's see, didn't you tell Felicity that Vernon was a client of your mother's before he'd met you?'

'That's right.'

'She'd know something about him, sexually speaking I mean, that might concur with some of the sexual behaviours that you experienced. Or that's what we'd be hoping anyway. If that's the case, we'd like to call her as a witness. Do you think she'd be in that?'

'I can only ask.'

'It would be good if we could talk to her first. Do you think she'd come and see us?'

'She doesn't live in Melbourne.'

'Well, even if she could phone and have a chat, that would be good. Do you think she'd do that?' Her speech is almost a drawl and there's something childlike about it. Maybe a bit too casual. Though I like Melanie, I wish Flick was still on the case.

'Like I said, I can only ask.'

Relations between Ma and me are strained. We never

fight but she gets on my nerves. It seems the only time I hear from her is when she wants me to do something, like open a dodgy phone betting account or forge a signature. It's years since I've helped in dodgy dealings. She respects that I now have a position in the community that's vulnerable. And it's the first time in my life I value a reputation. I care. Ma never presses when I say no but she's continued to ask all the same. In the past she would have sworn and been angry if I didn't help her. Now, in her mellow years, she accepts the refusals with grace, without going into a sulk. She is, in fact, proud of my success and doesn't want to jeopardise it.

I ring her in Canberra where she now lives and from where she runs her fantasy phone business.

'Ma. How are you?'

'Fine thanks. And you?'

'Pretty good. Not bad. Listen. You know I told you I'm taking Vernon to court?'

'Hmm.'

'I need witnesses. There's no way I can win without them and the solicitor says you'd be a good one.'

'Oh Barbara, what can I tell them? I was in Queensland when you lived with him,' she whines.

'She says you can talk about when he was your client.'

For a few seconds, there's silence on the other end of the phone.

'Barbara, I don't remember anything. You know I've got a shocking memory.'

'But anything you can tell them will be better than nothing.'

Another silence, then she says what's really on her mind.

'If I go on the stand and tell them all that, they'll think I'm a bad mother.' She says it with a 'so there' in her tone. Now she's said it. At least she's honest.

'Ma. It's not about you now,' I say. 'It's about me.'

She's thinking on the other end of the line. I know there's a threat in my voice: if you don't do this for me you can forget about playing happy families.

'Oh, alright then,' she says begrudgingly, but in a resigned kind of way. 'When is it?'

Thank God! I arrange for her to visit the solicitor next time she's in Melbourne. I have Sal as a character witness because I told her about Vernon ten years earlier but I also need some meat. Even I know I can't expect to face the ex-Solicitor-General of Victoria without something. Then I think of Jane, Vernon's ex-wife who'd had an overdose just before I lived with 'The Chief'. I track her down through her mother.

The weekend after we get back from Sydney, Jane comes home from hospital for the first time. She has weekend leave from the psych hospital.

The Chief told me how beautiful she was before she started on the Largactil. They give them to her for depression. Now she has a big bum. Because she's short, shorter than me and I'm small, she waddles when she walks. I can see she's been beautiful in the face, and still is, but she has a sleepy expression all the time.

From the minute Jane arrives in the house, I'm Cinderella and she's one of the ugly sisters. The first morning she wants a boiled egg for breakfast and I bring it to her in bed.

'This is hard inside, I wanted a soft boiled egg. Can't you even boil an egg? Go and do it again. This time with a soft yolk.'

'How do I know if it's soft until I cut it open?'

'Soft eggs are three-minute eggs. Didn't your grandmother teach you that? She knew how to boil an egg.'

I wonder for a second how she knows what Gran's cooking's like, then go back to make more eggs. This time they aren't cooked enough and the first one runs all over the toast when she cuts the top off.

'They're only boiled eggs,' says The Chief. 'All you have to do is boil the water. Can't you do that?' He's sighing a lot.

'I cooked them for three minutes just like you said.'

Four times I make boiled eggs. Four times. Why should I have to be her slave like that? I know this is her house, but I feel like it's mine too now. I don't think she should be able to tell me what to do. And The Chief's taking her side with everything.

In the end, Jane grumbles and has Vegemite on toast.

That's only the morning of the first day she's here.

In the afternoon, Kate poos her pants. She's never done that before. The only time she wears a nappy's at night and in the morning it just has wee in it. Those nappies are disposable and I throw them in the bin. So I take her undies off and throw them in the bin too.

'What did you just do with them?' says Jane when I come out of the kitchen.

'I put them in there.' I point into the kitchen.

'Where in there?'

'Just in there.'

'Where?'

I tell her I put them in the bin and she starts treating me like more of an idiot.

'Imagine if you threw away a pair of undies every time there's an accident. They'd never have any left. You go and get them out and wash them right this minute.'

'How?' I ask.

'What do you mean, how? You go and hose them down and then put them in the laundry of course.'

I can hear The Chief and Jane muttering and laughing as I leave. I can hear them laughing in my head even when I can't hear them anymore. My mantra pops into my head to ease the pressure. Hate, hate, hate ... I don't know who or what I hate. But you aren't supposed to think about what a mantra means.

When I've finished with the undies, Jane asks me to sew up the hem of a dress that's come undone.

By now I'm so mad I can't talk. She thinks I'm her slave. In a split second, The Chief must have seen some look on my face because he has me in the backyard so fast. He tells me he needs help with the laundry door Jane said was stuck.

'Pet, I know you think it's not fair, Jane asking you to do things like that, but she's sick. She's not well. Just do it. Humour her for me. Okay?'

'You're being so mean to me as well. I haven't done anything wrong,' I sulk.

'That's just to put her off the scent. Imagine what she'd think if she came home and saw a gorgeous young thing like you sharing the house with me and we got on well. It's just for the weekend. Humour her. Just for me. Okay?'

He puts his arms around me then. And in that moment I know if he wants me to, I can wash pooey pants and cook boiled eggs 'til the cows come home.

When I think about Jane, I think about how young and fresh and beautiful she'd been when she'd met Vernon. Only 18. In the photos I'd seen, at that age she'd looked as innocent as I'd been when I met him at 14. And a few years later she'd had two babies and was suicidal. Just like I'd been after nine months with him. I was never told why Jane was suicidal, but I figured, as sure as he'd driven me into a psych hospital, he'd driven poor Jane there as well.

'Barb, fancy hearing from you after all this time. How are you?'

I remember she was always so easily impressed. I think she'd married Vernon because a barrister was a good catch. So I tell her I'm a journalist doing a story on mental health and she immediately wants to meet for lunch.

Everyone thinks they have a story you can write about. I know I have to handle her delicately. When her kids were small, Vernon fought and won custody of them because, by then, she had a history of mental illness. I'm counting on her wanting to get back at him.

But when she answers my next question, I realise I couldn't be more wrong.

'Do you ever see The Chief?'

'The Chief. That's so funny. I remember you used to call him that. Yes, I do actually. About once a year or so. Sometimes I spend Christmas at their place. You know he's moved to Brisbane?'

'No, I didn't,' I lie. I wonder if Jane's swallowed Vernon's PR about himself over all these years. She still thinks he's Mr Wonderful just because he's a barrister.

We arrange to meet for lunch the next week but it never happens. Vernon makes sure of that. I find out through Melanie.

'His solicitor's sent us a letter demanding that we cease and desist harassing his ex-wife. That she has no desire to talk to us and doesn't want to hear from us again.'

'That's bullshit. She's happy to talk. We're having lunch next week.'

'If she's going voluntarily, there's nothing he can do about it.'

I ring Jane straight away to confirm our arrangement.

'I can't talk.' And she hangs up.

I ring again and she won't take the call. The next day I phone and say quickly, before she cuts me off: 'Jane. Please. Don't hang up. Can you just tell me why you can't see me?'

'Look. He says the girls'll never speak to me again if I talk to you. I can lose them forever. He's done it before. I'm sorry. I can't help you.'

The 'girls' are now 28 and 30 by my calculations. Even now I can see he was a charismatic personality. I have no doubt he's shaped their reality to suit himself as much as he had mine. I knew he would have kept control of Jane through the children, forever telling them how crazy and irresponsible their mother was – he'd done it when I was living there. 'Mummy's not very well and we have to look after her, don't we?' Always treating and portraying Jane as a helpless, slightly retarded child. I have no doubt it's within his power to stop them talking to their mother. Poor Jane.

When Ma comes down from Canberra she says she's rung Lionel, my brother Peter's father, to see if he can help her with dates and incidents she can talk about at the tribunal. She says he's good with trivial detail likes dates, locations and times. They were an item in the early 60s when Vernon was a client. Lionel's wife died 18 months ago and Ma says he's over the moon about seeing her again.

'I think he put a private detective onto me to try and find me because he knew I'd lived in New Zealand before I'd even told him. There's no way he could've known that otherwise 'cause I changed me name when I was there.'

'You don't think you're having a bit of a fancy, do you Ma?'

'No! He says since his wife died he's just been sitting in his flat staring at the walls.'

'I'm sure he didn't put it like that.'

'Not quite, but virtually. Anyway, I'm meeting him on the corner of Toorak Road and St Kilda Road tomorra. Could you give me a lift?' I wouldn't miss it for the world.

Before then we have an appointment with Melanie. I think I know about Ma's life on the street when we were young, but I have another thing coming.

She tells Melanie how Vernon paid her to be outside the window of his home while he had sex with boys or women, sometimes two at once.

'He'd tell me how he'd go to the beach or to Caulfield Park and pick up young boys and bring them home and fuck 'em. I never knew if it was true but I presumed it must be if he said it. I never actually saw him fucking a boy but sometimes he'd have a kid in the room while he was fucking the sheila.' One thing about Ma is that she always calls a spade a spade when it comes to sex. Working in the fantasy phone call business makes her able to talk about it with a casualness most people would reserve for an omelette recipe.

When she was outside the window, one of the women she saw him having sex with was Jane.

'He was rooting really hard and she was crying. It made me feel sick, actually.'

I look at Melanie to see how she's taking it. She looks kind of naive but I'm impressed with the way she's not judging Ma.

'And Lionel used to drive you to the jobs?'

'Mmm. But he'd wait in the car. He'd just give me a lift.'

'But you'd tell him what you'd seen?'

'Yes.'

'Would he be prepared to be a witness?'

'I don't know. I can ask, I suppose.'

'What else can you tell us? Was he interested in Barbara before she went to live with him? She's told us about the times he paid her grandmother to let him get at her. Do you remember that?'

'I don't know about that but he was always at me to let him look through the window at the kids after their bath. I always said "no," of course.'

'In what ways was he always at you? What was the offer?'

'Oh, I don't know. He was always at me. He never let it alone. He'd offer me money. But I never let him.'

'Can you remember any other sexual behaviour? What else did he ask you to do? Anything?' There's nothing hard edged about the way Melanie asks questions, but they're the right ones. I can see she's trying to build a case and I can see, like I'm sure she can, that Ma's going to make a great witness.

'Well, I never actually had sex with him. He was a voyeur. You know, he got off on looking. He'd get me to come into his office in the city and stand there with me tits hanging out while he wanked. He'd never touch me. I'd just stand there. Oh, and he liked to talk about things he did with women too. He used to have parties and he'd get sausages or carrots he'd put up some sheila and cut them up and put them on biscuits and he'd also put cum in the milk they'd put in their coffee, stuff like that.'

I feel a bit sick myself. I don't want to have these images of my mother in my head. Now I can see why Ma had at first been reluctant. It isn't a good look. But Melanie says it's riveting evidence and that it will tally with my own. She's sharp as a tack Melanie, despite the country drawl. She says Ma's our key witness.

The next day at midday I drop Ma off near Toorak Road in St Kilda Road outside McDonalds. I don't drive away, but wait to see how she and Lionel greet each other. It's not every day you catch up with someone you haven't seen for 30 years. Let alone that he's the father of your child.

Lionel's standing with his hands behind his back, rocking backwards and forwards on the balls of his feet. He's a tiny, wizened old thing who looks for all the world like Mister Magoo. As soon as he spots Ma his face lights up and it can't help warming your heart. They stumble around each other, not knowing whether to hug or kiss on the lips or cheek. They half-try to do all three and miss, both taking a step back in the confusion of it all. But I can see they'll be fine. They're beaming like teenagers on a date.

Ma's staying with us while she's down and she rings to say she won't be home. Well, well, well. Ma hasn't had a boyfriend for at least a decade but at 62 she hasn't given up the ghost yet. David and I can't wait to grill her when she gets home.

'He's still in love with me,' she tells us the next day.

'How do you know,' I ask.

'Well, apart from it being written all over his face, he told me.' So put that in your pipe and smoke it!

'And how do you feel? Do you still love him?'

'Not really.' Ma's matter-of-fact.

'Do you feel anything?'

'No.'

'Nothing?'

'Nothin'.' Ma doesn't play games. It's just the way it is.

'So why did you stay with him?'

'Because he's probably loaded.' She makes no bones about it. Then she adds, 'And he's a bit of a sweet old thing. I don't dislike him, there's just nothing there after all these years.'

Ma stares into space. I wish I could travel with her and see the memories that are playing on her face like movies.

'It's funny. When we were going out together I used to hold his hand walking down the street and he'd shake me off. I'd get real hurt, you know? Now he's all over me like a rash and I'm the one shaking him off.' She laughs at the way life can turn out.

'Oh, and he says there's no way he'd be a witness either. He hates courts and says if he never goes in one again it'll be too soon.'

Great.

The weekend after Ma leaves I'm in the chemist in Daylesford and who should I spy through the tissue shelf, but Joanne. I know she must have already spotted me because she has a fake nonchalant air about her like she knows you're watching. It's good to see her again, but in the time we'd been apart, I'd come into my own here. It's the longest I've ever lived anywhere. Kel Tori had persuaded me to join the school council. Through that I'd met parents at the school and local businessmen on the council. They smile and wave at me in the street. Stop me in the supermarket to say hello. It feels good.

At the end of last year on awards night, council members

were called to the stage to hand out prizes to kids. I know they do it so we, who leave our fires and trudge to the school for mid-winter monthly meetings, feel appreciated. Part of me wondered how anyone could get off on handing a present over for God's sake. But while I was up there, looking down at the hall full of people, good people, I couldn't work out how I'd managed to get here. There I was beating down my stupid cynicism because I was proud I'd earned the little privilege of giving a bunch of kids awards for their achievements. I could barely believe it. I felt ... humble. It was that night I realised Daylesford was my town. That I wasn't just passing through. Now, I belong here.

I don't know exactly why, but it wouldn't have happened if Joanne and I had been seeing each other. In our break, I'd claimed more than just the town as my own. Maybe that's why I'm able to be the first one to say something.

'Joanne! How the fuck are you, you old bag?'

She laughs instead of cries at the reference to her age.

'You're not a spring chicken yourself anymore, BB. Fancy seeing you here. I wondered when we'd run into each other. I can't believe in this tiny place ... it's been almost a year hasn't it?' Like she hadn't counted.

'Nearly two.'

'No! That long! Who'd have believed in old Daylesford we'd go that long without running into each other. In the street at least. We'll have to have a wee drinky poo to celebrate BB. Would you like that?' She's being careful. Respectful. I like it.

'Okay. I'll meet you at your place in 15. I'll get some champagne.'

During our hiatus I'd worked out that what had really been going on with Joanne and me was a power struggle. That's what our rift had been about. The friendship had started out 22 years ago with her nurturing me like a daughter. The price was unconditional love, even if that meant her bullying or shouting, me never disagreeing, me always backing down or taking her side against others even when she was wrong. It had taken me a long time to work out that I didn't want to do it anymore. I didn't want to be like 'the daughter she never had'. I wanted to get out from under her.

As soon as we're settled in with champagne, Joanne starts her old tricks again. Stroking me with what I want most. Or what she thinks I want. The idea is for me to be putty in her hands. I'd weathered Joanne's agoraphobic prima donna persona when other friends had long given up. In exchange? She shaped me like one of her ceramic pieces. The best of me is her doing. But now I'm grown-up, fully-formed and it's time to take myself in hand. I'm ready for it. To be free I have to lose something. In the two years of longing for and missing her, I'd decided when we got together again, as we always had, to trade our intensity for independence.

'You look so beautiful, what have you done to yourself?'

I caught it mid-air. She knows just how to suck me back into the honey. I'm an ugly duckling. She knows all my weak spots.

I'm supposed to say 'Really', and 'No' and 'Do you think so', but I ask instead about the new man I'd heard she'd met. She lets me go, but she's patient, Joanne. She tells me about her new man, Ron, who draws all day like her and is 15 years younger. 'He'll leave me. You'll see.'

But half an hour later she sets the bait again.

'Are you sure you haven't done something to yourself, BB? You look positively radiant. It's around the eyes. You look stunning.'

'No. Nothing at all,' I say coldly. That's when she knows the game's up. Rejecting the compliments frees me to reject the rest. She knows it and so do I.

After we settle into the new order, we catch up on the goss, get pissed and laugh like hyenas. The new footing is holding.

I tell her about the court case and she agrees to write a letter.

'But I can't come to Melbourne, BB. I haven't been there for years and I just know I'll have a panic attack. How about I make it a really good letter?'

I tell her about Ma and Lionel. Joanne's laughter is raucous and saucy and puts everything in perspective. She tells me about the men still hovering around. She says she doesn't like so much attention but you can tell she does and that they drive her crazy but you can see she loves it. Joanne's worrying herself to death over her age, Ron running off with a younger woman. Never mind you have to search for crevices on her 47-year-old face.

At home, I tell David about running into Joanne and he's overjoyed at the prospect of us all being friends again.

'I've missed the old Joanne, Barb.'

He's in a good phase, not harassing me to be with him every second. He doesn't say so but I know he's barracking for me to win the case and giving me space to do it. It occurs to me that my victory might be a vicarious one for him too.

Dan's 16 and talks more to David and Judy Tori than he does to me. Maybe that has something to do with why one night I decide to go where only I can with him. I have my upside too. Even if Dan can't be open with me, I sure as hell can with him. Especially when it comes to sex education.

I'm driving him and his friend, sexually active Matthew, home from a comedy performance in Melbourne that I had to review. We've had two beers each. Enough to make us relaxed. It's late on the way home when Matthew asks about female orgasms. I explain in brief but his questions are endless. And detailed. I relay the graphic information he's seeking with a dry, studied casualness. Me? Shy talking about sex? Me? Deny boys essential info about how to make girls happy? Never. If nice boys can learn this, girls won't be so vulnerable to manipulative and sex crazy guys who have the physical know-how to worm their way into women's hearts without their own heart connections to go with it. I want my son to have both.

'In the womb we all start out the same. We have clitorises. Then, if you've got an XY chromosome, in the third month of pregnancy the foetus marinates in testosterone and the tiny clitoris grows into a penis while the ovaries fall down to make balls. So that little sensitive part of your dick, just on the head where the ring meets at the front, that spot on a girl is her clitoris. It's where all the action is.'

Worried I'm getting too graphic, I look in the rearview mirror at Dan and sideways at Matthew. They're interested. Their mouths are hanging open. I could stop there. I *do* feel uncomfortable, but this is an opportunity for them to learn something that maybe even their girlfriends won't tell them. But I figure it'll help them in their relationships with women for life.

'Anyway, the main thing you need to know as a guy, is that the girl's orgasm's going to make yours better. You can have an okay orgasm even if the girl just lies there, right? But a girl's orgasm can take you to a kind of launching pad from which you can then have your own orgasm which will be bigger and better the higher she gets you first. Like the better her orgasm is, the better yours will be.'

'Yeah, yeah, but how do you make it good?' asks Matthew. I glance over at him and hope he can't see me squirming in the dark. I know if they think I'm embarrassed, they'll get embarrassed too. It's a delicate conversation.

'Everyone's different. The most important thing is to find

out what she likes. And no matter how weird you think it is, don't think, oh, what she really means is this other thing that you really like. Do what she wants because all women are different. My clitoris is supersensitive, so the less touched it is the better, which is a big fat drag because a lot of guys think if they're not being energetic nothing's happening. But if a guy touches me all over with his fingertips, gently, sensuously, everywhere *except* there, after half an hour I'm so hanging out just the lightest touch will get me there.'

I want them to know. If they could get through to a girl's heart the way Vernon had to mine, but without the manipulative stuff, wouldn't that be the best? Two people the same age able to communicate and touch each other on that level. I think back to my first boyfriend after Vernon, John, and how if he hadn't been so hopeless sexually, if he'd been able to connect with me, how differently things might have turned out.

'Sounds a bit boring.' Thanks Matthew.

'Think of it as an investment.'

'In what?'

'Your own orgasm, moron.'

'Right. Right. So that's it?'

'Well, teasing's pretty good too. Like going near the clitoris and around it, massaging everywhere but there. Then when you do touch it, make sure it's wet. Never touch a dry clitoris. Even if you have to spit on your fingers. Anyway, you go around and then touch it just a bit, maybe with the tip of your tongue, and pull back and do the whole thing over again and again until the girl's climbing the walls to come. At that point – you'll know because she's arching her back and writhing around – lick her clitoris lovingly, like a cat eating cream, give it a gentle, delicate suck like it's the most precious jewel in the world, and Bob's your uncle. That's the best actually and it's amazing how exciting it can be for the guy if he gets into it. You have to be into it like a meditation, otherwise she knows. If you're bored she'll be bored. But you'll see from the breathing. If she's just lying there while you're going for it and you're not sure if you're doing it right, listen to her breathing. Even if she's not doing anything, if her lips are open and she starts to pant, you're on your way.'

I look at Dan again to see if he's embarrassed but his mouth's still hanging open. They're both deeply concentrated.

'But can't you come together?' asks Matthew. 'Wouldn't that be better?'

'Don't ask me why, but a lot of women, and I know because I ask just about everyone sooner or later, just don't have vaginal orgasms. Some do, but not many. I've never had one. It's damn inconvenient but what can you do?'

'But when do we get our turn?'

'Once the girl's come she'll be desperate for you to be inside her. That's when she's launching you into Blissville. She'll be like an animal.'

'Yeah?' Dan Biggs is impressed.

Even though I can't look Matthew in the eye again, I'm happy I've done my duty. I know if they don't hear it from me, it might be years before a girl gets up the courage to tell them. I know why women find it so hard to tell guys what they like. It's got something to do with the guy's ego. She doesn't want to offend him. And God knows that's happened to me enough times. I remember one guy I slept with jumped on and off and we both fell asleep. Then when he wanted to have another go, I said, 'What about me?' He asked what I meant and I told him I hadn't come yet. He got straight out of bed, got dressed and stormed off.

In any case, the incident with the boys, coupled with my occasional partaking in the green weed when the young things offer it, makes me the coolest mum. This means I'm the most likely candidate to host their next party where how much they can drink is only practise for how much they can throw up before morning.

But they're not brutes. No. Even country mums are vaguely feminist and produce kids with a sophistication lacking in previous generations.

One night Dan and Chris invite two girls for a dinner party. The boys design and cook the Indian menu and Chris's dad chooses the wines. Joanne makes some hash cookies and gives them one each, so it's really her fault the night doesn't yield romantic fruit. Not even a kiss. She says she thought they knew the cookies were for after dinner. The poor lambs were hungry when they arrived and hoed in. The second the meal was over they sprawled on couches, chairs and beds, separately, and fell fast asleep – which is how David and I find them when we arrive home at midnight.

While David drags himself through the last of the renovations, he leaves me alone to finish the garden. The work gets more frenzied as the day for confronting Vernon looms closer. In the garden, earthmoving's going on out the back. A central pathway, which leads from the house down to the goat gate, is being scraped away. I'm building retaining walls with sandstone from the chimney freestanding in the horse paddock next door. Now the shape's made I can't wait to start construction. I hire someone and we mix concrete and carry stones together. Our backs ache and hands blister. We have the wall, paths and steps built in three weeks. I buy ten advanced trees and plant them to give an instant established look. When I'm not preparing for the case, I'm spending every second in my paradise, feverish about finishing. I can't shake the feeling it has to be finished before the court case starts.

As the tribunal hearing draws near, David and I fight less.

One night on the verandah after dinner I say pointedly, 'It's next week you know. On my birthday.' In ten years he's only acknowledged my birthday twice.

'How do you feel about seeing him again?'

Sigh. I tried.

'Nervous. I think. Yes, but not too much. I don't know really. I guess I won't know until I see him.'

'What you're doing's a good thing, Barb.'

I check him out. Positivity isn't his strong suit.

'Thank you, sweetheart.'

'If I had the guts I'd do the same thing. You're a strong woman, Barb. It's one of the reasons you're my girl.'

We don't talk for a while. David's looking behind me at the garden. He usually says nothing about my work there.

'It's a damn good garden you're making there, Barb.'

EIGHTEEN

GIVE HER AN INCH

With just a week to go I see the senior barrister found by the felicitous Felicity. Okay, he's not a Queen's Counsel, but he's very experienced in these types of cases, Felicity tells me. He's a short, cocky guy who seems more interested in getting advice on shares from his new social project who happens to have moved to the finance desk of Melbourne's biggest paper. Like I'd know. I can't even afford his fees.

He doesn't want to know the story. He'd read that in the brief.

'Just leave it to me. Your job's just to answer the questions in a straightforward way without getting too emotional. Do you think you can do that?'

'I'll do my best,' I say, but I have no confidence in that at all.

The day before the hearing, Melanie calls.

'Bad news. Your barrister's just found out a case he's been working on for months is listed for tomorrow. He can't get out of it.'

'You're kidding.'

'I wish I were.'

'That's all we need. What now? We can't go in there with no-one.'

'He does have a junior. He can do it and he's prepared to.'

'But Vernon's got a QC.'

'Well, James *is* only a junior, but he's also very experienced.'

'How old is he? How many cases has he done?'

'I don't know. He's probably in his late 20s, something like that. He's done a lot of cases like this. Anyway, it's not like you've got a lot of choices at this point. Come in early, about nine o'clock, and we'll run through everything with him.'

Great. The morning before the case and I end up with a junior. A baby barrister against Hartog Berkeley. Even *I* know *that* name, and I usually don't know anything.

I stay at Sal's that night. David asks if I want him to be there but I can see he doesn't want to come. I also don't need a stresshead on my hands as well. Lionel and Ma are meeting us at 9.30 at the barrister's office which is, coincidentally, in Owen Dixon Chambers, the place I'd been to when I went to tell Vernon's protege I was in love with The Chief when he'd kicked me out. It's around the corner from the magistrate's court building where the Crimes Compensation case will be held.

Lying in bed, I remember back to the last time I'd seen Vernon when I shook all night at the prospect of the meeting. But I don't feel nervous this time. I realise it will probably be different when I see him, maybe then I'll be nervous. But now I feel excited. It doesn't matter what the outcome is. I want to get up there and tell my story publicly for the first time. And I want him to sit and listen. In detail. I'm about to finish what I'd started at the St Kilda Sea Baths 13 years ago. I also realise, that more than anything, I want him to be sorry.

The next morning, Sal and I drive in but I have my blades in the car. She has to go off to work after the case.

'How're you feeling Babsie? You're not going to let him get to you, are you?'

'No. Not at all. I'm quite calm.'

'You'll be fine. You seem fine. Just don't look at him, okay? He can't spook you if you don't look at him.'

We meet the barrister in his office. His name's James Nixon. Great, not only is he a baby barrister, he even looks like a baby, with a smooth, white, hairless face that looks like he's only just started shaving. I like young people but find them a bit boring because they don't know about life yet. He's keen like a puppy, excited about his first wrangle with the big mutt. Baby Face doesn't inspire me with confidence.

'I'm sorry you've ended up with me at the last minute but I'm not all that bad. I've done quite a few cases like this, actually.' He's very lovely. Very sweet. But right now lovely and sweet's the last thing I need.

'And besides, we've got some good news that might turn the whole case around,' Melanie tells me.

'And what's that? Vernon's dropped dead?'

'Not quite. But in some ways even better. The case was to be heard by a male justice and now we've got Wendy Wilmoth. She's perfect. It's unbelievably good news in a case like this.'

'There wouldn't be too many women on the bench I guess. That's great.'

We head down in the lift and cross the road to the magistrate's court and conference in a small room outside the courtroom waiting for Ma to show up. I'd phoned her the night before to make sure she was coming and everything was okay. But she isn't here.

'If she doesn't turn up we'll have to ask for an adjournment.'

'She'll come. I've got her mobile number. I'll give her a call.'

As I'm dialling, the door opens and Ma comes huffing in.

'Sorry I'm late. Lionel drove in and he can't find a bloody park anywhere. In the end he dropped me outside.'

Her phone rings and she puts her hand over her mouth and starts explaining to the caller about her fantasy phone service.

'Ma!'

'Look, I'll give you another number to call ...' But she doesn't get it out. Melanie interrupts.

'If that happens in the courtroom the bench will take a very dim view of it indeed. Mobile phones are a pet hate. I'd turn it off now if I were you.'

Ma switches off that phone mid-sentence and rolls her eyes. She reaches into her bag and one by one turns off four mobile phones.

'Why've you got so many?' I've always wondered, but for God's sake, why am I asking now?

'Different payment plans. Don't ask,' says Ma.

Someone from the court sticks his head in and tells us it's time.

As we walk into the lobby, I see Vernon sitting on a seat outside the courtroom. He doesn't look at me.

'Which one is he, Babsie? Don't look. Just point him out, but whatever you do, don't look,' Sal says.

But I do look. It's easy because he isn't looking at me. I nod in his direction to point him out. I take a long look.

He's hardly changed. Less hair, more grey, a little more jowly, but the man inside the watery blue eyes is The Chief. He's in a suit, in business mode, talking earnestly to Berkeley, but the eyes look like they could cry any second, a strange baby quality completely at odds with his thin-lipped and arrogant wolf smile.

'He's still got the piggy eyes. I'd know those eyes anywhere,' says Ma dryly.

'He looks like a creep, Babs,' says Sal.

'Let's get the show on the road,' says Baby Face.

When the judge arrives in the small courtroom, we all stand. She's a short, tired, self-possessed woman. Despite the deadpan mask of professionalism, I can see her humanity between the cracks. It gives me hope.

Vernon and I sit at the tables with our counsels while Sal and Ma sit behind on the benches. Berkeley and Baby Face give their opening speeches. I'm more impressed with Baby Face than I expect to be. His opening is inspiring and clear. Strong. Maybe there's more under that smooth face than meets the eye.

I'm first to give evidence.

'Please state your name, address and date of birth.'

'Barbara Louise Biggs, 26 Western Ave, Daylesford, 3/12/56.'

'Can you tell the court how old you are.'

'Forty ... today.'

'Now, can you tell the court in your own words how you came to know Mr Vernon here.'

I tell my story clearly and simply, as if I'm talking about someone else. Baby Face may be less experienced than Hartog, but he's asking all the right questions that encourage me to tell the whole story in my own words. Once I start, nerves that have made me shake during the opening speeches, knowing I'd be up next, disappear.

I tell about how I first saw Vernon when I was about eight and he came home with Ma as one of her clients. How they'd walked in on Pommy and me dancing naked after our bath and he'd offered us money to dance for him. How, after that he'd often been caught looking in our windows at night around bath time. And again, when I was 11, how one night Gran had encouraged me to go to the shops at night alone with him to buy ice-creams for the rest of the kids. Then, finally, how I came to live at his house.

I'd hitched to Gran's place in Melbourne after running away from a convent in Queensland where Ma had put me after the rape on my 14th birthday. Gran wasn't allowed to have anyone stay with her otherwise she'd be kicked out of the housing commission flats. I had no clothes, no money and refused to go home. She phoned Vernon to ask if he had a job for me. I tell how Vernon told me while I was living with him that he'd paid Gran for that introduction and for the ice-cream incident a few years before. I didn't go into my feelings now about that part of the story. That I now think while what Gran did was terrible, the fact that Vernon told me I'd been virtually sold, seemed unnecessarily cruel.

I tell about all the weird and confusing sex we had while I was employed as a nanny to his two small daughters. How I tried to kiss him on the mouth but he'd never let me. How I had almost no contact with anyone else for the nine months I lived with him and was half crazy with loneliness.

Of all the things I have to say, I only choke up once. I'm telling about the incident at the swimming pool on the way up to Sydney to visit Vernon's parents.

'We were watching a guy diving from the high board. Vernon kept insisting I was looking at the bulge in the guy's bathers and that I was horny. I told him I wasn't thinking that at all, but he didn't believe me. His talk about sex never stopped. He took everything about me and turned it into something to do with sex … I just wanted to be … ordinary … like all the other kids in the pool.'

I tell about falling in love with Vernon and how he'd kicked me out when I told him I was suicidal. How I'd ended up in a psych hospital the year after I left his place and spent the rest of my adolescence careering from one casual sex encounter to the next. The four suicide attempts before I was 20.

I'm on the stand all morning. When I finish, I feel fantastic. Exhausted, but fantastic.

At lunchtime Sal is told I'll be cross-examined for most of the afternoon and if she needs to go in to work she can come back tomorrow. If they finish with me today, Ma can take the stand first. Sal leaves.

'You're doing great Babs. Hang in there.' She squeezes my arm and kisses me goodbye. 'Tell me everything tonight.'

'Sal's right, you're playing it perfectly,' says Baby Face.

'I think I'm being too dry. I sound so … unemotional. Even to myself.'

'That's okay. That's fine. It's like you're not trying to convince anyone of anything. You're just telling your story. That's all we need. Just keep that up when Hartog gets into you and we'll be fine.'

Ma calls Lionel and tells him to pick her up at 4pm outside.

'He hates courts. There's no point him sitting here whining about when it's going to end.'

Melanie, Ma and me have lunch in a bar nearby while Baby Face goes to his office.

'We'll probably put you on tomorrow, Pat,' Melanie tells Ma.

'Will you want me all day or just part?'

'Look, it's really hard to say. It depends on what Hartog does with Barbara today, how long he takes. I'd set aside the whole day just in case.'

'Hmmmm.'

I can see Ma's mind ticking over. She fills her days with a million things and she's reordering like a computer file.

The easy part of the evidence is over. I know the hard part will be the cross-examination. My nerves are on alert but a calm resolve is settling. I have no reason to be nervous. I'm telling the truth and there's nothing he can say or ask me that will change that.

'Will he really try to get me?' I ask.

'I don't think so. In a case like this, I think the judge would take a dim view of harassment or bullying. It's not like a criminal trial. He'll have to use kid gloves if he doesn't want to risk alienating this judge. I think he's smart enough to realise that.'

'Let's hope.'

We reconvene at one o'clock and I'm straight back on the witness stand.

'Miss Biggs, it is *Miss* isn't it?'

'Yes.'

'Miss Biggs, you've made some extraordinary claims about my client and some of them don't quite tally I'm afraid. I'd just like to ask you a few specific questions, if you don't mind. Earlier this morning you told Her Worship how when you and my client drove to Sydney to visit his parents he asked you to take your top off in the car so truck drivers could see your naked breasts. Is that correct?'

'Yes.'

'You also said that Mr Vernon was a caring father who valued his daughters above almost everything else. Is that right?'

'Yes.'

'Can you explain to us Miss Biggs, how a caring father would allow his daughters to witness such extraordinary behaviour while on a family holiday! Doesn't this seem a little out of character? Can you explain how my colleague Mr Vernon here could be both a model father, as you freely admit, *and* orchestrate this bizarre event? I put it to you that both could not possibly be true.'

'Yes, I can. When he asked me to take my top off the older girl, Nita, was asleep on the back seat and the younger one, Kate, was asleep on the floor at my feet.'

'Wasn't he concerned they might wake up? Wouldn't that be a legitimate concern of such a caring father?'

'Yes. He was very concerned. He was quite nervous about it, in fact.'

'Then why did he take such a risk when the consequence of one of them waking up to such a spectacle would be extreme discomfort to say the least. Can you explain why he would create such a compromising situation for his children whom you acknowledge were his prime concern?'

'A risky situation seemed to make it more exciting for him. In general I'd say that added another dimension to the sexual experience.'

'And the girls didn't wake up?'

'No.'

'You've also, Miss Biggs, accused my client of such diverse sexual perversities as wearing women's clothing, going to sex shows at Kings Cross, watching pornographic movies involving animals and voyeurism of the most lurid kind. Are you seriously asking the court to believe that one person could be capable of enjoying such a diverse range of sexual gratification?'

'I'm not asking to the court to believe anything. I'm just telling you what happened.'

'Indeed.'

He goes on for the next two hours. There's no bullying, but keeps up a steady flow of detailed questions. He tries to trip me up with times and dates but if I'm vague about a date I've already said so in my initial testimony.

'We have no further questions, Your Worship.'

The tribunal is scheduled to reconvene at 10am the following day.

'He didn't ride you hard but when he pushed the boundaries you came back at him. That's good. What do you think, Melanie? I don't think he scored a single point.'

'No. James is right. You handled it very well. Let's just hope your mother's just as good tomorrow.'

We disperse and agree to meet at 9.30am in Baby Face's office the next day. Ma hurries off to meet Lionel and I phone Joanne and David to tell them how the day went.

I go to work and have a birthday drink with angelface Sue, my Daylesford work colleague, at the bar downstairs.

'It must be an incredibly hard thing to do. Are you glad you started it or do you wish you'd left it all alone?'

'No. I feel good. It feels good. The worst is over and it isn't that bad.'

'But what about seeing him? That must be hard.'

'He didn't look at me once all day. When I first started giving evidence I was terrified of talking while he was watching me, but it was incredible, he didn't look at me. Not that I saw anyway. Maybe he had a squizz when I didn't notice but every time I looked he was staring at notes in front of him or at the floor.'

'Why do you think that is?' Sue's lovely. She really listens and takes in everything you say.

'No idea. All I know is that if he was trying to spook me all he'd have to do is stare at me with those eyes of his. I can't tell you how relieved I am. Maybe he's scared. I don't know. Either that or he's letting me know I mean nothing whatever to him and he's trying to spook me that way. But you know what? For the first time in all these years, he actually doesn't mean anything to me. All I care about is telling my story.'

When I get back to Sal's she has a birthday dinner waiting for me with a cake and four candles, one for each decade.

'We've only got wine, this time, Babsie. We're keeping the champagne for next week when this whole bloody thing's over and you win.'

'We wish.'

'You've got a good chance. Balance of probabilities, remember.'

The next day Ma's first up on the stand. Some of the things she tells about what she's done and seen Vernon do are chilling. Some make me squirm. Working in the sex industry has given Ma a comfort level for talking about explicit sex that other people find fascinating, if not exactly shocking. It isn't even so much what she says, I've heard it all before, it's the way she says it.

'He'd go to the toilet block at Caulfield Park and get young boys and have me watch through the window while they were watching him in the room rooting some sheila … he was fucking her up the bum while she was crying … I'd just stand there with me tits hangin' out … he never wanted to fuck me, he just wanted me to watch while he fucked other sheilas …'

It isn't easy to have those indelible images of your mother planted like booby traps in your mind. Anyway, Melanie and Baby Face think her ingenuousness makes her the best witness.

Then Sal. Sober, serious Sal, is the best character witness a girl could have. Ex-*Age* journalist, script writer, media liaison for the Environment Protection Authority, a cog in the wheels of the city. She wears stylish and trendy square glasses and has a professional, no-nonsense demeanour. She's only on the stand for ten minutes but, after Ma's testimony, if anyone had any doubts about me being a loony loose cannon, Sal dismisses them completely.

Vernon's up the next day. He knows the drill. Melanie thinks he's going to be too smart for his own good. He's cocky, in subtle ways aligning himself with the court by knowing its ways and mannerisms. He does everything right, including crying, but just a little, just enough.

'I'm sorry Your Worship, it's just that every time I think of that time in my life, when I had my two gorgeous little girls to take care of on my own ... it was just such a ... sorry Your Worship ... it was just such a terrible time ... such a stressful time ... I did my best ... sorry ... sorry Your Worship ...'

The clerk of courts rushes an emergency box of tissues to him, he dries his eyes and continues the testimony. Perfectly choreographed.

He denies everything as we already knew he would. But he makes so many mistakes with his dates that don't tally, like he'd come to Ma's home with me when I worked for him because he wanted to assure Ma he was taking good care of me. But he couldn't have done that because Ma had moved to Queensland the year before I lived with him.

When Baby Face cross-examines him, he's picked up all the discrepancies. What a genius. He occasionally turns to me to clarify if what I'd said in my testimony and what Vernon said could both have been true. I say no, the dates are all wrong. He may have a baby face, but he sure knows what he's doing. Thank God.

The whole thing gives me faith in the court process. That when people are lying they do trip up, even if they're famous criminal barristers who know all the pitfalls.

I don't know how he times it, but just after Vernon has given evidence, his only witness walks in. His daughter Kate. She's up next.

'I only have vague memories of Miss Biggs. She used to look after us when I was little. We used to call her Mummy Barb.'

'Did you ever see Miss Biggs again after that time?'

'Yes. Once when we lived at Rippon Lea, when I was about ten, my sister and I saw her once in the grounds there.'

'Did Miss Biggs come to your house?'

'No. I don't think she did.'

'Are you sure about that?'

'Yes. I'd remember. She didn't come to the house.' She must have forgotten. Either that or there's some reason they don't want to mention that incident.

'Can you tell us what kind of man your father is? In fact, in your opinion, what kind of father has he been?'

'He's been the best father any girl could wish for. I can't believe anyone would accuse him of anything like this. He's a good man. A kind man. A kind father who never thought of anything except our welfare ...' Her voice starts to break.

As soon as Kate finishes her testimony she sits in the pews of the courtroom, but Vernon's solicitor steams up to her and speeds her outside. Even though I've already given my evidence, there's no way he's going to let her hear the smutty allegations that are being made against Vernon.

When I meet Nita and Kate, I can see they're nice little girls with good manners.

'You can call her Mummy Barb because she's going to be your mummy for a bit while your real mummy's getting better in hospital,' The Chief tells them.

'But she's not our real mummy, is she Daddy?' asks Nita.

'No sweetheart. She's not your real mummy. No-one can ever replace your real mummy.'

A week later Nita starts kindy. She's never been to a kindy before. She screams when I try to leave her. She hangs on to my legs and I want to take her home. I don't exactly remember my first day of school but I remember the feeling. I tell the kindy teacher I'm not leaving until Nita isn't crying anymore. She tries to push me out the door saying Nita will be better after I leave, but I say I'm going to stay for awhile. The teacher doesn't know what to do, so she lets me stay. From that day onwards Nita really loves me. Then Kate does too because little sisters always want to be like their big sisters. The three of us become like sisters after that day.

Often The Chief comes home in the middle of the afternoon and waters the garden to 'unwind'. That's his time. The girls know that and keep watching television while I make him a cup of tea. We all go out and tell him about our day, then go to the park or play catchy. I learn to cook a bit but it's pretty basic. We eat a lot of baked beans and spaghetti from cans and The Chief sometimes brings takeaway food home. The girls and me love Kentucky Fried Chicken, with coleslaw for nourishment.

Then I bath the girls and they're ready for bed. That's their favourite time of day.

'Daddy, Daddy, tell us about Ninja Nita and Karate Kate and Flying Dog, Daddy.'

'Into bed first. Have you done your teeth? Kate, has Mummy Barb put your nappy on?'

'We're ready, Daddy, we're ready.'

Then The Chief lies on the floor between the beds holding one each of their little hands and tells the next part of a story about the girls and the Yarra River near the house where all their adventures happen. I lie next to one of the girls on the bed and he puts me into the stories too. I'm the rescuer. If Kate gets lost, me and Nita find her. If Nita's drowning, Kate rides the Flying Dog to get me and carry me back for the rescue. I'm there to protect them.

I love these stories so much I try to tape The Chief once, so I can play them to the girls when he isn't home. When the recorder clicks at the end of the tape and The Chief finds out what I'm doing he shouts at me.

'If you ever tape me without my knowledge you'll be out of here so fast you won't know what happened.'

In bed that night The Chief warns me.

'You know if you ever try to tell anyone what goes on here with us, they won't believe you, don't you? There are no witnesses and it'd just be your word against mine. And if you think anyone would believe you over me, think again.'

Apart from that one time when he's mad at me though, these are our best times together. When I go back to the couch after nights like that, I imagine how it would be if Nita and Kate and me *were* sisters and The Chief was my dad, too.

The next morning at Sal's I wake up and know I've had a dream. I almost never remember dreams. My routine is to wake up, jump into my clothes, put on my blades and within minutes be out of the house heading to work. But this morning I can't shake the feeling I'd dreamt something important. As I skate through the heavy morning traffic on my way into town, I feel unsettled. Blading down St Kilda Road, I try to remember, but dodging lights, potholes, cyclists and pedestrians, the thought only hums under the cardio workout. I arrive at my work shower block 45 minutes later, strip and jump under the shower head. Suddenly, standing there naked, violent sobs burst out of me like explosions. I fall against the wall. Tears aren't coming out of my eyes, although I'm crying. It seems that the water on my face is only from the shower. The reason for the outburst is a mystery except that it has something to do with the dream.

That's when I know that the dream is about Gran. I don't remember anything except that my feelings for her are so intense they strangle me until I can't breathe. Realising it's love and loss is like waking up in a fog. Then I feel sorry and sorriness rains down on me like water from the shower. I'm sorry for Gran, sorry for me. I forgive her more in that minute than I ever had when she was alive. I try to recall even one scene from the dream but nothing comes. I don't want to feel sorry for her. I don't want to love her. I know the forgotten scenes hold the key to why I should. Why I do. The more I try to remember, the knottier it becomes, like a brain teaser you'll never get. All I do know is that I don't blame Gran for anything. And when I realise that, the suffocating love I feel for her stops being so intense too and I don't care anymore about Gran. She seems far away but a hard knob in me is turning to dust.

When I arrive in Baby Face's office we go down in the lift together.

'You know I've had more colleagues stop me in the lift over this case than anything I've ever worked on,' he tells me.

'Really? What are they saying?'

'Just asking about it. Word travels like wildfire in this place. He was a bit of a legend at Owen Dixon Chambers, you know. Worked on some pretty famous cases.'

'I know. I read the papers. What have you been telling them?'

'Anything they want to know. The truth as far as I know it. He'd have been better off not defending this case. Once something like this gets around it's hard to wash the stain out.'

If I won the case it would be the state that paid compensation, not Vernon. I'm happy he's already paying with his reputation, whichever way the decision falls.

We know Vernon's not going to be here. He had to go back to Queensland after the third day. The judgment's scheduled for today, the fourth day.

Neither Ma, Sal or Melanie can be here either. It's only me and Baby Face.

I'm sitting at the back of the courtroom waiting for the judge.

I try to imagine losing. Vernon always said no-one would believe me if I ever told my story. It's easy to see now what he'd meant. He'd been eminent way back in 1971 when I was the daughter of a prostitute. Now I can see how odds stack differently when you both have professions on your side. I tell myself the judgment doesn't matter. But to not be believed. I can't even think about it.

Sitting on the benches waiting, I'm shaking. Crying too. Sobbing actually. Trying to imagine the judge saying she doesn't believe me. There's no bloody privacy in these places. Baby Face is sitting beside me looking at the floor.

'Sorry. Wait outside if you like,' I tell him. 'Better I get this over before she comes. Better now than later, right?'

'No. It's fine. Really. I'm a bit surprised that's all. You were such a good witness. No emotion. Straight down the line. It was perfect. Great. I didn't know it still affected you. I'm not saying it shouldn't, I just wasn't expecting it, that's all.'

'Got a tissue?' I'm drenched. He gives me a white hanky.

'You know you shouldn't think about winning or losing. Often people just want their day in court. The outcome's only part of it.'

He's sitting close. It makes me want to cry more. I recross my legs and move away half a bum space. Crying hasn't been a big part of my repertoire since I've been with David. He laughs at me if I'm upset. I suggest we get a coffee from the machine outside.

'She'll just give the judgment and then that'll be it. She'll ask if you have anything to say and we can go. Shouldn't take more than a few minutes. If you want to say anything, that's your chance. What do you think? Do you want to say something?'

Do I want to say something? It's taken half a lifetime for me to spew this out. I'm not going to let my chance to say something about it get away.

'Probably. I don't know what exactly.'

I start thinking.

By the time we're called 20 minutes later, I've pasted myself back together.

Judge Wendy comes in and we all stand.

'I see Mr Vernon and his representatives are not present.'

'Yes Your Worship, Mr Vernon had engagements in Queensland and Mr Berkeley has another case listed today. They've agreed that the judgment be handed down in their absence.'

'Very well then. As you know in this tribunal I've made my judgment on the balance of probability that the evidence presented was true and correct. There were some anomalies in Miss Biggs' testimony. We note that in her evidence, relating an incident in a car on the way up to Sydney, Mr Vernon allowing such alleged activities while his children were in the car, sleeping or not, seems an unlikely story given the undisputed evidence that Mr Vernon was an exemplary father. Nevertheless there were significant enough discrepancies in Mr Vernon's evidence …'

I look at Baby Face and know it was him who'd pointed out the gaping holes in Vernon's testimony. He's more than just a pretty face. In fact, I realise he's been quite brilliant.

'… his alleged visit to Miss Biggs' mother's home in Melbourne after she had already moved to Queensland …'

I can't believe how calm I am. She might as well be

telling me her shopping list. I float inside my own thoughts. Working out what I'm going to say when she invites me to speak. I want to tell her how I feel about the process, the Tribunal. I'm glad it's available. I'm glad we got a woman judge. God knows there's few enough. I want to tell her why I've brought the case. Why I'm not claiming compensation for being raped on my 14th birthday instead. At least that's a clear-cut crime. It was, technically, a rape. But here I was with Vernon, a willing participant. Nobody forced me into anything.

Whatever the judgment, I want to tell her that Vernon shaped me. When I was metamorphosing from girl to woman, he set emotional traps that would trip every time I loved. Every time I wanted to love. Every time someone loved me. Every time I had sex. Every time someone didn't love me.

'... But, overall, I find her and her witnesses to be credible and on the balance of probabilities, that the evidence they gave at this tribunal credible. I find that Miss Biggs has suffered psychologically as a result of the alleged crime against her. The Tribunal finds you eligible for compensation under the Crimes Compensation Act. I hereby award you $20,000, the maximum amount available to this Tribunal under the Act. Miss Biggs, do you understand the judgment?'

'Yes, I do, Your Worship.'

'Do you have anything you'd like to say?'

I stand up and put my hands on the table in front of me to steady myself.

'This Tribunal may have wondered why I applied for compensation for a crime that happened so long ago. And if I'm concerned about a crime that happened then, why I didn't make an issue of ...'

My words catch in my throat. I try again.

'The thing is, you can get over a single rape. That's done

to your body. You move on. But how your attitudes are formed ...'

Suddenly my body convulses and a sob erupts like a sneeze. Even a wail vomits up out of my bowels. The tears inside me, like a lava flow, won't stop. I can hardly speak but I'm getting this out if it's the last thing I do.

'It wasn't just nine months ...' I take deep breaths but every time I go to let it out a fresh torrent of crying collides with the words trying to escape.

'... wasn't just nine months, it affected ...'

Baby Face puts his hand on my arm trying to get me to sit down. I shake him off. I'm not doing all this crying for nothing. His hanky's sopping. I see him digging around in his pocket. I pray there'll be another starched white hanky down there somewhere.

'... it affected my whole ...'

A grunt and then a groaning wail crashes into the last word as Baby Face's hanky ambulance is shoved hastily into my hand.

'... life ...'

Then, as suddenly as it started, it stops. There's nothing left. With my new white hanky I mop up the damage. Judge Wendy sees her opportunity and grabs it.

'Is that all, Miss Biggs?'

It's an easy question. But the answer? How can I tell her, or anyone, that the emotional roller-coaster with Vernon was one thing and the sex was another? Every aspect of it is complicated. My first orgasm with him blew my mind. It also blew my heart right open. Since my first sexual experience, the rape on my 14th birthday, I'd just been a hole for men to put their dicks into. Vernon was adept with women's bodies. I think how if a guy, even if he is a dirty old man, happens to know how to give a girl an orgasm and bothers to do it, why wouldn't a teenage girl enjoy it? Why would a 20-year-old, an 18-year-old, a 16-year-old, but not a 14-year-old? People don't think about these things. Worse than that, they don't talk about them either and if you try, they're shocked and think you're being disgusting. They make out like you're some kind of nymphomaniac, that you were asking for it, that it was you rather than him that's responsible because you enjoyed it. They don't stop to think that the guilt and childlike love you have for the guy is the worst part that goes on and on forever. They like to think 14-year-old girls don't have sexual and romantic feelings or fantasies. They like to think everything's simple. I want to say all this, but I can't. I know nobody's interested. And I'm just glad she believed me. Glad it's finally over.

'Yes … No. I'd like to thank the Tribunal for considering my case. Thank you.'

When it's over Baby Face gives me space but tells me he thinks I've been brave. All of a sudden he doesn't look so young anymore. It's him and Melanie who won the case. I put my hand out to shake his.

'Thanks for everything, James.'

On the way home I'm racing down St Kilda Road like the wind. But I know it isn't me racing. That sobbing routine in the court has let her out. It's Pet, punching her way up from my guts, dancing over cracks in the pavement, jumping over gutters so I nearly break my neck, sobbing with I don't know what, but it's closer to elation than pain. Give her an inch and she'll take a mile every time. But let her have her moment. After all, it's her, not me, who's been stretched like a rubber band for 26 years.

After the case, Dan's social is waving on the horizon, a call to arms, a ritual down whose throat all will be swallowed and regurgitated the next day in a What Now void. We go to the Toris' to prepare the battle dress. Judy takes the photos. After all the photos that have gone west in my life, I still refuse to get a camera. We drop off the gaggle of too-long legs and arms in ill-fitting suits. I'm under orders not to enter the hall when I pick Dan up at midnight. But I'm a disobedient mother. At 11pm I drive there and sneak around to a side window to catch a glimpse of my boy. Tired balloons loaf on the floor, half-eaten party pies lie in ambush on seats. Even streamers have given up, but tomorrow's adults are still spurting energy like blood from a war wound. There's Dan, jacket off, shirt sleeves up, linedancing with classmates as if they'd invented it. Arms holding waists, throwing legs in the air. There's Shannon with his pop-up toaster smile, kicking up a cloud of fun enough for everyone; Chris, of the Indian dinner night; Matthew, who threw up on my lounge room rug after the last party; mountainous Toni with his stick girlfriend and Lovely Lena, Dan's wan, anaemic first love, who for once doesn't look like she'd break. And all the Kates. Exquisite ice queen, brain, student council rep, Dan's-first-kiss Katy Donald; Katie Mobbs of Mobbsville, a family compound with its own postcode and finally, freckle-faced, red-haired Kate Green. They don't know they're a carnival of fresh-picked fruit. Unsullied by nasty parasites or time.

They disappear into another room and I sneak around the front to go back to the car. There the headmaster, Mr Beecher, spots me and drags me into the hall. No, no, no. I'll just wait outside. I'm a bit early. Don't be silly, come, enjoy yourself. He loves me since I've joined the school council and written an article for the Melbourne paper on one of his students. Dan spots me and laughs. Mother dearest, are you being bad? A head above me now, he puts his arm around my waist and swings me round. He looks so grown-up even with his praying mantis limbs. He lets me stay and I breathe them in. Can you have nostalgia for something you never had? Of course you can.

NINETEEN

BUNGEY JUMPING
WITHOUT A ROPE

At work I'm writing freelance travel stories for extra money. David's doing some part-time work with a local builder but we still don't have enough money for holidays. The travel stories are a way of having a break.

There's a Victorian mansion in Torquay that's been turned into a glamorous guesthouse and I have to stay there for the weekend. I'd hoped to take David so we could try to have a romantic time together but he doesn't like free things. I invite Joanne instead. She's working for Lady Carol at

Lavandula, now a thriving lavender farm, hating every minute of being an employee for her friend. She jumps at the idea.

We arrive on a Friday afternoon and have dinner at a local pub.

Just before midnight we walk across the road to the beach and away from town. It's deserted and the wind makes our hair stand on end. We're intoxicated in several ways. Joanne takes off her clothes and wades into the sea.

'Come on, get your gear off BB. It's a full moon and you never know when you're going to be by the sea on a full moon again in your life.'

'What if someone sees us?'

'BB? Is this my BB? You? Worried about someone seeing you? You're becoming conservative in your old age. Is this the same girl who used to steal thousands on shoplifting sprees?'

'That was a lifetime ago. And yes, I have changed. I *am* more conservative. Anyway, you hated me back then. I hated me back then. Aren't you glad I've changed?'

'I am. Actually, BB, have I told you how proud I am of you?'

'Once or twice. But you can tell me again any old time. Do you know you're the only one who really knows where I came from?'

'You mean I'm the only one who was crazy enough to stick around?'

'If you want to put it like that. People who meet me now just see this moderately successful professional person who's only a bit weird around the edges.'

'Yeah, yeah. Just take your Miss Goody Two Shoes off for a minute. Just for me? Come on BB. Just a little dip.'

Joanne's drunk. Just like she doesn't 'do' public transport or queues, she doesn't usually do begging either. I take off my dress and undies and go in.

I start swimming out. When I swim away from shore I'm reminded of the time at the beach when I swam out hoping I wouldn't have enough strength to make it back. I think about dying now and realise for the second time that the feeling's still here. I don't want to die. We're swimming next to each other and moonlight's washing over our white skin, shining wetly.

'You know, I haven't wanted to die for ages now. In fact, I don't think I want to die at all anymore.'

'Lucky you.'

I groan. I shouldn't have said anything. I don't want Joanne talking about how she does want to die just when I don't. Those trips make me feel tired. She used to talk about killing herself all the time when I first got back from Guatemala. You don't have your brother and sister and friend kill themselves without realising there's nothing you can do to help. That it's one lonely decision you make and no-one can take away the anguish of it. I know she wants me to help her. But I just can't. She uses the suicide talk to make me feel sorry for her, to draw me into her sticky web. I'm not buying into it. I start swimming back and get out.

Joanne doesn't seem to take offence. She knows the days when she'd tug the string and I'd come running are over, but she's a stubborn thing and has to give it one last go. She keeps swimming and gets out and we start walking back to the guesthouse without our clothes on under the moonlight while we dry off.

We spend the rest of the weekend laughing raucously like when we first met, behaving like stupid teenagers. Our new equality is holding. After 22 years, we've finally resolved our friendship into something healthy. No mother-daughter routine, no manipulation, just two friends having a wild old time. Together, we've come of age.

When Joanne lived in Melbourne she used to buy a special biodynamic bread from a shop near her house. Where I stay at Sal's isn't far from there so I buy a loaf of the casalinga for Joanne every week. I usually dropped it off at her place on Saturday night on my way past.

But this Saturday I'm tired. A visit with Joanne's never less than an hour or two and I want to get home.

The next morning I wake up late. David's spraying weeds in the back paddock when Dan calls that Ron's on the phone for him. Ron and David have become friends. Ron's already built a pigeon house at Joanne's and wants to build a chook house as well. He's asked David for help. They're two inept dreamers not meant for this world.

'Barb!'

'Yes David.'

'Ron wants me to go over. I think it's about the chooks. I'll be back soon. Do we need anything at the shop?'

'Only milk.'

'Back soon.'

Not likely, I think. Those boys can talk for hours.

It's only half an hour later, almost midday, when David returns. I'm in the kitchen making toast when he comes in. He stops for a second in the doorway before stretching his arms out towards me in a gesture that means I should come into them. What's he up to? Some new joke I haven't seen before. I look at him, puzzled, trying to head off this new tease at the pass. Then he starts walking towards me.

'I'm so sorry, Barb. I'm so sorry.'

He hugs me but I push him away so I can see his face. He's up to no good for sure.

'What are you doing?'

'Barb. I'm sorry. I'm sorry.'

'What are talking about? What are you sorry about? Stop it.'

'Barb. It's Joanne.'

'What about her? This isn't funny, David.'

'Stop, Barb. It's Joanne. Something terrible's happened.'

He keeps trying to pull me towards him to cuddle me but I keep pushing him away to read his face. He's never teased like this before.

'This isn't funny, David.'

'Barb. It's not a joke. She's dead.'

I push him off me and stare, now trying to believe he's joking. It would be just like him to try and scare me like this.

'David, you don't joke about things like that.'

'It's why Ron phoned, Barb. It's true.'

In my heart I already know it's suicide. I think about how I'd almost dropped in to see her last night.

'Tell me she didn't kill herself.'

'Just come, Barb. I told Ron I'd be straight back. He's there on his own. Just come. You'll see.'

We drive the couple of blocks to her house without talking. It's come to this. Again. Will it ever stop? I don't have it in me to be devastated. Not again.

We pull up behind Joanne's car in her driveway and get out. I see Ron kneeling at the open door of her car. He's stroking her face and talking to her. I think that means she must really still be alive. But he's crying and telling her he's sorry. I look at Joanne who's stiff in the driver's seat and I know she's dead. There are blankets stuffed up against the car windows. I hug Ron.

'Are you okay?'

'It's all my fault.' It's almost a whisper.

'What happened?'

'I came home about 11 and found her. It's all my fault.'

'You weren't even here. Don't be silly. It's nobody's fault.'

'No. It's all my fault. I stayed out last night. I didn't come home. I was going to but I didn't. It's the first time I haven't come home. She thought I was coming.'

'Where were you?'

'I stayed at a girl's house. I slept with another woman. It was the first time. It's all my fault.'

Eventually the whole story comes out. They'd been fighting for three days but were expected to go to a mutual friend's birthday party together last night. He took Sally dachshund for a walk and Joanne went to the party alone. Ron arrived half an hour later and saw her walking to the shops to get some wine. It's the last time he saw her. We don't know if she came back from the bottle shop and saw Ron flirting with the woman or what happened. All we do know is that she left a note saying goodbye to Ron. She'd stuffed up the exhaust and car windows, taken a pillow and blanket out to make herself comfortable and turned on the ignition. Carbon monoxide is heavier than air. It sinks. At some point she collapsed onto the passenger seat with her head near the floor where there's the greatest concentration of poisonous gas.

I'm making phone calls inside the house when David comes in and tells me the worst news.

'She turned the ignition off and opened the driver's side window. She changed her mind Barb.'

I can see now how it happened. She'd wanted to punish Ron for the fight, or flirting with the other woman. She set it up so he'd find her when he came home from the party. She'd gone far enough to make it look convincing, then turned off the ignition and opened the window. She wasn't counting on him not coming home until morning.

Ron hasn't called anyone yet. I call the police then start phoning Joanne's stepmother in Sydney, her two ex's Robert and Russell, others who need to know.

I go out to the car a couple of times to look at her. I stay only a few seconds. Her greatest fear in life has always been getting old. Even when she was 26 I remember her erupting in tears when I, all of 18, said she was brave for ice-skating 'at her age'. Now she'll never get old.

Nobody knows what to do. An old friend comes and finds a big, old wooden box in Joanne's garage.

'That'd make a great coffin, BB. Why don't you get David to do something with it? You don't want her being buried in one of those horrible shiny things. She'd hate that, Barbara. You know she would.'

He's right, but David laughs nervously.

'It's not the right shape.'

'You're a carpenter, surely you can do something.'

He ties the box onto the roof racks, takes it home and sets to work while I finish phoning friends in Joanne's address book. I haven't cried yet. I can't. Too many suicides make you immune. You just shake your head. Over and over.

I come back home and find David in the shed. The coffin's nearly finished.

'I thought it was a stupid idea, Barb. But it's just what I needed. I had to do something.'

The next day we set the handmade, rustic coffin up in Joanne's garden and her friends, mostly artists, paint it with their farewells, messages, pictures, all symbols of an inspired life lived on the edge.

We wait for Robert and Maggie Stepmother to turn up from Sydney and have the funeral three days after Joanne dies.

There's no service. People speak at the graveside. Her artist friend Maggie says how Joanne had never recovered from her mother dying when she was 12. It's when her agoraphobia started. I tell the story of when she was a child and her grandmother would take her by the hand to the incinerator and they'd burn money and furs and jewellery her bookmaker grandfather had given the old woman. How she'd stolen money from her grandfather's desk drawer to buy buckets and buckets of fire crackers and set them off under his petunias. How she'd bawled out the headmistress for her best friend when they'd been in trouble at school.

'Just leave the poor girl alone. Can't you see she's terrified?'

After the funeral both Ron and I have an obsession about having Joanne's things. Her stepmother, Maggie, thought I was the beneficiary of Joanne's will but nothing to this effect is found. One written years ago was made out to her, so she starts throwing things out, getting auctioneers in. Ron's going through the rubbish, even rescuing paper doodles. I'm buying what I can.

Maggie says she'll give me back the $5000 I'd given Joanne and I want to buy her favourite bits of furniture with it. We talk about keeping her house exactly as it is, a museum of her artwork and collections, but the practicalities are too much. I get an art dealer to come and look at Joanne's work, dreaming of her becoming famous posthumously. They're not interested.

After the funeral David and Dan are quiet around the house. In bed with David at night he's tender with me and asks if I'm okay. I'm grateful, but wish the price for his small window of sincerity wasn't so high.

One day I'm at Sal's place and she tells me her barrister brother Ray, who works at Owen Dixon Chambers, where Vernon had worked, saw a notice in the lift about his funeral. Three months after he'd lied shamelessly during the Tribunal hearing, he'd died of tongue cancer. I feel nothing. I'm not sad. Or happy. That's when I know that the vestiges of the emotional attachment that still had me hooked in when I was 27, had dissolved when I'd won the case. Now, his death, is simply interesting news. A postscript to a 30-year saga.

The year after the case and Joanne's death is my worst time in ten years. It starts with having to take legal action against Maggie, who refuses to return the money I'd given Joanne. She instead wants to give it to Joanne's sister who she'd barely seen since we'd first become friends 22 years ago. At work, two friends can't cope with my grief and start avoiding me. Then I tell my boss in the pub after work one night that people at work are bored and need to be moved around. He takes offence and none of my work colleagues talk to me for the rest of the year. I come into work one day and on my desk I find a doll with pins stuck all over it. Every week I'm crying in the toilets or the sick room. I feel like I'm having a nervous breakdown.

It doesn't start out with anything to do with me and David, and there's nothing conscious about it, but how I cope ends up shifting the battle between David and me to a final and unexpected front.

At work I'd changed from general news to writing for the real estate and finance section of the paper. Anything to get from under the editor and chief-of-staff. This job runs its own show. No news conferences, no unnecessary mixing with the other staff. I start getting interested in auctions and house prices and notice they're going up.

I see a two bedroom art deco flat for sale in Chapel Street, St Kilda. It seems cheap so I see a bank about raising a deposit by increasing the mortgage on our house which has gone up in value since the major rebuild. They agree and I buy the flat with no up-front money. David's furious.

'You don't just go out and buy a flat like you'd buy a hat, Barb.'

'Don't worry, the rent will cover the repayments.' I wish he'd just go away. He hadn't wanted to put his name on this house when I bought it. He didn't want to take a risk.

'It's my money too if you're mortgaging this house. You should have asked me.'

Now it's my turn to tune out.

In the next five months I get a fever for real estate. As pressure on me mounts at work and home, like Zeus refusing to be done in by a storm, I sweep my wits and manic energy behind me and charge off to buy property as if my life depends on it. My survival instincts have returned. My life motto? When the underbelly's threatened, create chaos on the surface.

In one weekend I buy two flats. Then I buy one in joint names with Beacon who's on the dole and depressed about having nothing to leave her son Dennis. We'd known each other since Dan and Dennis were babies and I don't want to lose my old friends on my roller-coaster ride to financial security. I lend her the deposit by upgrading the mortgage on Daylesford again. We paint and furnish it together and rent it out to backpackers for twice the normal rent. She pays me back from the weekly rental profit.

David's stressed by my real estate madness and starts harassing me again.

One day he comes into the bedroom and finds me reading in the afternoon. I know he'll take my book so I take it and run out the front door and jump into the car. He's a shadow behind me when I lock the door just in time. I laugh happily because I've won and continue reading my book. He goes behind the house and brings around a piece of old carpet and covers the car so I can't see. By then Dan's come out and both boys are laughing. So am I, but sitting there in the dark car I'm also mad. I'm not getting out in defeat, so I drive down the road with my head out the window to see where I'm going.

I wonder again, if David's so funny, it must be me who is the problem in this relationship.

Every day he gets in my way with the garden and cooking. I'm percolating with rage. One day it occurs to me the reason I haven't played piano for ten years is because every time I'd started practising in the early days he'd interrupted at first by talking to me, and then later, when I resisted that, he'd pick up my hands and start making them dance like I was a marionette. I just gave up. The realisation galvanises me into greater rebellion.

We have to move to Melbourne next year when Dan starts uni, so when I see two double-storey Victorian terrace houses, I decide to buy one to live in. They're to be auctioned on the same morning. My bank manager agrees to finance the purchase. The second house is my preference but the first goes so cheap I buy that instead. I'm so manic about it I sit in the gutter bidding with my hand in the air until it's knocked down to me. I go to the second auction just to see how much it goes for. The bidding's at $50,000 less than the agents have quoted. I know it has to be sold because of the owners' separation. I end up buying both houses.

After the auctions, I realise I've spent, or rather committed to borrowing, $670,000 in a day.

For David, this is tantamount to bungey jumping without a rope. He's livid and stressed to breaking point. That's when I decide I don't care. That I'm not going to let him hold me back anymore. We couldn't be more different. I can't stay running on the spot anymore because he's frightened of risk. Really, afraid of life itself.

Things hot up between us when my bank manager reneges on her agreement to fund both purchases and says I no longer fit their lending criteria.

I have four months to find the money to settle or lose my deposit which I've raised by mortgaging everything I own. Instead of slinking off to cry in the toilets at work, I'm now sneaking off to meet loan officers in the boardroom. I apply to eight lending institutions and they all turn me down.

Finally, one lender helps with a friendly tip that reminded me of Elizabeth's advice with my first loan 20 years ago.

'Don't tell them you bought two houses. Just apply for one at a time through two different banks. On paper you look like a nutcase. If they think you just bought one house you might get two separate banks to come to the party.'

I take his advice and it works. I have the finance organised but have a $30,000 shortfall. If I can dig up that, settlement's in the bag. I lie awake at night jigging figures to try and make them fit.

Friends listen politely to my financial woes. While I'm obsessed with real estate, by comparison, my troubles at work and with David fade into insignificance.

I don't think there's anything strange about my behaviour until my friend Lissa and I go out for a coffee and find ourselves driving by an open-for-inspection sign. I've got her in there, pen poised over the dotted line, before the caffeine has even worn off. 'You can do it Lissa. You've almost paid the whole mortgage off on your flat. Just mortgage it again for the deposit for this place and you can buy it now! Right now, Lissa. Just think about it.' I'm not happy being a house junkie by myself. In my mania I want to take others with me on the road to success. It's her backing away from me kind of look that makes me think maybe I should calm down and deal with what's already on my own plate.

As the date for settlement looms, lavender Lady Carol says kindly, 'You don't think you've bitten off more than you can chew do you, BB?'

People at work who catch me in the act of trying to borrow a million dollars think I'm finally cracking. Others dismiss it as a Walter Mitty fantasy. So, Biggs, I hear you're trying to borrow a million bucks.

While I'm manoeuvring to make settlement on the two new houses, the two flats I'd bought settle on the same day.

I have to renovate, furnish and get them rented as fast as possible to be able to start making the mortgage payments. I take two weeks holidays from work. I plan to renovate and furnish one flat in the first week and the other in the second. I'm stressed to the eyeballs.

While I'm working on the first, Christian's released from jail. I'd refused to visit him while he was 'away' on his last stint because he'd stolen $800 when he'd borrowed my bankcard to buy groceries one day. He's been in jail twice now. But Ruthy Baby and I keep in touch. She tells me Christian wants to work off the money he'd stolen.

'He'll do anything you like Barb. Paint, run around, anything. He's changed.'

I don't want to have anything to do with him. He'd stolen the money the night I'd taken him and Ruth out for his 21st birthday. I don't trust him. He's so much like Neville.

'Come on Auntie Barb. He's family. Have a heart.'

I only find out later that Ruthy had finally broken up with Christian after a night when a dealer burst into their house with a machine gun and pointed it at their heads. Christian had been dealing. It suddenly wasn't an exciting game anymore.

But now I relent and Christian starts helping the painter I've hired. He messes up everything, more trouble than he's worth. One day I come home and find a wall I've told him to paint deep strawberry he's decided would look better orange.

The stress of the past 12 months mushrooms like an atom bomb, raining fallout over Christian in a venomous attack.

'Get the fuck out of here. I don't care about the money. I don't like you. I've never liked you. You're just like your father. You lie just like him. You sound just like him. The only reason I have anything to do with you is because you're Pommy's son. I do it for her, not for you. Get out. I never want to see you again.'

His face crumbles, then turns to stone.

'You fuckin' bitch. I'm nothing like Neville. I'm Mum's son too, you fuckin' bitch.'

He storms off and I set my mouth into a tight crack. The guy I'm paying to help paint keeps his eyes glued steadfastly to the wall.

With a month to go before settlement Ma calls out of the blue. We've both been busy and have barely spoken since the Tribunal hearing. She asks how I am and I tell her about the real estate deals and the trouble I'm having finding the money for settlement. She doesn't bat an eye. After all, the underbelly strategy's her very own.

'What about if I buy into the house with you?'

'Have you got $30,000?'

'Yeah. Just. And I can't buy anything because I don't have a credit rating so it'd be good for me, too.'

'Ma, thank you, thank you, thank you. That's fantastic.'

It's the beginning of the tide turning. For me, actions speak louder than words. She'd helped me with the Vernon case and now this. I swallow the lump in my throat.

By the end of the year I've done it. On a three-day-a-week salary I've bought five properties and borrowed over a million dollars in five months.

TWENTY

WELCOME HOME

The last two house settlements are both in January 1998, a month after I turn 41. The fire and brimstone are over and life starts having some semblance of normality.

The Daylesford place, the finishing touches finally done only because we're moving out, is rented to tourists on weekends. We move into one of the terrace houses I've bought. Now I own eight properties: four flats and one house rented to backpackers, the two in Daylesford and the five-bedroom one in Gourlay Street, East St Kilda we live in with Ruthy Baby and my Peter Pan-sized gay friend, Robby. I'm easily managing to meet the mortgage repayments with backpacker tenants.

Suddenly I've become a property mogul to friends who'd smiled benevolently months before. Now they're asking advice as if I'd really known what I was doing, buying up half of Melbourne when everyone else was ditching it. They didn't realise I was just trying to stay sane by self-immolation. Property prices have already started to rise. Where I'd started out geared at 88 per cent, I soon own 60 per cent of what I've bought. It looks like I'll be a modest millionaire. And not in the too distant future.

David, studying his fourth year of project management, hasn't quite forgiven me for the real estate madness. Dan finishes high school with flying colours and enrols in software engineering at Monash University. He and his country friends hoist their social lives on their backs to the bigger playground of Melbourne.

Work becomes more bearable after colleagues decide the heat's off and a few slowly stop ignoring me.

I have another Bed and Breakfast review in Port Fairy, a fishing village three hours from Melbourne along the Great Ocean Road. David doesn't want to come, so I invite Lissa.

I end up sleeping with a young guy. His kisses are tender and he looks into my eyes. His smile is shy. His touch isn't at all. He makes love like David did the first time. I feel like a rescued castaway, incredulously taking a bath and eating a hot meal for the first time after a decade of berries and raw fish.

Afterwards he asks about Dan, my life, work. He listens while he strokes my face. He gives his mobile number and asks me to call. He has to get home.

'Don't you want your jumper?' I ask. He'd given it to me earlier when I was cold.

'Nah. Keep it. That way I might see ya again.' He reminds me of young Lindsay, the boy who used to sit in my lounge room in Adelaide while I practised piano. The one who made love like a poem. The one I'd betrayed for silly Ian.

When he has to go, he stands in the doorway staring at me. Then comes back to kiss me tenderly, no tongue, just sensual lips. Three times he makes it to the door and comes back. The last time he brushes a stray hair away from my face while he stares dreamily into my eyes. When he goes, I lie in blissful shock.

The next day, on the way back to Melbourne, I wish I were alone to savour the feelings. The only strong emotions I've felt for so long have been anger and frustration. Now, this powerful softness is like an alien substance seeping into me. But Lissa's here and she knows, maybe better than me, that I'm travelling through a gate. I wonder if she knows it's slowly closing behind me.

I lay my head back, eyes closed. This boy, like Lindsay before, has plucked strings that have started a cacophony of old passions. It's a sticky mix. Longing, for sure, and a touch of infatuation. But I know it isn't really about him. It's about me. I don't feel invisible today. I'm taking shape. Mentally, like a blind person, I feel for the shape of me. Below the braille reading, a distant storm is brewing. On my internal horizon I see faint bolts of lightning and hear muffled thunder roar.

Before we arrive back in Melbourne, the gate has clanged shut.

It takes David a week to acclimatise to my suggestion that we try living separately. Our housemate Robby wants to move back into his flat and I talk him into sharing with David.

They've got on well in the past year and Robby needs the extra cash. I can't believe how easy it is.

I decide to sell our Daylesford house and David doesn't object. Three months after my infidelity, Bloss splits up with her husband Bernie and he visits. She's found a new man and set Bernie up with the kids' babysitter. Now he's in love. She's always been a good organiser, Bloss.

'You know, you wouldn't believe how much love you can experience when you both open your hearts to it,' Bernie's saying.

'There's no danger of that here, Bernie. I gave up on that years ago.' David's smirking. It's one of his big jokes on me. The trouble is, we both know it's no joke. He'd loved his first girlfriend, Mary, for three years. When she slept with another man he put that bit of himself in a padlocked trunk. I stare at David with my mouth open. Like I'd found out once years before, while something remains unsaid you can kid yourself in all kinds of creative ways. But now he's finally spelt it out, it's like riding backwards on a ferris wheel. Part of me can't believe the world's completely changed direction.

Bernie and David leave together and I go up to my room. I write the goodbye letter. It's short. I tell him I still love him but until he has more faith in himself and more trust in life he won't be able to love me the way I need to be loved. I say I can't live like that anymore.

David lets himself into the house at dawn and comes up to my room. He hasn't done that since he moved out. He's always been intuitive.

'Come for a walk, Barb. I want to talk.'

I take my letter with me and give it to him under a streetlamp. I don't want to hear what he has to say. I've jumped on a world going the other way and David's already receding into the distance, dropping over the edge.

He reads it.

'Come and sit in the park for a bit, Barb.' I'm looking at David aged ten. He's terrified.

'It's too late.'

'Just for a minute.'

We sit on a bench in the playground at the end of the street.

'Give me a week. I can change.'

'I don't want you to change for a week. You'd have to change for good. You can't.'

'Please, Barb. I never thought you'd do it. I just can't believe it. I didn't see it coming.'

'David, I asked you to move out and sold our house.'

He cries. A first with me. I hold his hand but my heart has stopped beating.

It takes another three months. We're having a trial separation. No sex. He visits every day and finally gives me what I've wanted all these years. He tells me how much he admires and adores me. He strokes my face and buys me roses. He half convinces me he can change.

I go for a five-week holiday to Bali and when I get back he has another girlfriend. Now I am devastated. But I see that if it hadn't been for that, we'd still be together and, really, I still know that's not what I want. But like Fernando says, whatever's holding us together is like Tarzan's Grip.

I ask David to call once a week at a certain time to help me with the final break-up. He agrees but the first day he's supposed to ring, he doesn't. I fume. The scale of the unfairness hooks me in again. When I pulled the plug he'd been at my house every day. I ring and discover he's invited his new girlfriend for dinner.

I explode like a landmine and rage at him that I'm coming with a hammer to smash his car. no-one's ever going to do this to me again is the gist of it.

But he manages to calm me down, promising to call the next day.

By then I have enough sense to wonder why, in our final death throes, I expect him to be any different from the past ten years. Isn't this why I'd left him?

In that instant, I give up, finally let go. The mystery of Fernando's glue becomes clear. All along, David might, in part, have been my sister or Ma or Vernon. But most of all, he was me. I'd always understood he tortured me because he was tortured. My back was wider than his. I endured and let out slack because we were both kids gone wrong. I thought, if I can hold on long enough, be understanding long enough, supporting long enough, he'll come through. I'll come through. I'd wanted to arrive together. Sadness smothers me. David isn't my damaged self? Now I have to make it alone.

I decide to move out of the big house in Gourlay Street. Ruthy wants to move in with her new boyfriend, so I decide to rent four rooms to backpacker couples and leave Dan there to manage it. He'll meet travellers and get a taste of the big wide world.

My beautiful flat in Hawsleigh Avenue has tenants, so I rent another huge art deco one and make it exactly how I want. I've never liked living alone, never liked my own company. But now I love being here. The walls are freshly painted white, my piano's here and I've furnished it with Joanne's furniture and art work. It could be her old home.

Now I'm living alone and have space, I start dabbling in writing. I write about Ma's life, using some of the short stories I'd written when Dan was a baby and others from my TAFE short story course.

One day, I realise when I'm dropping off the dogs at the old house after a walk, that I've locked my house keys in my flat.

Dan's working on the computer. He dropped out of software engineering three weeks ago because he isn't enjoying it. He's starting History and Philosophy of Science, Psychology and Criminology next year. Nothing practical, but that's not what real education's about anyway. Now he's happy learning.

'Hello sweetie.' It's a pantomime of sweetness, an irony we've both adopted from David's teasing ways. I go to kiss him and he pulls me onto his knee.

'Hello Mother dearest.' A parody of filial bliss. Just like me with my own mother, it's never just plain 'Mum'. Only when I was small did I use 'Mum', then it became 'Mother', then 'Ma'. Each one expressing how I felt about her. In Dan's case it's his way of playing, teasing, lightening things up, but also of distancing just a little, of not being vulnerable. Because he senses he can't rely on me? I'm not sound and solid and predictable like the Tori family?

'I'm locked out.'

'How'd you do that?' Admonishment, another trait he learnt from David. But I don't take offence with Dan. I know it's something to do with him growing up, the changing roles of parent and child. I tell him.

'You can get in the bathroom window if you take the louvres out.'

'I'm too old to be climbing on rubbish bins and through windows.'

'You don't have to get on the rubbish bin.' He grabs me around my legs and lifts me high above his head into the air. 'I just get you like this and push you in.'

He carries me into the hall and drops me.

'That hurt.'

'You're so short.' In my socks, I come up to Dan's shoulders.

'I am not.' Hmph.

He offers to climb in the window himself.

He revs his new secondhand turbo Nissan Pulsar to show off. He's proud of the car, bought with his check-out chick money. He's been working part-time since he started uni, independent early like his mum. But not too early.

At my flat, he hands me the louvres one by one. In a second he's leapt in the tiny opening head first. His lanky legs dangle in the air.

'Don't drown in the toilet.'

I hear him laughing. His legs wriggle down until I can only see his Nikes. Then he's gone.

'Have to go,' he says, as he opens the door. He loves being clever. But he's gotta be cool. 'Got basketball. Then I'm driving to Daylesford for Cinta's birthday.' The Tori kids are his surrogate siblings.

'Drive carefully.' I know it's futile. He drives how he drives. A responsible hoon.

'I love you Mum.' He kisses me and is off.

I stare at him for just a second. He often says it, but only after me.

I think it's because I tell him to drive carefully. It reminds him of the Tori family who make him phone when he drives from Daylesford back to Melbourne.

I consider telling him to ring when he gets to Daylesford, but decide it sounds contrived. He's always onto me straight-away. I never worry about bad things happening. It's the optimism I inherited from Ma.

I'm reminded for the millionth time how disconnected we are. How we don't talk much. He doesn't volunteer much. He figures I'm not interested because I don't remember what he tells me.

It's true. I try to be more interested, but he makes me work so hard at getting information. Because I miss the in-between bits there's no continuity. It's like tuning into *Melrose*

Place for snippets without getting the inside goss. I wonder if it's a mother/son thing or I'm repeating Ma's pattern. I always feel guilty. But not for long. Like mother like daughter.

As soon as I'm inside, Ma rings. She tells me about Lionel going into hospital tomorrow to start chemo. Doctors don't think anything can be done. They've given him four months to live. But both Lionel and Ma are relieved something is at last being done. He changed his will and Ma discovered he's much richer than she ever imagined. He's worth three million dollars of which she'll get half and Peter eight hundred thousand. I wonder if it will be some kind of compensation for his son that Lionel didn't take time to get to know him in his last three years. Ma will enjoy the money after spending a lifetime chasing it, but I know it won't be compensation for losing her sweetheart. She says he's the only man in her life who ever really loved her.

After Ma finishes telling me about the chemo, she stays on the line. Not talking.

I don't like it when she does that. But having just had the same feeling with Dan, it occurs to me that maybe she wants to talk and doesn't know how.

'Why don't you come and stay with me while Lionel's in hospital?' I ask.

'Well, I was thinking of that but your flat's so cold.'

We're both cold-blooded.

I think about mentioning my blow heater but I know she'll have it on all day and night for the four days. Things are tight with all the mortgages. And her presence is a stony reminder of how we can't communicate.

'How's the book going?' she asks. I'm writing the story of her incredible life. I admire her hugely even if I don't feel that close.

'Good.' It's what I always say because I can't be bothered

telling her. She may want to know, but she puts no effort into leading up to the big questions, or starting out with something more specific. Something she might have to think about. It's this feeling that usually makes our telephone calls last about three minutes. Always efficient, about practical stuff. Since she met Lionel again she's been saying 'love ya' before hanging up. I say 'you too'. It's all there is, no knowing each other, just saying it.

I decide to try something new.

'How's Jenny going?'

'Well, she's become a volunteer firefighter. She's joined the sea scouts and she's doing ambulance driving part-time. She's also abseiling on the weekends.'

I'm astonished. I had no idea.

We talk for about 20 minutes.

I come clean about having a heater.

'Well, in that case maybe I will come and stay on Saturday. I'm going out with one of the ladies on Sunday night.' Ma is friends with the 'ladies' she hires to make the fantasy calls for her service.

'That's good because I'm going dancing on Sunday night. Do you want to come after your dinner?' I think she might want to watch, forgetting for a second she's not like other people's mothers.

'Nah, I'm not sure I could dance with me leg. And I don't think I like Latin. With partner dancing it'd be too hard for the man with me limping around.' She conjures an image for herself to laugh at.

'Do you want to come and watch?'

'No thanks.' I can see her screwing up her nose. 'I'd want to dance. I can't just watch.'

The last time she'd danced was on a cruise five years ago. Big, lop-sided, old Ma. Once a dancer. The thing she enjoyed in her teenage motherhood. A fun lovin' girl pregnant with responsibility. She hasn't lost it yet. I can see her on the dance floor. Grey-haired granny boogeying, having the time of her life, not caring what anybody thinks.

When she hangs up, maybe sustained by a taste of the real thing, she doesn't say 'love ya'.

I think about Jenny and how I don't know her at all. Then about Peter and how I don't know him at all. Bloss is different because she insists I have a relationship with her two kids and harasses me to make it so.

I think about the times Jenny tried to connect with me and I'm full of regret. There's a poignancy about our courage and hopefulness that we made attempts at being family despite all evidence that we were only in name.

Like the time Peter invited me to his pool championship and Bloss knitting jumpers for siblings that never kept in touch. Like Jenny pleading for understanding from the rehab centre about the hell that was her life and my guilt-appeasing cake bake that day at Peter's.

Only a grumble followed half-hearted attempts at support when we'd swallow a drop of bitter bile as the other pushed us away. Like the time I rang and *almost* sent flowers when Bloss had her stillborn baby: Do you want me to come over, No, it's okay, I'll be all right. As we get older we make attempts but there's no faith in the gestures. Better half-hearted than be reminded these acts of family others take for granted are alien customs we never mastered.

Our small gestures to be like other families are like cooees across a canyon that might be answered years later or not at all, with no hard feelings or regret because, in our family, we understood early that in life we go it alone. We were flies in a bottle looking for escape. Every man for himself. Only the strongest survived. And what a shock when we discovered, too late, that Pommy wasn't the strongest. She was more fragile than any of us. For me she was the best one, the most generous, the brightest star, whose sensitivities doomed her to crash into earth's realities.

It's late and I've run a bath. In this place, my place, I'm basking in my own company for the first time. Throwing a few goodies my own way instead of waiting for someone else to do it. I deserve it. Before, I stuffed diversions into my mind like a cushion. Now, I loll luxuriously in nothingness. It's not that hard. Lying in the bath eating mandarins, steam fuzzing tea candle lights dotted around the room, I begin to think about Ma and me. Dan and me.

I straddle two generations worlds apart. Dan's stable. Sensible. Happy because, I saw, before it was too late – David helped me see – that a kid needs stability. Knowing my limitations, I let him go out to find what he needed. The big-hearted Tori family volunteered for the job. Can a parent do anymore? Do I expect Ma to have done more?

Dan understands I had a life different from his. That he has a wacky family. When he was 12, he listened to me tell Joanne about the New Zealand trip and the sex toys in the cupboard. He said: I wish I had a granny who made cakes. Now he likes having a funny grandma. He dines out on her stories like I have. And he accepts my shortcomings and loves me anyway. I wonder if I accept Ma's? Knowing who you are, your place in the world, can be a great comfort. Dan knows his place. I've been looking for mine for as long as I can remember, limping and rushing, obsessing and fighting my way from society's fringes to its core.

I get out of the bath, twirling to Aretha Franklin in mandarin swollen air, drying off with a fluffy white towel. I change the CD to Nina Simone, light vanilla incense I bought in Bali at Christmas, boil the kettle before putting on my fresh, white cotton nightgown with tiny buttons from neckline to floor, made during Joanne's Victorian Ladies Nightie Making Weekend. I switch on the soft light inside a small ceramic house with shuttered windows and little bears with vests welcoming us inside, another gift from Joanne for one of Dan's birthdays. I'm keeping it for his kids because he can be a careless boy. I make a pot of raspberry leaf tea and put it, with a riotous cup, next to my bed. I turn the CD player off and sit at the piano. I've been practising again since I've moved here, alone. It's a cliché but I play *Moonlight Sonata* every day like a meditation. It never fails to move me.

I get into bed to read for a bit but then put the book down. I don't have to be busy.

I sit up in crispy clean sheets, drink my tea.

Sometimes pivotal moments in life are fleeting, a blinding recognition or sudden awakening to something you only then realise has always been. As if all the struggle - self-help books, counselling, interminable workshopping with friends and endless, endless mental masturbation — suddenly converge to bear fruit.

Or maybe I kid myself. Maybe, in the end, a person only hears when they're ready and not a moment earlier.

I'm not a religious person. I don't believe in visions or voices. That's why I'm so suspicious about an ineffable peace that pounces on me when a few simple words pop into my head. I'm shocked because everyone: from Pet, who I think is long dead and Barbie of the mantra I used to chant when I was in my tortured teens - Hate, hate, hate; to motherless daughter BB, barb-riddled Barb and all the rest, appear out of nowhere and claim the words are positively dripping with meaning.

'Welcome home. I've been waiting for you.'

Then this stranger - witness, saviour, flighty Joan of Arc - steps out from behind a curtain in my mind. In a second, I know that she's been here all along, watching the whole drama of my life unfold, waiting for me to realise who I really am.

I lie, tea mid-air, as the loose live wires of my former selves fly around. It's like some kind of high school reunion for God's sake. Oh, you, hi, I know you. Yes, and you, I'm here. Me too. No! Hate, hate, hate … it comes from a quiet girl in the corner. The hate mantra. All these years I thought you meant the world. So, Pet, you meant us all along. Okay, now I get it! Now all the attention's on Joan. Hey, gorgeous, look, I knew there was something going on back there. Where'd you get those shoes, and those wings? Girls, girls, get a load of the wings on those shoes …

I realise these selves are not the essence of me. They are *in* me, but they are not me. I drift off to sleep with peace hanging about soaking everything in angel juice.

In the morning, I wake up and remember the night before. Disappointment grips me. Maybe it was an aberration, some crazy thoughts you have late at night. But I put a feeler out and the juice is still there.

It's there all day. All week.

Months pass before I really believe it. My old selves are here, but they're quiet in the peace that keeps hanging about. Joan's in charge and slowly shaking them down into a whole. I'm not just feeling who I am on the inside, I'm on a journey. The discovery about how she, as me, will manifest. Like a developing photo, or the birth of a child, I can't wait to see what's there …

If you enjoyed this,
please see over

'confronting, distressing AND funny ...'

IN
MORAL
DANGER

A True Story

BARBARA BIGGS

GET THE
WHOLE STORY ...

The 1970s were dangerous, a time and place where lingering Victorian values and hypocrisy collided head-on with the permissive society. There were many casualties. Barbara Biggs was almost one of them. Branded a 'wayward girl', she seemed doomed to destruction—but survived to tell a remarkable tale.

The Road Home is the sequel to Biggs's controversial best-selling memoir, *In Moral Danger*, an expose of sexual exploitation. If you haven't read both books, you haven't got the full story.

A true story
of recklessness
and romance

By Barbara Biggs
bestselling author of
In Moral Danger

The
**Accidental
Renovator**
— A PARIS STORY —

AVAILABLE NOW

Incorrigible romantic, writer and renovator Barbara Biggs thought she knew about sex and real estate. Then she went to Paris. The self-described 'foot-in-mouth Aussie chick' can't help 'just looking' at apartments for sale. Big mistake. She speaks little French, knows no-one in Paris and has never thought of living there. But when the agent assures her the owner will insist on the asking price, she makes a low offer 'just for fun'. It is accepted— and her life goes haywire. Biggs smuggles in a handsome Australian builder to renovate the apartment. But he doesn't speak French, doesn't have any tools and when the budding romance goes sour he vanishes and Barbara's dream renovation becomes a nightmare. Undeterred, she joins the Lazy Pigs Millionaires' Club and is soon lunching in grand chateaux, partying until dawn and learning about continental men in the nicest possible way. Then writes about it.

Barbara Biggs

CHAT ROOM

A cautionary tale
for every teenager using chatrooms
and their parents

AVAILABLE NOW

Sam, 13, has just moved from Sydney to Melbourne. Normally a confident kid, she suddenly finds herself lonely. Both high powered parents work late and Sam turns to chatrooms for company.

Chatman, a charming 17-year-old, tells Sam everything she wants to hear. Too young for romance, she welcomes the developing friendship … until something more sinister starts to emerge.

Chatroom was written in consultation with Det. Sen. Sgt. Chris O'Connor, from Victoria Police's Sexual Crime Squad and co-author of *Rockspider*. If you think you know about internet predators, this book will make you think again.

Forewarned is forearmed.

THE THINKING PERSON'S GUIDE
TO WEALTH AND HAPPINESS

SEX

AND

MONEY

HOW TO GET MORE

Barbara Biggs

Former finance journalist *and* sex worker

AVAILABLE NOW

Sex and Money: How to Get More, is a roller coaster ride through your psyche with plenty of hair-raising laughs along the way.

Barbara Biggs has been a writer for the *Australian Financial Review* and Melbourne *Herald Sun* finance section. She became a millionaire through property investing.

In her early years as a sex worker, having 'more sex than most people have had hot dinners', her sexual exploits were legendary – once advertising for a sugar daddy. Since then, she has found a way to deeply fulfilling sex. Barbara also draws on the grass roots wisdom from her mother's 30 years in the fantasy phone call business.

In this easy-to-read, chatty manual, she tells us why people read finance and sex books but don't follow the advice. Because making money (and sex) isn't about strategies, it's about emotional qualities like fear, risk-taking ability, going against the crowd and our underlying beliefs.

Hold on while Biggs takes you where others fear to tread. This book just might change your life.